QUANTUM FIELD THEORY: NEW RESEARCH

QUANTUM FIELD THEORY: NEW RESEARCH

O. KOVRAS
EDITOR

Nova Science Publishers, Inc.
New York

For permission to use material from this book please contact us:
Telephone 631-231-7269; Fax 631-231-8175
Web Site: http://www.novapublishers.com

LIBRARY OF CONGRESS CATALOGING-IN-PUBLICATION DATA

Quantum field theory: new research / O. Kovras, editor.
p. cm.
Includes bibliographical references and index.
ISBN 1-59454-509-X
1. Quantum field theory--Research. I. Kovras, O.
QC174.45.Q38 2005
530.14'3--dc22

2005014611

Published by Nova Science Publishers, Inc. ✦ New York

CONTENTS

PREFACE

Chapter 1 contains a detailed investigation of free neutral (Hermitian) or charged (non-Hermitian) scalar fields and the describing them (system of) Klein-Gordon equation(s) in momentum picture of motion. A form of the field equation(s) in terms of creation and annihilation operators is derived. An analysis of the (anti-dash)commutation relations on its base is presented. The concept of the vacuum and the evolution of state vectors are discussed.

In Chapter 2, the authors show that in the search of a unified mean field description of finite nuclei and of nuclear and neutron matter even at high densities, the relativistic nuclear model derived from effective field theory and density functional theory methods constitutes a competitive framework. The model predicts a soft equation of state, owing to the additional meson interaction terms, consistently with the results of the microscopic Dirac-Brueckner-Hartree-Fock theory and recent experimental observations from heavy ion collisions. In finite systems, after inclusion of the pairing correlations, the model is able to describe both stable and exotic nuclei. The authors address two examples at the limits of the nuclear landscape. On the one hand, we analyze the giant halo effect and the isoscalar giant monopole resonance in very neutron-rich Zr isotopes. On the other hand, we discuss the structure of superheavy nuclei with double shell closures.

Chapter 3 presents a new Lagrangian density $L = L_f + L_w$, L_f describes F-particles which form the given left-handed world, L_w describes W-particles which form the unknown right-handed world, L_f and L_w are symmetric, independent of each other before quantization and dependent on each other after quantization. $(0|H|0)$ is naturally obtained. From this it is possible to determine the cosmological constant and to correct non-perturbational methods which depend on the energy of the vacuum state.

On the basis of preceding paper, in Chapter 4, the authors discuss quantization for interacting fields, construct the coupling operators and mass operators, derives scattering operators and Feynman rules. We see that though independent of each other before quantization, L_f and L_w are dependent on each other after quantization. In contrast with the conventional *QED*, in the present theory, there is only one sort of parameters which are all finite and measurable, there are two sorts of corrections originating S_f and S_w and all Feynman integrals are convergent.

Chapter 5 takes one-loop correction as example to illustrate the perturbation method in the Quantum Field Theory Without Divergence, and to show that there are two sorts of corrections originating from S_f and S_w, Feynman integrals of loop-diagrams are all determined by the sum of integrands originating from S_f and S_w and are all convergent, thus it is unnecessary to introduce regularization and counter-terms. Three supplementary Feynman rules are given. On the same basis as the new QED, they obtain naturally a new generalized SU(2)XU(1) electroweak unified model which is left-right symmetric and does not contain unknown massive particles. Thus, the world is left-right symmetric in principle, but the part observed by us is asymmetric because L_w and L_f are all asymmetric. If the interaction between the W-matter and the F-matter is gravitation, W-matter is the candidate for dark matter.

In Chapter 6 is presented the so-called Einstein-Podolsky-Rosen (EPR) and Bell's theorems which are often supposed to prove that the local causality of Quantum Field Theory (QFT) is spoiled by the measurement process. This would imply an instantaneous, unphysical influence between distant measurements which would be hardly compatible with Special Relativity. Recently, actual experiments inspired in a proposal by Popper have been argued to disprove such 'nonlocal collapse' of the state vector. As a consequence, the 'orthodox' interpretation of the quantum theory, in which the state vector is used to describe the single events, has to be abandoned. It is then necessary to search a way out of the apparent contradiction between locality versus EPR and Bell's theorems. QFT may help, since it prevents the production of entangled states with a definite number of particles, that are postulated by EPR. A 'minimal statistical interpretation' can then allow for a full reconciliation with locality, although it renounces to understand the single event.

Chapter 7 illustrates that an effective Hamiltonian field theory for a (given scale) can be obtained by systematically decoupling irrelevant degrees of freedom (e.g., high-energy modes and many-body states) from relevant ones using a consistent renormalization scheme. Such a procedure is usually rather complicated and is plagued by the so-called Tamm-Dancoff renormalization problem. Here they present a succinct discussion of recent studies of such problems. Our method is based on many-body techniques and the Wilsonian exact renormalization group. In one sense, it resembles similarity renormalization group. However, neither perturbation theory nor unitarity of the similarity transformation are essential for this method. The non-unitarity of the approach is related to the fact that we have a biorthogonal representation of the given many-body problem. This, in fact, simplifies the diagonalization of the Hamiltonian matrix. The authors discuss its (non-)perturbative implementation. As illustrative examples we obtain results for the one-loop renormalized extended Lee model and the two-loop renormalized ϕ^4 theory.

In: Quantum Field Theory: New Research
Editor: O. Kovras, pp. 1-66

ISBN 1-59454-509-X

Chapter 1

Lagrangian Quantum Field Theory in Momentum Picture

Bozhidar Z. Iliev[*†]
Laboratory of Mathematical Modeling in Physics,
Institute for Nuclear Research and Nuclear Energy,
Bulgarian Academy of Sciences,
Boul. Tzarigradsko chaussée 72, 1784 Sofia, Bulgaria

Abstract

The work contains a detailed investigation of free neutral (Hermitian) or charged (non-Hermitian) scalar fields and the describing them (system of) Klein-Gordon equation(s) in momentum picture of motion. A form of the field equation(s) in terms of creation and annihilation operators is derived. An analysis of the (anti-)commutation relations on its base is presented. The concept of the vacuum and the evolution of state vectors are discussed.

1 Introduction

This paper pursuits a twofold goal. On one hand, it gives a detailed illustration of the methods of Lagrangian quantum field theory in momentum picture, introduced in [1, 2], on the simplest examples of free Hermitian (neutral, real) or non-Hermitian (charged, complex) scalar field. On another hand, it contains an in-depth analysis of the (system of) Klein-Gordon equation(s) in momentum picture describing such fields. Most of the known fundamental results are derived in a new way (and in a slightly modified form), but the work contains and new ones.

We have to mention, in this paper it is considered only the Lagrangian (canonical) quantum field theory in which the quantum fields are represented as operators, called field operators, acting on some Hilbert space, which in general is unknown if interacting fields are studied. These operators are supposed to satisfy some equations of motion, from them are constructed conserved quantities satisfying conservation laws, etc. From the view-point

*E-mail address: bozho@inrne.bas.bg
†URL: http://theo.inrne.bas.bg/~bozho/

of present-day quantum field theory, this approach is only a preliminary stage for more or less rigorous formulation of the theory in which the fields are represented as operator-valued distributions, a fact required even for description of free fields. Moreover, in non-perturbative directions, like constructive and conformal field theories, the main objects are the vacuum mean (expectation) values of the fields and from these are reconstructed the Hilbert space of states and the acting in it fields. Regardless of these facts, the Lagrangian (canonical) quantum field theory is an inherent component of the most of the ways of presentation of quantum field theory adopted explicitly or implicitly in books like [3–10]. Besides, the Lagrangian approach is a source of many ideas for other directions of research, like the axiomatic quantum field theory [5, 9, 10].

The basic moments of the method, we will follow in this work, are the next ones:

(i) In Heisenberg picture is fixed a (second) non-quantized and non-normally ordered operator-valued Lagrangian, which is supposed to be polynomial (or convergent power series) in the field operators and their first partial derivatives;

(ii) As conditions additional to the Lagrangian formalism are postulated the commutativity between the components of the momentum operator (see (2.6) below) and the Heisenberg relations between the field operators and momentum operator (see (2.7) below);

(iii) Following the Lagrangian formalism in momentum picture, the creation and annihilation operators are introduced and the dynamical variables and field equations are written in their terms;

(iv) From the last equations, by imposing some additional restrictions on the creation and annihilation operators, the (anti)commutation relations for these operators are derived;

(v) At last, the vacuum and normal ordering procedure are defined, by means of which the theory can be developed to a more or less complete form.

The main difference of the above scheme from the standard one is that we postulate the below-written relations (2.6) and (2.7) and, then, we look for compatible with them and the field equations (anti)commutation relations. (Recall, ordinary the (anti)commutation relations are postulated at first and the validity of the equations (2.6) and (2.7) is explored after that [11].)

In Sect. 2 are reviewed the basic moments of the momentum picture of motion in quantum field theory.

The rest of the work is divided into two parts.

Part A, involving sections 3–9, deals with the case of neutral (Hermitian, real) free scalar field. The contents of its sections is as follows:

In Sect. 3, the material of Sect. 2 is specialized to the case of free Hermitian (neutral, real) scalar field; in particular, the Klein-Gordon equation in momentum picture is derived.

Sect. 4 is devoted to analysis of the Klein-Gordon equation (in momentum picture) in terms of operators similar to (and, in fact, up to a phase factor and normalization constant, identical with) the Fourier images of field operators in Heisenberg picture. From them, in Sect. 5, are constructed the creation and annihilation operators which turn to be identical, up to a phase factor and, possibly, normalization constant, with the ones known from Heisenberg picture. Their physical meaning is discussed (or recalled). In Sect. 6, the 3-dimensional creation and annihilation operators (depending on the 3-momentum) are introduced and the field equation is written in their terms. It happens to be a tri-linear equation relative to them. This new form of the field equation is utilized in Sect. 7 for a detailed analysis of the (additional) conditions leading to the known commutation relations. In particular, it is proved that, excluding the vanishing field case, the quantization of a free Hermitian scalar field by *anti*-commutators is rejected by the field equation without an appeal to the spin-statistics theorem (or other equivalent to it additional assertion).

Sect. 8 is devoted to the introduction of the concept of vacuum (state) which requires a modification of the developed theory by a normal ordering of products of creation and/or annihilation operators. The vacua of Heisenberg and momentum pictures happen to coincide. The problem of state vectors, representing in momentum picture a free Hermitian scalar field, is considered in Sect. 9. It turns to be rather trivial due to the absence of any interaction. However, the construction of Fock base is recalled and the basic ideas of scattering theory are illustrated in this almost trivial case.

The second part B of our work is devoted to the general case of charged or neural free scalar field. Regardless of some overlap with part A, it concentrates mainly on the case of non-Hermitian field. Most of the proofs in it refer or are based, at least partially, on similar ones in the Hermitian case, investigated in part A. The problems of the choice of the initial Lagrangian and the 'right' definitions of the energy-momentum and charge operators are partially discussed. The layout of part B, involving sections 10–17, is similar to the one of part A.

The description of arbitrary free scalar field is presented in Sect. 10.

An analysis of the system of Klein-Gordon equations describing free scalar fields is presented in Sect. 11. A feature of the momentum picture is that, in a case of non-Hermitian field, the two equations of this system are not separate equations for the field and its Hermitian conjugate; they are mixed via the momentum operator. The creation and annihilation operators are introduced in Sect. 12 and the field equations are written in their terms in Sect. 13. They turn to be trilinear equations similar to the ones appearing the parafield theory. The commutation relations are extracted from them in Sect. 15. These reveal the non-equivalence of the theories build from different initial Lagrangians. To agree the results, one needs different additional hypotheses/conditions, depending on the concrete Lagrangian utilized. The 'best' Lagrangian (of three considered) is pointed out. The charge and orbital angular momentum operators are considered in Sect. 14. The vacuum is defined in Sect. 16, where the normal ordering of the dynamical variables is described too. We point that the last operation is the final step which leads to identical theories build from different initial Lagrangians. Some problems concerning the state vectors of free scalar fields are discussed in Sect. 17.

Sect. 18 closes the paper by pointing to its basic results.

The books [3–5] will be used as standard reference works on quantum field theory. Of course, this is more or less a random selection between the great number of papers on the theme.[1]

[1] The reader is referred for more details or other points of view, for instance, to [6, 12, 13] or the literature

Throughout this paper $\hbar$ denotes the Planck's constant (divided by 2π), c is the velocity of light in vacuum, and i stands for the imaginary unit.

The Minkowski spacetime is denoted by M. The Greek indices run from 0 to $\dim M - 1 = 3$. All Greek indices will be raised and lowered by means of the standard 4-dimensional Lorentz metric tensor $\eta^{\mu\nu}$ and its inverse $\eta_{\mu\nu}$ with signature $(+\,-\,-\,-)$. The Einstein's summation convention over indices repeated on different levels is assumed over the whole range of their values.

At the end, a technical remark is in order. The derivatives with respect to operator-valued (non-commuting) arguments will be calculated according to the rules of the classical analysis of commuting variables, which is an everywhere silently accepted practice [3, 11]. As it is demonstrated in [14], this is not quite correct but does not lead to incorrect results (except the non-uniqueness of the conserved quantities) when free scalar fields are concerned. We shall pay attention on that item at the corresponding places in the text.

2 The momentum picture

The momentum picture in quantum field theory was introduce in [1, 2]. Its essence is in the following.

Let us consider a system of quantum fields, represented in Heisenberg picture of motion by field operators $\tilde{\varphi}_i(x)\colon \mathcal{F} \to \mathcal{F}$, $i = 1, \dots, n \in \mathbb{N}$, in system's Hilbert space $\mathcal{F}$ of states and depending on a point x in Minkowski spacetime M. Here and henceforth, all quantities in Heisenberg picture will be marked by a tilde (wave) "$\tilde{\ }$" over their kernel symbols. Let $\tilde{\mathcal{P}}_\mu$ denotes the system's (canonical) momentum vectorial operator, defined via the energy-momentum tensorial operator $\tilde{\mathcal{T}}^{\mu\nu}$ of the system, viz.

$$\tilde{\mathcal{P}}_\mu := \frac{1}{c} \int\limits_{x^0=\mathrm{const}} \tilde{\mathcal{T}}_{0\mu}(x)\,\mathrm{d}^3\boldsymbol{x}. \tag{2.1}$$

Since this operator is Hermitian, $\tilde{\mathcal{P}}_\mu^\dagger = \tilde{\mathcal{P}}_\mu$, the operator

$$\mathcal{U}(x, x_0) = \exp\Big(\frac{1}{\mathrm{i}\hbar} \sum_\mu (x^\mu - x_0^\mu)\,\tilde{\mathcal{P}}_\mu\Big), \tag{2.2}$$

where $x_0 \in M$ is arbitrarily fixed and $x \in M$,[2] is unitary, i.e. $\mathcal{U}^\dagger(x_0, x) := (\mathcal{U}(x, x_0))^\dagger = \mathcal{U}^{-1}(x, x_0) = (\mathcal{U}(x, x_0))^{-1}$ and, via the formulae

$$\tilde{\mathcal{X}} \mapsto \mathcal{X}(x) = \mathcal{U}(x, x_0)(\tilde{\mathcal{X}}) \tag{2.3}$$

$$\tilde{\mathcal{A}}(x) \mapsto \mathcal{A}(x) = \mathcal{U}(x, x_0) \circ (\tilde{\mathcal{A}}(x)) \circ \mathcal{U}^{-1}(x, x_0), \tag{2.4}$$

---

cited in [3–6, 12, 13].

[2] The notation x_0, for a fixed point in M, should not be confused with the zeroth covariant coordinate $\eta_{0\mu}x^\mu$ of x which, following the convention $x_\nu := \eta_{\nu\mu}x^\mu$, is denoted by the same symbol x_0. From the context, it will always be clear whether x_0 refers to a point in M or to the zeroth covariant coordinate of a point $x \in M$.

realizes the transition to the *momentum picture*. Here $\tilde{\mathcal{X}}$ is a state vector in system's Hilbert space of states $\mathcal{F}$ and $\tilde{\mathcal{A}}(x)\colon \mathcal{F} \to \mathcal{F}$ is (observable or not) operator-valued function of $x \in M$ which, in particular, can be polynomial or convergent power series in the field operators $\tilde{\varphi}_i(x)$; respectively $\mathcal{X}(x)$ and $\mathcal{A}(x)$ are the corresponding quantities in momentum picture. In particular, the field operators transform as

$$\tilde{\varphi}_i(x) \mapsto \varphi_i(x) = \mathcal{U}(x, x_0) \circ \tilde{\varphi}_i(x) \circ \mathcal{U}^{-1}(x, x_0). \tag{2.5}$$

Notice, in (2.2) the multiplier $(x^\mu - x_0^\mu)$ is regarded as a real parameter (in which $\tilde{\mathcal{P}}_\mu$ is linear). Generally, $\mathcal{X}(x)$ and $\mathcal{A}(x)$ depend also on the point x_0 and, to be quite correct, one should write $\mathcal{X}(x, x_0)$ and $\mathcal{A}(x, x_0)$ for $\mathcal{X}(x)$ and $\mathcal{A}(x)$, respectively. However, in the most situations in the present work, this dependence is not essential or, in fact, is not presented at all. For this reason, we shall *not* indicate it explicitly.

As it was said above, we consider quantum field theories in which the components $\tilde{\mathcal{P}}_\mu$ of the momentum operator commute between themselves and satisfy the Heisenberg relations/equations with the field operators, i.e. we suppose that $\tilde{\mathcal{P}}_\mu$ and $\tilde{\varphi}_i(x)$ satisfy the relations:

$$[\tilde{\mathcal{P}}_\mu, \tilde{\mathcal{P}}_\nu]_{\_} = 0 \tag{2.6}$$

$$[\tilde{\varphi}_i(x), \tilde{\mathcal{P}}_\mu]_{\_} = \mathrm{i}\hbar\partial_\mu \tilde{\varphi}_i(x). \tag{2.7}$$

Here $[A, B]_\pm := A \circ B \pm B \circ A$, $\circ$ being the composition of mappings sign, is the commutator/anticommutator of operators (or matrices) A and B. The momentum operator $\tilde{\mathcal{P}}_\mu$ commutes with the 'evolution' operator $\mathcal{U}(x, x_0)$ (see below (2.12)) and its inverse,

$$[\tilde{\mathcal{P}}_\mu, \mathcal{U}(x, x_0)]_{\_} = 0 \qquad [\tilde{\mathcal{P}}_\mu, \mathcal{U}^{-1}(x, x_0)]_{\_} = 0, \tag{2.8}$$

due to (2.6) and (2.2). So, the momentum operator remains unchanged in momentum picture, viz. we have (see (2.4) and (2.8))

$$\mathcal{P}_\mu = \tilde{\mathcal{P}}_\mu. \tag{2.9}$$

Since from (2.2) and (2.6) follows

$$\mathrm{i}\hbar\frac{\partial\mathcal{U}(x, x_0)}{\partial x^\mu} = \mathcal{P}_\mu \circ \mathcal{U}(x, x_0) \qquad \mathcal{U}(x_0, x_0) = \mathsf{id}_\mathcal{F}, \tag{2.10}$$

we see that, due to (2.3), a state vector $\mathcal{X}(x)$ in momentum picture is a solution of the initial-value problem

$$\mathrm{i}\hbar\frac{\partial\mathcal{X}(x)}{\partial x^\mu} = \mathcal{P}_\mu(\mathcal{X}(x)) \qquad \mathcal{X}(x)|_{x=x_0} = \mathcal{X}(x_0) = \tilde{\mathcal{X}} \tag{2.11}$$

which is a 4-dimensional analogue of a similar problem for the Schrödinger equation in quantum mechanics [15–17].

By virtue of (2.2), or in view of the independence of $\mathcal{P}_\mu$ of x, the solution of (2.11) is

$$\mathcal{X}(x) = \mathcal{U}(x, x_0)(\mathcal{X}(x_0)) = \mathrm{e}^{\frac{1}{\mathrm{i}\hbar}(x^\mu - x_0^\mu)\mathcal{P}_\mu}(\mathcal{X}(x_0)). \tag{2.12}$$

Thus, if $\mathcal{X}(x_0) = \tilde{\mathcal{X}}$ is an eigenvector of $\mathcal{P}_\mu$ $(= \tilde{\mathcal{P}}_\mu)$ with eigenvalues p_μ,

$$\mathcal{P}_\mu(\mathcal{X}(x_0)) = p_\mu \mathcal{X}(x_0) \quad (= p_\mu \tilde{\mathcal{X}} = \tilde{\mathcal{P}}_\mu(\tilde{\mathcal{X}})), \tag{2.13}$$

we have the following *explicit* form of the state vectors

$$\mathcal{X}(x) = \mathrm{e}^{\frac{1}{\mathrm{i}\hbar}(x^\mu - x_0^\mu)p_\mu}(\mathcal{X}(x_0)). \tag{2.14}$$

It should clearly be understood, *this is the general form of all state vectors* as they are eigenvectors of all (commuting) observables [5, p. 59], in particular, of the momentum operator.

In momentum picture, all of the field operators happen to be constant in spacetime, i.e.

$$\varphi_i(x) = \mathcal{U}(x, x_0) \circ \tilde{\varphi}_i(x) \circ \mathcal{U}^{-1}(x, x_0) = \varphi_i(x_0) = \tilde{\varphi}_i(x_0) =: \varphi_{(0)\,i}. \tag{2.15}$$

Evidently, a similar result is valid for any (observable or not such) function of the field operators which is polynomial or convergent power series in them and/or their first partial derivatives. However, if $\tilde{\mathcal{A}}(x)$ is an arbitrary operator or depends on the field operators in a different way, then the corresponding to it operator $\mathcal{A}(x)$ according to (2.4) is, generally, not spacetime-constant and depends on the both points x and x_0. As a rules, if $\mathcal{A}(x) = \mathcal{A}(x, x_0)$ is independent of x, we, usually, write $\mathcal{A}$ for $\mathcal{A}(x, x_0)$, omitting all arguments.

It should be noted, the Heisenberg relations (2.7) in momentum picture transform into the identities $\partial_\mu \varphi_i = 0$ meaning that the field operators φ_i in momentum picture are spacetime constant operators (see (2.15)). So, in momentum picture, the Heisenberg relations (2.7) are incorporated in the constancy of the field operators.

Let $\tilde{\mathcal{L}}$ be the system's Lagrangian (in Heisenberg picture). It is supposed to be polynomial or convergent power series in the field operators and their first partial derivatives, i.e. $\tilde{\mathcal{L}} = \tilde{\mathcal{L}}(\varphi_i(x), \partial_\nu \varphi_i(x))$ with ∂_ν denoting the partial derivative operator relative to the νth coordinate x^ν. In momentum picture, it transforms into

$$\mathcal{L} = \tilde{\mathcal{L}}(\varphi_i(x), y_{j\nu}) \qquad y_{j\nu} = \frac{1}{\mathrm{i}\hbar}[\varphi_j, \mathcal{P}_\nu]_{\_}, \tag{2.16}$$

i.e. in momentum picture one has simply to replace the field operators in Heisenberg picture with their values at a fixed point x_0 and the partial derivatives $\partial_\nu \tilde{\varphi}_j(x)$ in Heisenberg picture with the above-defined quantities $y_{j\nu}$. The (constant) field operators φ_i satisfy the following *algebraic Euler-Lagrange equations in momentum picture* :[3]

$$\Big\{ \frac{\partial\, \tilde{\mathcal{L}}(\varphi_j, y_{l\nu})}{\partial \varphi_i} - \frac{1}{\mathrm{i}\hbar} \Big[\frac{\partial\, \tilde{\mathcal{L}}(\varphi_j, y_{l\nu})}{y_{i\mu}}, \mathcal{P}_\mu \Big]_{\_} \Big\} \Big|_{y_{j\nu} = \frac{1}{\mathrm{i}\hbar}[\varphi_j, \mathcal{P}_\nu]_{\_}} = 0. \tag{2.17}$$

Since $\mathcal{L}$ is supposed to be polynomial or convergent power series in its arguments, the equations (2.17) are *algebraic*, not differential, ones. This result is a natural one in view of (2.15).

By virtue of (2.4) and (2.9), the momentum operator (2.1) can be written as

$$\mathcal{P}_\mu = \tilde{\mathcal{P}}_\mu = \frac{1}{c} \int\limits_{x^0 = x_0^0} \mathcal{U}^{-1}(x, x_0) \circ \mathcal{T}_{0\mu} \circ \mathcal{U}(x, x_0)\, \mathrm{d}^3 \boldsymbol{x}. \tag{2.18}$$

This expression for $\mathcal{P}_\mu$ will be employed essentially in the present paper.

Part A

Free neutral scalar field

The purpose of this part of the present work is a detailed exploration of a free neutral (Hermitian, real, uncharged) scalar field in momentum picture.[4]

After fixing the notation and terminology, we write the Klein-Gordon equation in momentum picture and derive its version in terms of creation and annihilation operators. The famous commutation relations are extracted from it. After defining the vacuum for a free Hermitian scalar field, some problems concerning the state vectors of such a field are investigated.

[3] In (2.17) and similar expressions appearing further, the derivatives of functions of operators with respect to operator arguments are calculated in the same way as if the operators were ordinary (classical) fields/functions, only the order of the arguments should not be changed. This is a silently accepted practice in the literature [4,5]. In the most cases such a procedure is harmless, but it leads to the problem of non-unique definitions of the quantum analogues of the classical conserved quantities, like the energy-momentum and charge operators. For some details on this range of problems in quantum field theory, see [14]; in particular, the *loc. cit.* contains an example of a Lagrangian whose field equations are *not* the Euler-Lagrange equations (2.17) obtained as just described.

[4] A classical real field, after quantization, becomes a Hermitian operator acting on the system's (field's) Hilbert space of states. That is why the quantum analogue of a classical real scalar field is called Hermitian scalar field. However, it is an accepted common practice such a field to be called (also) a real scalar field. In this sense, the terms real and Hermitian scalar field are equivalent and, hence, interchangeable. Besides, since a real (classical or quantum) scalar does not carry any charge, it is called neutral or uncharged scalar field too.

3 Description of free neutral scalar field in momentum picture

Consider a free neutral (Hermitian) scalar field with mass m. The corresponding to such a field operator will be denoted by $\tilde{\varphi}$. It is Hermitian, i.e.

$$\tilde{\varphi}^{\dagger}(x) = \tilde{\varphi}(x), \tag{3.1}$$

where the dagger $\dagger$ denotes Hermitian conjugation relative to the scalar product $\langle\cdot|\cdot\rangle$ of field's Hilbert space $\mathcal{F}$, and it is described in the Heisenberg picture by the Lagrangian

$$\tilde{\mathcal{L}} = \tilde{\mathcal{L}}(\tilde{\varphi}, \partial_\nu \tilde{\varphi}) = -\frac{1}{2} m^2 c^4 \tilde{\varphi} \circ \tilde{\varphi} + \frac{1}{2} c^2 \hbar^2 (\partial_\mu \tilde{\varphi}) \circ (\partial^\mu \tilde{\varphi}), \tag{3.2}$$

which in momentum picture transforms into (see (2.16))

$$\mathcal{L} = \tilde{\mathcal{L}}(\varphi, y_\nu)\big|_{y_\nu = \frac{1}{\mathrm{i}\hbar}[\varphi_0, \mathcal{P}_\nu]_{\_}} = -\frac{1}{2} m^2 c^4 \varphi_0 \circ \varphi_0 - \frac{1}{2} c^2 [\varphi_0, \mathcal{P}_\mu]_{\_} \circ [\varphi_0, \mathcal{P}^\mu]_{\_}. \tag{3.3}$$

Here φ_0 is the constant value of the field operator in momentum picture i.e. (see (2.15))[5]

$$\varphi(x) = \mathcal{U}(x, x_0) \circ \tilde{\varphi}(x) \circ \mathcal{U}^{-1}(x, x_0) = \varphi(x_0) = \tilde{\varphi}(x_0) =: \varphi_0. \tag{3.4}$$

Since the operator $\mathcal{U}(x, x_0)$ is unitary (see (2.2) and use the Hermiticity of the momentum operator), the (momentum) field operator φ_0 is also Hermitian, i.e.

$$\varphi_0^\dagger = \varphi_0. \tag{3.5}$$

So, we have [6]

$$\pi^\mu := \frac{\partial \tilde{\mathcal{L}}(\varphi_0, y_\nu)}{\partial y_\mu}\Big|_{y_\nu = \frac{1}{\mathrm{i}\hbar}[\varphi_0, \mathcal{P}_\nu]_{\_}} = -\mathrm{i}\hbar c^2 [\varphi_0, \mathcal{P}^\mu]_{\_} \tag{3.6}$$

$$\frac{\partial \mathcal{L}}{\partial \varphi_0} = \frac{\partial \tilde{\mathcal{L}}}{\partial \varphi_0} = -m^2 c^4 \varphi_0. \tag{3.7}$$

Consequently, equation (2.17), in this particular situation, yields

$$m^2 c^2 \varphi_0 - [[\varphi_0, \mathcal{P}_\mu]_{\_}, \mathcal{P}^\mu]_{\_} = 0. \tag{3.8}$$

This is the *Klein-Gordon equation in momentum picture*. It replaces the usual Klein-Gordon equation

$$\Big(\tilde{\Box} + \frac{m^2 c^2}{\hbar^2} \mathsf{id}_{\mathcal{F}}\Big) \tilde{\varphi}(x) = 0, \tag{3.9}$$

---

[5] The index "0" in φ_0 indicates the dependence on x_0, according to (3.4).

[6] As pointed at the end of the Introduction, the calculation of the derivatives in (3.6) and (3.7) below is not quite correct mathematically. However, the field equation (3.8) is correct; for its rigorous derivation, see [14].

where $\widetilde{\Box} := \partial_\mu \partial^\mu$, in Heisenberg picture.[7]

The energy-momentum tensorial operator $\mathcal{T}_{\mu\nu}$ has two (non-equivalent) forms for free Hermitian scalar field, viz.

$$\tilde{\mathcal{T}}_{\mu\nu} = \tilde{\pi}_\mu \circ \partial_\nu \tilde{\varphi} - \eta_{\mu\nu} \tilde{\mathcal{L}} = c^2\hbar^2 (\partial_\mu \tilde{\varphi}) \circ (\partial_\nu \tilde{\varphi}) - \eta_{\mu\nu} \tilde{\mathcal{L}} \tag{3.10a}$$

$$\begin{aligned} \tilde{\mathcal{T}}_{\mu\nu} &= \frac{1}{2}(\tilde{\pi}_\mu \circ \partial_\nu \tilde{\varphi} + \partial_\nu \tilde{\varphi} \circ \tilde{\pi}_\mu) - \eta_{\mu\nu} \tilde{\mathcal{L}} \\ &= \frac{1}{2} c^2\hbar^2 \big((\partial_\mu \tilde{\varphi}) \circ (\partial_\nu \tilde{\varphi}) + (\partial_\nu \tilde{\varphi}) \circ (\partial_\mu \tilde{\varphi}) \big) - \eta_{\mu\nu} \tilde{\mathcal{L}}, \end{aligned} \tag{3.10b}$$

which in momentum picture read respectively:

$$\mathcal{T}_{\mu\nu} = -c^2 [\varphi_0, \mathcal{P}_\mu]_{\_} \circ [\varphi_0, \mathcal{P}_\nu]_{\_} + \eta_{\mu\nu} \frac{1}{2} c^2 \big(m^2 c^2 \varphi_0 \circ \varphi_0 + [\varphi_0, \mathcal{P}_\lambda]_{\_} \circ [\varphi_0, \mathcal{P}^\lambda]_{\_} \big) \tag{3.11a}$$

$$\begin{aligned} \mathcal{T}_{\mu\nu} = &- \frac{1}{2} c^2 \big([\varphi_0, \mathcal{P}_\mu]_{\_} \circ [\varphi_0, \mathcal{P}_\nu]_{\_} + [\varphi_0, \mathcal{P}_\nu]_{\_} \circ [\varphi_0, \mathcal{P}_\mu]_{\_} \big) \\ &+ \eta_{\mu\nu} \frac{1}{2} c^2 \big(m^2 c^2 \varphi_0 \circ \varphi_0 + [\varphi_0, \mathcal{P}_\lambda]_{\_} \circ [\varphi_0, \mathcal{P}^\lambda]_{\_} \big). \end{aligned} \tag{3.11b}$$

Let us say a few words on the *two* versions, (3.10a) and (3.10b), of the energy-momentum operator. The former one is a direct analogue of the classical expression for the energy-momentum tensor, while the latter variant is obtained from (3.10a) by a 'Hermitian symmetrization'. The second expression is symmetric and Hermitian, i.e. $\tilde{\mathcal{T}}_{\mu\nu} = \tilde{\mathcal{T}}_{\nu\mu}$ and $\tilde{\mathcal{T}}^\dagger_{\mu\nu} = \tilde{\mathcal{T}}_{\mu\nu}$, while the first one is such if $\partial_\mu \tilde{\varphi}$ and $\partial_\nu \tilde{\varphi}$ commute for all subscripts μ and ν. However, as we shall see, both forms of $\mathcal{T}_{\mu\nu}$ lead to one and the same (Hermitian) momentum operator. In this sense, the both forms of $\tilde{\mathcal{T}}_{\mu\nu}$ are equivalent in quantum field theory. More details on this problem will be given in Sect. 10.

Before going on, let us make a technical remark. The derivatives in (3.6) and (3.7) are calculated according to the rules of classical analysis of commuting variables, which is not correct, as explained in [14]. However, the field equation (3.8) or (3.9) is completely correct for the reasons given in *loc. cit.* Besides, the two forms (3.10) of the energy-momentum tensor operator are also due to an incorrect applications of the rules mentioned to the region of analysis of non-commuting variables; the correct rigorous expression turns to be (3.10b). The reader is referred for more detail on that item to [14], in particular to section 5.1 in it. The only reason why we use a non-rigorous formalism is our intention to stay closer to the

---

[7] As a simple exercise, the reader may wish to prove that the D'Alembert operator (on the space of operator-valued functions) in momentum picture is $\Box(\cdot) = -\frac{1}{\hbar^2}[[\cdot, \mathcal{P}_\mu]_{\_}, \mathcal{P}_\nu]_{\_}\eta^{\mu\nu}$. (Hint: from the relation $\mathrm{i}\hbar \frac{\partial \mathcal{A}(x)}{\partial x^\mu} = [\mathcal{A}(x), \tilde{\mathcal{P}}^{\mathrm{t}}_\mu]_{\_}$ with $\tilde{\mathcal{P}}^{\mathrm{t}}_\mu = -\mathrm{i}\hbar \frac{\partial}{\partial x^\mu} + p_\mu \,\mathrm{id}_{\mathcal{F}}$ (see [18]), it follows that $\widetilde{\Box}(\tilde{\varphi}_i) = -\frac{1}{\hbar^2}[[\tilde{\varphi}_i, \tilde{\mathcal{P}}^{\mathrm{t}}_\mu]_{\_} \tilde{\mathcal{P}}^{\mathrm{t}}_\nu]_{\_}\eta^{\mu\nu}$; now prove that in momentum picture $\mathcal{P}^{\mathrm{t}}_\mu = \tilde{\mathcal{P}}^{\mathrm{t}}_\mu + \mathcal{P}_\mu$.) Now, the equation (3.8) follows immediately from here and the 'usual' Klein-Gordon equations (3.9). By the way, the above representation for $\Box(\cdot)$ remains valid in any picture of motion as it is a polynomial relative to $(\cdot)$ and $\mathcal{P}_\mu$; in particular, (3.8) is equivalent to $m^2c^2 \tilde{\varphi}_0 - [\tilde{\varphi}_0, \tilde{\mathcal{P}}_\mu]_{\_}, \tilde{\mathcal{P}}^\mu]_{\_} = 0$ which is equivalent to (3.9) due to the (Heisenberg) relation $[\tilde{\varphi}_0, \tilde{\mathcal{P}}_\mu]_{\_} = \mathrm{i}\hbar\partial_\mu \tilde{\varphi}$.

standard books on Lagrangian quantum field theory. This approach will turn to be harmless for the range of problems considered in the present paper.

A free neutral or charged scalar field has a vanishing spin angular momentum and possesses an orbital angular momentum, which coincides with its total angular momentum. The orbital angular momentum density operator is

$$\tilde{\mathcal{L}}^{\lambda}_{\mu\nu}(x) = -\tilde{\mathcal{L}}^{\lambda}_{\nu\mu}(x) = x_\mu \tilde{\mathcal{T}}^{\lambda}{}_{\nu}(x) - x_\nu \tilde{\mathcal{T}}^{\lambda}{}_{\mu}(x) \tag{3.12}$$

$$\mathcal{L}^{\lambda}_{\mu\nu} = -\mathcal{L}^{\lambda}_{\nu\mu} = x_\mu \mathcal{T}^{\lambda}{}_{\nu} - x_\nu \mathcal{T}^{\lambda}{}_{\mu} \tag{3.13}$$

in Heisenberg and momentum pictures, respectively. The angular momentum operator in Heisenberg and momentum picture, respectively, is

$$\begin{aligned}\tilde{\mathcal{L}}_{\mu\nu} &:= \frac{1}{c}\int\limits_{x^0=\text{const}} \tilde{\mathcal{L}}^{0}_{\mu\nu}(x)\,\mathrm{d}^3\boldsymbol{x} = \frac{1}{c}\int\limits_{x^0=\text{const}} \{x_\mu \tilde{\mathcal{T}}^{0}{}_{\nu}(x) - x_\nu \tilde{\mathcal{T}}^{0}{}_{\mu}(x)\}\,\mathrm{d}^3\boldsymbol{x} \\ &= \frac{1}{c}\int\limits_{x^0=\text{const}} \mathcal{U}^{-1}(x,x_0)\circ\{x_\mu \mathcal{T}^{0}{}_{\nu} - x_\nu \mathcal{T}^{0}{}_{\mu}\}\circ\mathcal{U}(x,x_0)\,\mathrm{d}^3\boldsymbol{x}\end{aligned} \tag{3.14}$$

$$\mathcal{L}_{\mu\nu}(x,x_0) = \mathcal{U}(x,x_0)\circ\tilde{\mathcal{L}}_{\mu\nu}\circ\mathcal{U}^{-1}(x,x_0). \tag{3.15}$$

Since the spin angular momentum of a free scalar field is zero, the equations

$$\partial_\lambda \tilde{\mathcal{L}}_{\mu\nu} = 0 \quad \frac{\mathrm{d}\,\tilde{\mathcal{L}}_{\mu\nu}}{\mathrm{d}x^0} = 0 \quad \partial_\lambda \tilde{\mathcal{L}}^{\lambda}_{\mu\nu} = 0 \tag{3.16}$$

express equivalent forms of the conservation law of angular momentum. As the treatment of the orbital angular momentum for a neutral and charged scalar fields is quite similar, we shall present a unified consideration of the both cases in Sect. 14.

A simple, but important, conclusion from (3.8) is that the operator

$$\mathcal{M}^2\colon \varphi_0 \mapsto \frac{1}{c^2}[[\varphi_0, \mathcal{P}_\mu]_{\_}, \mathcal{P}^\mu]_{\_} \tag{3.17}$$

should be interpreted as square-of-mass operator of the field in momentum (and hence in any) picture. This does not contradict to the accepted opinion that the square-of-mass operator is equal to the Lorentz square of the (divided by c) momentum operator. The problem here is in what is called a momentum operator and in what picture the considerations are done. Indeed, in Heisenberg picture, we can write

$$\begin{aligned}\tilde{\mathcal{M}}^2(\tilde{\varphi}) &= \frac{1}{c^2}[[\tilde{\varphi}, \tilde{\mathcal{P}}_\mu]_{\_}, \tilde{\mathcal{P}}^\mu]_{\_} = \frac{1}{c^2}[\mathrm{i}\hbar\partial_\mu\tilde{\varphi}, \tilde{\mathcal{P}}^\mu]_{\_} = \frac{(\mathrm{i}\hbar)^2}{c^2}(\partial_\mu\partial^\mu)(\tilde{\varphi}(x)) \\ &\Big(= -\frac{(\hbar)^2}{c^2}\,\square\tilde{\varphi}(x)\Big) = \frac{1}{c^2}\mathcal{P}^{\text{QM}}_\mu\circ\mathcal{P}^{\text{QM}\,\mu}(\tilde{\varphi}(x)) = \cdots = \frac{1}{c^2}[[\tilde{\varphi}, \tilde{\mathcal{P}}^{\text{t}}_\mu]_{\_}, \tilde{\mathcal{P}}^{\text{t}\,\mu}]_{\_},\end{aligned} \tag{3.18}$$

where [18] $\mathcal{P}^{\text{QM}}_\mu = \mathrm{i}\hbar\partial_\mu$ and $\tilde{\mathcal{P}}^{\text{t}}_\mu = \tilde{\mathcal{P}}^{\text{QM}}_\mu + p_\mu\,\mathsf{id}_{\mathcal{F}}$, with $p_\mu = \text{const}$ and $\mathsf{id}_{\mathcal{F}}$ being the identity mapping of $\mathcal{F}$, are respectively the quantum mechanical and translational momentum operators. So, we see that the conventional identification of $\tilde{\mathcal{M}}^2$ with the square of (divided by c) momentum operator corresponds to the identification of the last operator with $\tilde{\mathcal{P}}_\mu^{\mathrm{QM}}$ (or of its square with $-\hbar^2\tilde{\Box}$). For details on the last item the reader is referred to [18]. It should be noted, the eigenvalues of the operator (3.17) on the solutions of (3.8) characterize the field (or its particles), while the eigenvalues of $\frac{1}{c^2}\mathcal{P}_\mu \circ \mathcal{P}^\mu$ on the same solutions are characteristics of the particular states these solutions represent.

4 Analysis of the Klein-Gordon equation

Our next aim is to find, if possible the (general) explicit form of the (constant) field operator φ_0. The Klein-Gordon equation (3.8) is not enough for the purpose due to the simple fact that the (canonical) momentum operator $\mathcal{P}_\mu$ depends on φ_0. To show this, recall the definition (2.1) of $\mathcal{P}_\mu$ and the expression (2.18) for it through the energy-momentum operators $\mathcal{T}_{\mu\nu}$ and $\tilde{\mathcal{T}}_{\mu\nu}$, given in Heisenberg and momentum pictures, respectively, by (3.10) and (3.11). Therefore (3.8), (2.18), (3.11), and the explicit relation (2.2) form a closed algebraic-functional system of equations for determination of φ_0 (and $\mathcal{P}_\mu$).

At the beginning of our analysis of the equations defining φ, we notice the evident solution

$$[\varphi_0, \mathcal{P}_\mu]_{\_} = 0 \qquad \text{for } m = 0 \tag{4.1}$$

of (3.8) which, by virtue of the Heisenberg equations/relations

$$[\tilde{\varphi}(x), \tilde{\mathcal{P}}_\mu]_{\_} = \mathrm{i}\hbar \frac{\partial \tilde{\varphi}(x)}{\partial x^\mu} \tag{4.2}$$

leads to $\tilde{\varphi}(x) = \tilde{\varphi}(x_0) = \text{const}$ for $m = 0$. Consequently (in the zero mass case) our system of equations admits a, generally non-vanishing, solution (see also (3.4))

$$\tilde{\varphi}(x) = \tilde{\varphi}(x_0) = \text{const} = \varphi_0 \qquad \tilde{\mathcal{P}}_\mu = \mathcal{P}_\mu = 0 \qquad \text{for } m = 0. \tag{4.3}$$

Evidently, (4.1) implies

$$\mathcal{T}_{\mu\nu} = 0 \qquad \mathcal{L}^\lambda_{\mu\nu} = 0, \tag{4.4}$$

due to (3.11) and (3.13), and, consequently, the dynamical variables for the solutions (4.1) vanish, i.e.

$$\mathcal{P}_\mu = 0 \qquad \mathcal{L}_{\mu\nu} = 0. \tag{4.5}$$

For the general structure of the solutions of (3.8) is valid the following result.

Proposition 4.1. *Every solution φ_0 of (3.8) and (2.7) is of the form*

$$\varphi_0 = \int \mathrm{d}^3\boldsymbol{k} \{ f_+(\boldsymbol{k})\varphi_0(k)\big|_{k_0=+\sqrt{m^2c^2+\boldsymbol{k}^2}} + f_-(\boldsymbol{k})\varphi_0(k)\big|_{k_0=-\sqrt{m^2c^2+\boldsymbol{k}^2}} \} \tag{4.6}$$

which can, equivalently, be rewritten as

$$\varphi_0 = \int \mathrm{d}^4 k \delta(k^2 - m^2c^2) f(k) \varphi_0(k). \tag{4.7}$$

Here: $k = (k^0, k^1, k^2, k^3)$ *is a 4-vector with dimension of 4-momentum,* $k^2 = k_\mu k^\mu = k_0^2 - k_1^2 - k_2 - k_3^2 = k_0^2 - \boldsymbol{k}^2$ *with* k_μ *being the components of* k *and* $\boldsymbol{k} := (k^1, k^2, k^3) = -(k_1, k_2, k_3)$ *being the 3-dimensional part of* k*,* $\delta(\cdot)$ *is the (1-dimensional) Dirac delta function,* $\varphi_0(k)\colon \mathcal{F} \to \mathcal{F}$ *is a solution of the equation*

$$[\varphi_0(k), \mathcal{P}_\mu]_- = -k_\mu \varphi_0(k), \tag{4.8}$$

$f_\pm$ *are complex-valued functions (resp. distributions (generalized functions)) of* $\boldsymbol{k}$ *for solutions different from* (4.3) *(resp. for the solutions* (4.3)*), and* f *is a complex-valued function (resp. distribution) of* k *for solutions different from* (4.3) *(resp. for the solutions* (4.3)*). Besides* $f(k)|_{k_0=\pm\sqrt{m^2c^2+\boldsymbol{k}^2}} = 2\sqrt{m^2c^2 + \boldsymbol{k}^2} f_\pm(\boldsymbol{k})$ *for solutions different from* (4.3).

Remark 4.1. In fact, in (4.6) enter only those solutions of (4.8) for which

$$k^2 := k_\mu k^\mu = k_0^2 - \boldsymbol{k}^2 = m^2c^2. \tag{4.9}$$

Besides, a non-vanishing solution of (4.8) is a solution of (3.8) iff the condition (4.9) holds. (Proof: write (3.8) with $\varphi_0(k)$ for φ_0 and use (4.8) twice.)

Remark 4.2. Evidently, the l.h.s. of (4.8) vanishes for the solutions (4.3). Therefore, we have

$$\tilde{\varphi}_0(x, 0) = \tilde{\varphi}_0(x_0, 0) = \text{const} = \varphi_0(0) \qquad \mathcal{P}_\mu = \tilde{\mathcal{P}}_\mu = 0 \tag{4.10}$$

where

$$\tilde{\varphi}_0(x, k) := \mathcal{U}^{-1}(x, x_0) \circ \varphi_0(k) \circ \mathcal{U}(x, x_0). \tag{4.11}$$

In terms of (4.6), this solution is described by $m = 0$ and, for example, $f_\pm(\boldsymbol{k}) = (\frac{1}{2} \pm a)\delta^3(\boldsymbol{k})$, $a \in \mathbb{C}$ or $f(k)$ such that $f(k)|_{k_0=\pm|\boldsymbol{k}|} = (1 \pm 2a)|\boldsymbol{k}|\delta^3(\boldsymbol{k})$, $a \in \mathbb{C}$.

Remark 4.3. Since φ_0 is Hermitian (see (3.5)), we have

$$\big(f_\pm(k)\varphi_0(k)\big|_{k_0=\pm\sqrt{m^2c^2+\boldsymbol{k}^2}}\big)^\dagger = -f_\mp(-k)\varphi_0(-k)\big|_{k_0=\mp\sqrt{m^2c^2+\boldsymbol{k}^2}}. \tag{4.12}$$

due to (4.6). Also the similar relation

$$(f(\boldsymbol{k})\varphi_0(k))^\dagger = f(-\boldsymbol{k})\varphi_0(-k), \tag{4.13}$$

holds as a corollary of (4.7).[8]

[8] The same result follows also from the below-written equations (4.19) and (4.21). Indeed, (4.19) and $\tilde{\varphi}^\dagger = \tilde{\varphi}$ imply $\underline{\tilde{\varphi}}_0(k)^\dagger = \underline{\tilde{\varphi}}_0(-k)$, which, in view of (4.21), entails (4.13).

Proof. Since the proposition was proved for the 'degenerate' solutions (4.3) in remark 4.2, below we shall suppose that $(m,k) \neq (0,0)$ (and, hence $\mathcal{P}_\mu \neq 0$).

The equality (4.7) is equivalent to (4.6) (for solutions different from (4.3)) due to $\delta(y^2 - a^2) = \frac{1}{2a}(\delta(y-a) + \delta(y+a))$ for $a > 0$.

Let φ_0 be given by (4.7). Using (4.8), we get

$$[\varphi_0, \mathcal{P}_\mu]_- = -\int \mathrm{d}^4 k k_\mu \delta(k^2 - m^2c^2) f(k) \varphi_0(k). \tag{4.14}$$

Inserting this into (3.8) and, again, applying (3.8), we see that (4.7) is a solution of (3.8). So, it remains to be proved that any solution of (3.8) is of the form (4.7).

The equation (4.8) in Heisenberg picture reads (see (2.5))

$$[\tilde{\varphi}(x,k), \tilde{\mathcal{P}}_\mu]_- = -k_\mu \tilde{\varphi}(x,k). \tag{4.15}$$

Combining this with (4.2) (with $\tilde{\varphi}(x,k)$ for $\tilde{\varphi}(x)$), we find

$$\tilde{\varphi}(x,k) = \mathrm{e}^{-\frac{1}{\mathrm{i}\hbar}(x^\mu - x_0^\mu)k_\mu} \tilde{\varphi}(x_0,k) = \mathrm{e}^{-\frac{1}{\mathrm{i}\hbar}(x^\mu - x_0^\mu)k_\mu} \varphi_0(k) \tag{4.16}$$

as

$$\varphi_0(k) = \tilde{\varphi}(x_0,k). \tag{4.17}$$

Hence, due to (2.5), the equation (4.7) in Heisenberg picture reads

$$\tilde{\varphi}(x) = \int \mathrm{d}^4 k \delta(k^2 - m^2c^2) \mathrm{e}^{+\mathrm{i}\frac{1}{\hbar}k_\mu x^\mu} \mathrm{e}^{\frac{1}{\mathrm{i}\hbar}k_\mu x_0^\mu} f(k) \varphi_0(k). \tag{4.18}$$

At the end, recalling that any solution (different from (4.3)) of the Klein-Gordon equation (3.9), satisfying the Heisenberg relation (5.3), admits a Fourier expansion of the form [3–5]

$$\tilde{\varphi}(x) = \int \mathrm{d}^4 k \delta(k^2 - m^2c^2) \mathrm{e}^{\mathrm{i}\frac{1}{\hbar}k_\mu x^\mu} \underline{\tilde{\varphi}}(k) \tag{4.19}$$

for some operator-valued function $\underline{\tilde{\varphi}}_0(k)$ satisfying (4.8) under the condition (4.9), viz.[9]

$$[\underline{\tilde{\varphi}}(k), \mathcal{P}_\mu]_- = -k_\mu \underline{\tilde{\varphi}}(k) \qquad k^2 = m^2c^2, \tag{4.20}$$

the proof is completed by the identification

$$\underline{\tilde{\varphi}}(k) = e^{\frac{1}{\mathrm{i}\hbar}k_\mu x_0^\mu} f(k) \varphi_0(k) = e^{\frac{1}{\mathrm{i}\hbar}k_\mu x_0^\mu} f(k) \tilde{\varphi}(x_0,k) \tag{4.21}$$

[9] The first equality in (4.20) is the Fourier image of (2.7).

and subsequent return from Heisenberg to momentum picture. □

Meanwhile, we have proved two quite important results. On one hand, by virtue of (4.21) and the homogeneous character of (4.8), any solution of (3.8) can be written as

$$\varphi_0 = \int \delta(k^2 - m^2c^2)\underline{\varphi_0}(k)\,\mathrm{d}^4k \tag{4.22}$$

where $\varphi_0(k)$ are *appropriately normalized (scaled) solutions of* (4.8) which solutions can be identified, up to the phase factor $\mathrm{e}^{\frac{1}{\mathrm{i}\hbar}x_0^\mu k_\mu}$, with the Fourier coefficients of $\tilde{\varphi}(x)$, viz. (see (4.19) and (4.21))

$$\underline{\tilde{\varphi}}(k) = \mathrm{e}^{\frac{1}{\mathrm{i}\hbar}x_0^\mu k_\mu}\underline{\varphi_0}(k). \tag{4.23}$$

Therefore, by virtue of (4.13) and (4.21), the operators $\varphi_0(k)$ appearing in (4.22) satisfy the relation (cf. (4.13))

$$(\varphi_0(k))^\dagger = \varphi_0(-k). \tag{4.24}$$

On the other hand, this implies that the operator $\varphi_0(k)$, entering in (4.22), is (up to a constant) identical with the usual momentum representation of a scaler field $\tilde{\varphi}(x)$ in Heisenberg picture [3–5]. *Consequently, the operators* $\underline{\tilde{\varphi}}(k)$ *with* $k^2 = m^2c^2$, *representing a free Hermitian scalar field in momentum representation of Heisenberg picture of motion in quantum field theory, are nothing else but (suitably normalized) solutions of* (4.8) *under the condition* (4.9), *i.e. of the Klein-Gordon equation* (3.8), *which form a basis in the operator space of all solutions of* (3.8). In short, the momentum representation of a scalar field in Heisenberg picture is a suitably chosen base for the solutions of the Klein-Gordon equation in momentum picture. This result is quite important from two aspects. On one hand, it reveals the real meaning of the momentum representation in Heisenberg picture of quantum field theory. On another hand, it allows us to apply freely in momentum picture all of the already established results concerning the Fourier images of the field operators, observables and other operators in Heisenberg picture. In particular, this concerns the frequency decompositions and creation and annihilation operators theory.

5 Frequency decompositions and their physical meaning

Since the decomposition (4.6) (or (4.7) if the solutions (4.3) are excluded) is similar to the one leading to the frequency decompositions (in Heisenberg picture for free fields) in quantum field theory, we shall introduce similar (in fact identical) notation. Defining [10]

$$\varphi_0^\pm(k) = \begin{cases} f_\pm(\pm\boldsymbol{k})\varphi_0(\pm k) & \text{for } k_0 \geq 0 \\ 0 & \text{for } k_0 < 0 \end{cases}, \tag{5.1}$$

[10] Notice, we do not exclude the case $k_0 = 0$ as it is done in the literature.

we see that

$$\varphi_0 = \varphi_0^+ + \varphi_0^- \tag{5.2}$$

$$\varphi_0^\pm = \int \mathrm{d}^3\boldsymbol{k}\varphi_0^\pm(k)\big|_{k_0=\sqrt{m^2c^2+\boldsymbol{k}^2}} \tag{5.3}$$

$$[\varphi_0^\pm(k), \mathcal{P}_\mu]_\_ = \mp k_\mu \varphi_0^\pm(k) \qquad k_0 = \sqrt{m^2c^2+\boldsymbol{k}^2} \tag{5.4}$$

due to (4.6) and (4.8). Notice, since φ_0 and $\varphi_0(k)$ satisfy (3.5), (4.13) and (4.12), we have

$$(\varphi_0^\pm(k))^\dagger = \varphi_0^\mp(k). \tag{5.5}$$

The equation (5.4) implies the interpretation of a free scalar field in terms of particles. Indeed, if $\mathcal{X}_p$ is a state vector of a state with 4-momentum p, i.e.

$$\mathcal{P}_\mu(\mathcal{X}_p) = p_\mu \mathcal{X}_p, \tag{5.6}$$

then, applying (5.4), we obtain

$$\mathcal{P}_\mu(\varphi_0^\pm(k)(\mathcal{X}_p)) = (p_\mu \pm k_\mu)\varphi_0^\pm(k)(\mathcal{X}_p) \qquad k_0 = \sqrt{m^2c^2+\boldsymbol{k}^2} \tag{5.7}$$

So, $\varphi_0^+(k)$ (resp. $\varphi_0^-(k)$) can be interpreted as an operator creating (resp. annihilating) a particle (quant of the field) with mass m and 4-momentum k with $k_0 = \sqrt{m^2c^2+\boldsymbol{k}^2}$, i.e. a particle with energy $\sqrt{m^2c^2+\boldsymbol{k}^2}$ and 3-momentum $\boldsymbol{k}$. In this situation, the vacuum for a scalar field should be a state $\mathcal{X}_0$ with vanishing 4-momentum and such that

$$\varphi_0^-(k)(\mathcal{X}_0) = 0 \qquad k_0 = \sqrt{m^2c^2+\boldsymbol{k}^2}. \tag{5.8}$$

The action of the operators $\varphi_0^+(k)$ on $\mathcal{X}_0$ produces one- or multiple-particle states. More details concerning the definition of a vacuum and construction of state vectors from it will be given in sections 8 and 9.

For a comparison with existing literature (see, e.g., [3–5, 12]), we notice that the creation/annihilation operators $\tilde{\varphi}^\pm$, introduced in momentum representation of Heisenberg picture of motion, are defined by

$$\tilde{\varphi}^\pm(k) = \begin{cases} \underline{\tilde{\varphi}}(\pm k) & \text{for } k_0 \geq 0 \\ 0 & \text{for } k_0 < 0 \end{cases} \tag{5.9}$$

where $\underline{\tilde{\varphi}}(k)$ is the Fourier image of $\tilde{\varphi}(x)$ (see (4.19)). Therefore, by virtue of (4.21) and proposition 4.1, we have the following connection between the creation/annihilation operators in Heisenberg and momentum picture:

$$\tilde{\varphi}^\pm(k) = \mathrm{e}^{\pm\frac{1}{\mathrm{i}\hbar}x_0^\mu k_\mu}\varphi_0^\pm(k) \qquad k_0 = \sqrt{m^2c^2+\boldsymbol{k}^2}. \tag{5.10}$$

We leave to the reader to prove as an exercise that the general formula (2.5) implies

$$\varphi^\pm(k) = \mathrm{e}^{\mp\frac{1}{\mathrm{i}\hbar}x^\mu k_\mu}\,\mathcal{U}(x,x_0)\circ\tilde{\varphi}_0^\pm(k)\circ\mathcal{U}^{-1}(x,x_0) \qquad k_0 = \sqrt{m^2c^2+\boldsymbol{k}^2}, \tag{5.11}$$

which, in view of (2.7) and (5.4), is equivalent to (5.10). (Hint: apply the Fourier decomposition from Sect. 4, then show that $\frac{\partial}{\partial x^\mu}\varphi^\pm(k) = 0$ and, at last, set $x = x_0$ in (5.11).)

6 The field equations in terms of creation and annihilation operators

Let us return now to our main problem: to be found, if possible, the explicit form of the field operator φ_0 (and momentum operator $\mathcal{P}_\mu$).

At first, we shall express $\mathcal{P}_\mu$ in terms of the creation and annihilation operators $\varphi_0^\pm$. Regardless of the fact that the result is known (see, e.g., [3, eq. (3.26)] or [4, eq. (12.11)]), we shall reestablish it in a completely new way.

Since (5.2)–(5.4) entail

$$[\varphi_0, \mathcal{P}_\mu]_- = \int \mathrm{d}^3\boldsymbol{k}\{k_\mu(-\varphi_0^+(k) + \varphi_0^-(k))\}|_{k_0=\sqrt{m^2c^2+\boldsymbol{k}^2}},$$

from (3.11), after some algebra (involving (5.2) and (5.3)), we get the energy-momentum operator as

$$\begin{aligned} \mathcal{T}_{\nu\mu} = c^2 \int \mathrm{d}^3\boldsymbol{k}\,\mathrm{d}^3\boldsymbol{k}'\{(-k_\nu k'_\mu + \frac{1}{2}\eta_{\nu\mu}k_\lambda k'^\lambda)(-\varphi_0^+(k) + \varphi_0^-(k)) \\ \times(-\varphi_0^+(k') + \varphi_0^-(k')) + \frac{1}{2}\eta_{\nu\mu}m^2c^2(\varphi_0^+(k) + \varphi_0^-(k))(\varphi_0^+(k') + \varphi_0^-(k'))\} \end{aligned} \tag{6.1a}$$

$$\begin{aligned} \mathcal{T}_{\nu\mu} = \frac{1}{2}c^2 \int \mathrm{d}^3\boldsymbol{k}\,\mathrm{d}^3\boldsymbol{k}'\{(-k_\nu k'_\mu - k_\mu k'_\nu + \eta_{\nu\mu}k_\lambda k'^\lambda)(-\varphi_0^+(k) + \varphi_0^-(k)) \\ \times(-\varphi_0^+(k') + \varphi_0^-(k')) + \eta_{\nu\mu}m^2c^2(\varphi_0^+(k) + \varphi_0^-(k))(\varphi_0^+(k') + \varphi_0^-(k'))\}, \end{aligned} \tag{6.1b}$$

where $k_0 = \sqrt{m^2c^2 + \boldsymbol{k}^2}$, $k'_0 = \sqrt{m^2c^2 + \boldsymbol{k}'^2}$ and the two expressions for $\mathcal{T}_{\mu\nu}$ correspond to the two its versions in (3.11).

The idea is now the last result to be inserted into (2.18) and to commute $\varphi_0^\pm(k)$ and $\varphi_0^\pm(k')$ with $\mathcal{U}(x, x_0)$ in order to 'move' $\varphi_0^\pm(k)$ and $\varphi_0^\pm(k')$ to the right of $\mathcal{U}(x, x_0)$. Rewriting (4.8) as $\varphi_0(k) \circ \mathcal{P}_\mu = (\mathcal{P}_\mu - k_\mu \,\mathrm{id}_\mathcal{F}) \circ \varphi_0(k)$, by induction, we derive

$$\varphi_0(k) \circ (\mathcal{P}_{\mu_1} \circ \dots \circ \mathcal{P}_{\mu_a}) = \{(\mathcal{P}_{\mu_1} - k_{\mu_1}\mathrm{id}_\mathcal{F}) \circ \dots \circ (\mathcal{P}_{\mu_a} - k_{\mu_a}\mathrm{id}_\mathcal{F})\} \circ \varphi_0(k) \tag{6.2}$$

for any $a \in \mathbb{N}$, which, in view of the expansion of the r.h.s. of (2.2) into a power series, implies

$$\varphi_0(k) \circ \mathcal{U}(x, x_0) = \mathrm{e}^{-\frac{1}{\mathrm{i}\hbar}(x^\mu - x_0^\mu)k_\mu}\,\mathcal{U}(x, x_0) \circ \varphi_0(k). \tag{6.3}$$

So, we have (see (5.1))

$$\begin{aligned} \varphi_0^\pm(k) \circ \mathcal{U}(x, x_0) &= \mathrm{e}^{-\frac{1}{\mathrm{i}\hbar}(x^\mu - x_0^\mu)(\pm k_\mu)}\,\mathcal{U}(x, x_0) \circ \varphi_0^\pm(k) \\ \varphi_0^+(k) \circ \varphi_0^\pm(k') \circ \mathcal{U}(x, x_0) &= \mathrm{e}^{-\frac{1}{\mathrm{i}\hbar}(x^\mu - x_0^\mu)(k_\mu \pm k'_\mu)}\,\mathcal{U}(x, x_0)\varphi_0^+(k) \circ \varphi_0^\pm(k') \\ \varphi_0^-(k) \circ \varphi_0^\pm(k') \circ \mathcal{U}(x, x_0) &= \mathrm{e}^{-\frac{1}{\mathrm{i}\hbar}(x^\mu - x_0^\mu)(-k_\mu \pm k'_\mu)}\,\mathcal{U}(x, x_0)\varphi_0^-(k) \circ \varphi_0^\pm(k'). \end{aligned} \tag{6.4}$$

At the end, substituting (6.1) into (2.18), applying the derived commutation rules (6.4), performing the integration over x, which yields δ-functions like $\delta(\boldsymbol{k} \pm \boldsymbol{k}')$, and the integration over $\boldsymbol{k}'$, we finally get after, a simple, but lengthy and tedious, calculation, the following result

$$\mathcal{P}_\mu = \frac{1}{2} \int k_\mu|_{k_0=\sqrt{m^2c^2+\boldsymbol{k}^2}} \{\varphi_0^+(\boldsymbol{k}) \circ \varphi_0^-(\boldsymbol{k}) + \varphi_0^-(\boldsymbol{k}) \circ \varphi_0^+(\boldsymbol{k})\} \, \mathrm{d}^3\boldsymbol{k}, \tag{6.5}$$

where we have introduced the 3-dimensional renormalized creation and annihilation operators

$$\varphi_0^\pm(\boldsymbol{k}) := \{(2c(2\pi\hbar)^3 k_0)^{1/2} \varphi_0^\pm(k)\}|_{k_0=\sqrt{m^2c^2+\boldsymbol{k}^2}}. \tag{6.6}$$

Notice, the result (6.5) is independent of from what form of $\mathcal{T}_{\mu\nu}$, (3.11a) or (3.11b), we have started. The only difference of our derivation of (6.5) from similar one in the literature (see, e.g., [3, sec. 3.2]) is that we have *not* exclude the massless case and the degenerate solution (4.3) from our considerations. The operator $\varphi_0^+(\boldsymbol{k})$ (resp. $\varphi_0^-(\boldsymbol{k})$) is called the *creation* (resp. *annihilation*) operator (of the field).

We would like to emphasize on the relations

$$(\varphi_0^\pm(\boldsymbol{k}))^\dagger = \varphi_0^\mp(\boldsymbol{k}) \tag{6.7}$$

which follow from (6.6) and (5.5). Actually these equalities are equivalent to the supposition that φ_0 is Hermitian field operator.

As a result of (5.10), the operators $\tilde{\varphi}^\pm(\boldsymbol{k})$, corresponding to (6.5) in (the momentum representation of) Heisenberg picture of motion, are [3, Sec. 3.2]

$$\begin{aligned}\tilde{\varphi}^\pm(\boldsymbol{k}) :&= \{ \big(c(2\pi\hbar)^3\big)^{1/2} (2k_0)^{-1/2} \, \tilde{\varphi}^\pm(k)\}|_{k_0=\sqrt{m^2c^2+\boldsymbol{k}^2}} \\ &= \mathrm{e}^{\pm\frac{1}{\mathrm{i}\hbar}x_0^\mu k_\mu}|_{k_0=\sqrt{m^2c^2+\boldsymbol{k}^2}} \varphi_0^\pm(\boldsymbol{k}).\end{aligned} \tag{6.8}$$

Similarly, we have also the connection (see (5.11))

$$\tilde{\varphi}^\pm(\boldsymbol{k}) = \mathrm{e}^{\pm\frac{1}{\mathrm{i}\hbar}x^\mu k_\mu}|_{k_0=\sqrt{m^2c^2+\boldsymbol{k}^2}} \mathcal{U}^{-1}(x, x_0) \circ \varphi_0^\pm(\boldsymbol{k}) \circ \mathcal{U}(x, x_0). \tag{6.9}$$

Consequently, the integrand in (6.5) and similar ones which will be met further in this work, look identically in terms of $\varphi_0^\pm(\boldsymbol{k})$ and $\tilde{\varphi}^\pm(\boldsymbol{k})$.

Summarizing the above results, we are ready to state and analyze the following problem.

Problem 6.1. Let

$$\begin{aligned}\varphi_0 = \varphi_0^+ + \varphi_0^- &= \int (\varphi_0^+(k) + \varphi_0^-(k))|_{k_0=\sqrt{m^2c^2+\boldsymbol{k}^2}} \, \mathrm{d}^3\boldsymbol{k} \\ &= \int \Big(2c(2\pi\hbar)^3\sqrt{m^2c^2+\boldsymbol{k}^2}\Big)^{-1/2} (\varphi_0^+(\boldsymbol{k}) + \varphi_0^-(\boldsymbol{k})) \, \mathrm{d}^3\boldsymbol{k}\end{aligned} \tag{6.10}$$

be a solution of the Klein-Gordon equation (3.8). Find the general explicit form of the operators $\varphi_0^\pm(\boldsymbol{k})$ which are solutions of the equations (see (5.4))

$$[\varphi_0^\pm(\boldsymbol{k}),\,\mathcal{P}_\mu]_- = \mp k_\mu \varphi_0^\pm(\boldsymbol{k}) \qquad k_0 = \sqrt{m^2c^2+\boldsymbol{k}^2} \tag{6.11}$$

where $\mathcal{P}_\mu$ is given by (6.5).

Inserting the representation (6.5) into (6.11) and writing the expression $\mp k_\mu \varphi_0^\pm(\boldsymbol{k})$ as $\int \mp q_\mu \varphi_0^\pm(\boldsymbol{k})\delta^3(\boldsymbol{k}-\boldsymbol{q})\,\mathrm{d}^3\boldsymbol{q}$ with $q_0 = \sqrt{m^2c^2+\boldsymbol{q}^2}$, we, after a simple algebraic manipulation, obtain

$$\int q_\mu\big|_{q_0=\sqrt{m^2c^2+\boldsymbol{q}^2}} \big\{ [\varphi_0^\pm(\boldsymbol{k}), \varphi_0^+(\boldsymbol{q})\circ\varphi_0^-(\boldsymbol{q}) + \varphi_0^-(\boldsymbol{q})\circ\varphi_0^+(\boldsymbol{q})]_- \\ \pm 2\varphi_0^\pm(\boldsymbol{k})\delta^3(\boldsymbol{k}-\boldsymbol{q})\big\}\,\mathrm{d}^3\boldsymbol{q} = 0 \tag{6.12}$$

Consequently $\varphi_0^\pm(\boldsymbol{k})$ must be solutions of

$$[\varphi_0^\pm(\boldsymbol{k}), [\varphi_0^+(\boldsymbol{q}), \varphi_0^-(\boldsymbol{q})]_+]_- \pm 2\varphi_0^\pm(\boldsymbol{k})\delta^3(\boldsymbol{k}-\boldsymbol{q}) = f^\pm(\boldsymbol{k},\boldsymbol{q}) \tag{6.13}$$

where $[A,B]_+ := A\circ B + B\circ A$ is the anticommutator of operators (or matrices) A and B and $f^\pm(\boldsymbol{k},\boldsymbol{q})$ are operator-valued (generalized) functions such that

$$\int q_\mu\big|_{q_0=\sqrt{m^2c^2+\boldsymbol{q}^2}} f^\pm(\boldsymbol{k},\boldsymbol{q})\,\mathrm{d}^3\boldsymbol{q} = 0. \tag{6.14}$$

Looking over the derivation of (6.13), we see its equivalence with the initial system of Klein-Gordon equation (3.8) and Heisenberg relations (2.7) in momentum picture. Consequently, (6.13) is the *system of field equations in terms of creation and annihilation operators in momentum picture*.

As a simple test of our calculations, one can prove that the commutativity of the components $\mathcal{P}_\mu$ of the momentum operator, expressed by (2.6) (see also (2.9)), is a consequence of (6.5), (6.13), and (6.14).

7 The commutation relations

The equations (6.13) are the corner stone of the famous (anti)commutation relations in quantum field theory for the considered here free Hermitian scalar field.[11] The equations (6.13) form a system of two homogeneous algebraic equations of third order relative to the functions $\varphi_0^\pm(\boldsymbol{k})$. Generally, it has infinitely may solutions, but, at present, only a selected class of them has a suitable physical meaning and interpretation. This class will be described a little below.

[11] The idea for arbitrary (Hermitian/real or non-Hermitian/complex, free or interacting) fields remains the same: one should derive the Euler-Lagrange equations in momentum picture and to solve them relative to the field operators by using the explicit expression of the (canonical) momentum operator through the field operators.

Since for the physics is essential only the restriction of $\varphi_0^{\pm}(\boldsymbol{k})$ on the *physically realizable states*, not on the whole system's Hilbert space $\mathcal{F}$, we shall analyze (6.13) in this case, following the leading idea in similar cases in, e.g., [3, subsec. 10.1], or [4, § 70], or [5, p. 65]. It consists in *admitting* that the commutator or anticommutator of the creation and/or annihilation operators (for free fields) is a c-number, i.e. it is proportional to the identity mapping $\mathsf{id}_{\mathcal{F}}$ of the system's Hilbert space $\mathcal{F}$ of states. In particular, in our case, this (additional hypothesis) results in

$$[\varphi_0^{\pm}(\boldsymbol{k}), \varphi_0^{\pm}(\boldsymbol{q})]_{\varepsilon} = \alpha_{\varepsilon}^{\pm}(\boldsymbol{k}, \boldsymbol{q})\, \mathsf{id}_{\mathcal{F}} \qquad [\varphi_0^{\mp}(\boldsymbol{k}), \varphi_0^{\pm}(\boldsymbol{q})]_{\varepsilon} = \beta_{\varepsilon}^{\pm}(\boldsymbol{k}, \boldsymbol{q})\, \mathsf{id}_{\mathcal{F}} \tag{7.1}$$

where $\varepsilon = \pm$, $[A, B]_{\pm} := A \circ B \pm B \circ A$, and $\alpha_{\varepsilon}^{\pm}$ and $\beta_{\varepsilon}^{\pm}$ are complex-valued (generalized) functions. It should clearly be understood, the conditions (7.1) are *additional* to the Lagrangian formalism and do not follow from it. In fact, they or the below written commutation relations (7.28) (which under some conditions follow from (7.1)) have to be *postulated.*

Defining

$$[A, B]_{\eta} = A \circ B + \eta B \circ A \qquad \eta \in \mathbb{C} \tag{7.2}$$

and applying the identity

$$[A, B \circ C]_{\eta} = [A, B]_{-\eta\varepsilon} \circ C + \eta\varepsilon B \circ [A, C]_{\varepsilon} \qquad \varepsilon = \pm 1 \tag{7.3}$$

for $\eta = -1$, viz.

$$[A, B \circ C]_{-} = [A, B]_{\varepsilon} \circ C - \varepsilon B \circ [A, C]_{\varepsilon}, \tag{7.4}$$

due to $\varepsilon = \pm 1$ and $[A, B]_{\pm 1} = [A, B]_{\pm}$, we rewrite (6.13) as

$$\begin{aligned}
&[\varphi_0^{\pm}(\boldsymbol{k}), \varphi_0^{+}(\boldsymbol{q})]_{\varepsilon} \circ \varphi_0^{-}(\boldsymbol{q}) - \varepsilon\varphi_0^{+}(\boldsymbol{q})\circ[\varphi_0^{\pm}(\boldsymbol{k}), \varphi_0^{-}(\boldsymbol{q})]_{\varepsilon}\\
&+[\varphi_0^{\pm}(\boldsymbol{k}), \varphi_0^{-}(\boldsymbol{q})]_{\varepsilon} \circ \varphi_0^{+}(\boldsymbol{q}) - \varepsilon\varphi_0^{-}(\boldsymbol{q})\circ[\varphi_0^{\pm}(\boldsymbol{k}), \varphi_0^{+}(\boldsymbol{q})]_{\varepsilon}\\
&\qquad\qquad \pm 2\varphi_0^{\pm}(\boldsymbol{k})\delta^3(\boldsymbol{k} - \boldsymbol{q}) = f^{\pm}(\boldsymbol{k}, \boldsymbol{q}).
\end{aligned} \tag{7.5}$$

Now, substituting the *additional conditions* (7.1) into (7.5), we get

$$\begin{aligned}
&(1 - \varepsilon)\varphi_0^{-}(\boldsymbol{q}) \circ [\varphi_0^{\pm}(\boldsymbol{k}), \varphi_0^{+}(\boldsymbol{q})]_{\varepsilon}\\
&\qquad + (1 - \varepsilon)\varphi_0^{+}(\boldsymbol{q}) \circ [\varphi_0^{\pm}(\boldsymbol{k}), \varphi_0^{-}(\boldsymbol{q})]_{\varepsilon} \pm 2\varphi_0^{\pm}(\boldsymbol{k})\delta^3(\boldsymbol{k} - \boldsymbol{q}) = f^{\pm}(\boldsymbol{k}, \boldsymbol{q}).
\end{aligned} \tag{7.6}$$

For $\varepsilon = +1$, this equality reduces to $\pm 2\varphi_0^{\pm}(\boldsymbol{k})\delta^3(\boldsymbol{k} - \boldsymbol{q}) = f^{\pm}(\boldsymbol{k}, \boldsymbol{q})$ which, when inserted into (6.14), entails

$$k_{\mu}\big|_{k_0=\sqrt{m^2c^2+\boldsymbol{k}^2}}\varphi_0^{\pm}(\boldsymbol{k}) = 0 \tag{7.7}$$

for any $\mu = 0, 1, 2, 3$ and k. Consequently, the choice $\varepsilon = +1$, i.e.

$$[\varphi_0^{\pm}(\boldsymbol{k}), \varphi_0^{\pm}(\boldsymbol{q})]_{+} = \alpha_{+}^{\pm}(\boldsymbol{k}, \boldsymbol{q})\,\mathrm{id}_{\mathcal{F}} \qquad [\varphi_0^{\mp}(\boldsymbol{k}), \varphi_0^{\pm}(\boldsymbol{q})]_{+} = \beta_{+}^{\pm}(\boldsymbol{k}, \boldsymbol{q})\,\mathrm{id}_{\mathcal{F}}, \tag{7.8}$$

leads, in view of (6.5) and (7.7), to

$$\mathcal{P}_{\mu} = 0 \tag{7.9}$$

which, by virtue of Klein-Gordon equation (3.8), implies

$$m^2c^2\varphi_0 = 0. \tag{7.10}$$

So, if $m = 0$, we get the solution (4.3) and, if $m \neq 0$, we derive

$$\varphi_0 = 0 \qquad \text{for } m \neq 0 \tag{7.11}$$

and, consequently,

$$\varphi_0^{\pm}(\boldsymbol{k}) \equiv 0 \qquad \text{for } m \neq 0 \tag{7.12}$$

We interpret the obtained solution (7.11) (or (7.12)) of the Klein-Gordon equation (3.8) as a complete absence of the physical scalar field.[12]

Consider now (7.6) with $\varepsilon = -1$. Writing it explicitly for the upper, "+", and lower, "−", signs, we see that (7.6) is equivalent to

$$\varphi_0^{\mp}(\boldsymbol{q}) \circ [\varphi_0^{\pm}(\boldsymbol{k}), \varphi_0^{\pm}(\boldsymbol{q})]_{-} + [\varphi_0^{\pm}(\boldsymbol{k}), \varphi_0^{\mp}(\boldsymbol{q})]_{-} \circ \varphi_0^{\pm}(\boldsymbol{q}) \pm \varphi_0^{\pm}(\boldsymbol{q})\delta^3(\boldsymbol{k} - \boldsymbol{q}) = \frac{1}{2} f^{\pm}(\boldsymbol{k}, \boldsymbol{q}) \tag{7.13}$$

where, in accord with (7.1), the commutators are

$$[\varphi_0^{\pm}(\boldsymbol{k}), \varphi_0^{\pm}(\boldsymbol{q})]_{-} = \alpha^{\pm}(\boldsymbol{k}, \boldsymbol{q})\,\mathrm{id}_{\mathcal{F}} \qquad [\varphi_0^{\mp}(\boldsymbol{k}), \varphi_0^{\pm}(\boldsymbol{q})]_{-} = \beta^{\pm}(\boldsymbol{k}, \boldsymbol{q})\,\mathrm{id}_{\mathcal{F}}. \tag{7.14}$$

Here, for brevity, we have omit the subscript "−", i.e. we write $\alpha^{\pm}$ and $\beta^{\pm}$ for $\alpha_{-}^{\pm}$ and $\beta_{-}^{\pm}$ respectively.

The properties of $\alpha^{\pm}$ and $\beta^{\pm}$ can be specified as follows.[13]

Let $\mathcal{X}_p$ be a state vector with fixed 4-momentum p (see (5.6)). Defining

$$\mathcal{X}_{k,q}^{\pm} := (\varphi_0^{\pm}(\boldsymbol{k}) \circ \varphi_0^{\pm}(\boldsymbol{q}))(\mathcal{X}_p) \qquad \mathcal{Y}_{k,q}^{\pm} := (\varphi_0^{\pm}(\boldsymbol{k}) \circ \varphi_0^{\mp}(\boldsymbol{q}))(\mathcal{X}_p), \tag{7.15}$$

we, applying (5.7), get

$$\mathcal{P}_{\mu}(\mathcal{X}_{k,q}^{\pm}) = (p_{\mu} \pm k_{\mu} \pm q_{\mu})\,\mathcal{X}_{k,q}^{\pm} \qquad \mathcal{P}_{\mu}(\mathcal{Y}_{k,q}^{\pm}) = (p_{\mu} \pm k_{\mu} \mp q_{\mu})\,\mathcal{Y}_{k,q}^{\pm}. \tag{7.16}$$

[12] Since, for a scalar field, the solutions (4.3) do not lead to any physically predictable results, they, in the massless case, should also be interpreted as absence of the field.

[13] For the initial idea, see [3, subsec. 10.1], where the authors (premeditated or not?) make a number of implicit assumptions which reduce the generality of the possible (anti)commutation relations.

Noticing that

$$\mathcal{X}_{k,q}^{\pm} + \varepsilon\, \mathcal{X}_{q,k}^{\pm} = [\varphi_0^{\pm}(\boldsymbol{k}), \varphi_0^{\pm}(\boldsymbol{q})]_{\varepsilon}(\mathcal{X}_p) \qquad \mathcal{Y}_{k,q}^{\mp} + \varepsilon\, \mathcal{Y}_{q,k}^{\pm} = [\varphi_0^{\mp}(\boldsymbol{k}), \varphi_0^{\pm}(\boldsymbol{q})]_{\varepsilon}(\mathcal{X}_p)$$

for $\varepsilon = \pm 1$, we see that

$$\begin{aligned} (\mathcal{P}_\mu \circ [\varphi_0^{\pm}(\boldsymbol{k}), \varphi_0^{\pm}(\boldsymbol{q})]_{\varepsilon})(\mathcal{X}_p) &= (p_\mu \pm k_\mu \pm q_\mu)[\varphi_0^{\pm}(\boldsymbol{k}), \varphi_0^{\pm}(\boldsymbol{q})]_{\varepsilon}(\mathcal{X}_p) \\ (\mathcal{P}_\mu \circ [\varphi_0^{\mp}(\boldsymbol{k}), \varphi_0^{\pm}(\boldsymbol{q})]_{\varepsilon})(\mathcal{X}_p) &= (p_\mu \mp k_\mu \pm q_\mu)[\varphi_0^{\mp}(\boldsymbol{k}), \varphi_0^{\pm}(\boldsymbol{q})]_{\varepsilon}(\mathcal{X}_p). \end{aligned} \tag{7.17}$$

It is worth to mention, in the derivation of (7.17) no additional hypothesis, like (7.1), have been used.

Applying (7.17) for $\varepsilon = -1$ and imposing the *additional conditions* (7.14), we, due to (5.6), find

$$(\boldsymbol{k} + \boldsymbol{q})\alpha^{\pm}(\boldsymbol{k}, \boldsymbol{q}) = 0 \qquad (\boldsymbol{k} - \boldsymbol{q})\beta^{\pm}(\boldsymbol{k}, \boldsymbol{q}) = 0 \tag{7.18}$$

$$\left.\begin{aligned} \left(\sqrt{m^2c^2 + \boldsymbol{k}^2} + \sqrt{m^2c^2 + \boldsymbol{q}^2}\right)\alpha^{\pm}(\boldsymbol{k}, \boldsymbol{q}) = 0 \\ \left(\sqrt{m^2c^2 + \boldsymbol{k}^2} - \sqrt{m^2c^2 + \boldsymbol{q}^2}\right)\beta^{\pm}(\boldsymbol{k}, \boldsymbol{q}) = 0. \end{aligned}\right\} \tag{7.19}$$

Here, with necessity, $\alpha^{\pm}$ and $\beta^{\pm}$ must be regarded as distributions (generalized functions) as otherwise the equations (7.18) have only the trivial solutions

$$\alpha^{\pm}(\boldsymbol{k}, \boldsymbol{q}) = 0 \quad \text{for } \boldsymbol{k} + \boldsymbol{q} \neq 0 \qquad \beta^{\pm}(\boldsymbol{k}, \boldsymbol{q}) = 0 \quad \text{for } \boldsymbol{k} - \boldsymbol{q} \neq 0 \tag{7.20}$$

which, as it can easily be seen, reproduce the trivial solution (7.11) of the Klein-Gordon equation. Rewriting (7.18) as $\boldsymbol{q}\alpha^{\pm}(\boldsymbol{k}, \boldsymbol{q}) = -\boldsymbol{k}\alpha^{\pm}(\boldsymbol{k}, \boldsymbol{q})$ and $\boldsymbol{q}\beta^{\pm}(\boldsymbol{k}, \boldsymbol{q}) = \boldsymbol{k}\beta^{\pm}(\boldsymbol{k}, \boldsymbol{q})$, we see that

$$f(\boldsymbol{q})\alpha^{\pm}(\boldsymbol{k}, \boldsymbol{q}) = f(-\boldsymbol{k})\alpha^{\pm}(\boldsymbol{k}, \boldsymbol{q}) \qquad f(\boldsymbol{q})\beta^{\pm}(\boldsymbol{k}, \boldsymbol{q}) = f(\boldsymbol{k})\beta^{\pm}(\boldsymbol{k}, \boldsymbol{q}) \tag{7.21}$$

for a function $f(\boldsymbol{k})$ which is supposed to be polynomial or convergent power series. [14] As a result of (7.21), the second equation in (7.19) is equivalent to the identity $0 = 0$, while the first one reduces to

$$\sqrt{m^2c^2 + \boldsymbol{k}^2}\alpha^{\pm}(\boldsymbol{k}, \boldsymbol{q}) = 0. \tag{7.22}$$

Inserting (7.14) into (7.13), we find

$$\frac{1}{2}f^{\pm}(\boldsymbol{k}, \boldsymbol{q}) = \varphi_0^{\mp}(\boldsymbol{q})\alpha^{\pm}(\boldsymbol{k}, \boldsymbol{q}) + \varphi_0^{\pm}(\boldsymbol{q})(\beta^{\mp}(\boldsymbol{k}, \boldsymbol{q}) \pm \delta^3(\boldsymbol{k} - \boldsymbol{q})). \tag{7.23}$$

At the end, besides (7.22), the condition (6.14) is the only one remaining to be satisfied. Substituting (7.23) into it and using (7.21) for $f(\boldsymbol{q}) = \sqrt{m^2c^2 + \boldsymbol{q}^2}$ in the case $\mu = 0$ and for $f(\boldsymbol{q}) = q_a$ in the one with $\mu = a = 1, 2, 3$, we obtain

[14] We cannot write, e.g., $\alpha^{\pm}(\boldsymbol{k}, \boldsymbol{q}) = \text{const} \times \delta^3(\boldsymbol{k} + \boldsymbol{q})$ as the equation $yg(y) = 0$, $y \in \mathbb{R}$, has a solution $g(y) = \text{const} \times \delta(y)$, but this is *not* its general solution; e.g., its solutions are $g(y) = \alpha_0\delta(y) + \alpha_1 y\frac{\mathrm{d}\delta(y)}{\mathrm{d}y} + \alpha_2 y^2\frac{\mathrm{d}^2\delta(y)}{\mathrm{d}y^2} + \cdots$ with $\alpha_0, \alpha_1, \ldots$ being constant numbers.

$$0 = k_a \int \{ -\alpha^{\pm}(\boldsymbol{k},\boldsymbol{q})\varphi_0^{\mp}(\boldsymbol{q}) + (\beta^{\mp}(\boldsymbol{k},\boldsymbol{q}) \pm \delta^3(\boldsymbol{k}-\boldsymbol{q}))\varphi_0^{\pm}(\boldsymbol{q}) \} \,\mathrm{d}^3\boldsymbol{q} \tag{7.24a}$$

$$0 = \sqrt{m^2c^2 + \boldsymbol{k}^2} \int \{ +\alpha^{\pm}(\boldsymbol{k},\boldsymbol{q})\varphi_0^{\mp}(\boldsymbol{q}) + (\beta^{\mp}(\boldsymbol{k},\boldsymbol{q}) \pm \delta^3(\boldsymbol{k}-\boldsymbol{q}))\varphi_0^{\pm}(\boldsymbol{q}) \} \,\mathrm{d}^3\boldsymbol{q}, \tag{7.24b}$$

where, in the second equation, the term containing $\alpha^{\pm}$ vanishes due to (7.22). Since these equations must be valid for arbitrary $\boldsymbol{k}$, the integrals in them should vanish if $\boldsymbol{k} \neq 0$. Forming the sum and difference of these integrals in that case, we get

$$\int \alpha^{\pm}(\boldsymbol{k},\boldsymbol{q})\varphi_0^{\mp}(\boldsymbol{q}) \,\mathrm{d}^3\boldsymbol{q} = 0 \tag{7.25a}$$

$$\int (\beta^{\mp}(\boldsymbol{k},\boldsymbol{q}) \pm \delta^3(\boldsymbol{k}-\boldsymbol{q}))\varphi_0^{\pm}(\boldsymbol{q}) \,\mathrm{d}^3\boldsymbol{q} = 0. \tag{7.25b}$$

If $(m, \boldsymbol{k}) \neq (0, \boldsymbol{0})$, the standard (Bose-Einstein) commutation relations are extracted from equations (7.24) (or (7.25) if $\boldsymbol{k} \neq 0$) by imposing a *second, after* (7.1), *additional condition*. If we demand (7.24) to be valid for *arbitrary* $\varphi_0^{\pm}(\boldsymbol{q})$ whose commutators are c-numbers, then (7.24) entail

$$\alpha^{\pm}(\boldsymbol{k},\boldsymbol{q}) = 0 \qquad \beta^{\mp}(\boldsymbol{k},\boldsymbol{q}) = \pm\delta^3(\boldsymbol{k}-\boldsymbol{q}) \tag{7.26}$$

which convert (7.22) into identity.

Let us say also a few words on the special case when $m = 0$ and $\boldsymbol{k} = \boldsymbol{0}$. In it one cannot extract any information from (7.24) and (7.22). Recall, if $m = 0$, the operators $\varphi_0^{\pm}(\boldsymbol{0})$ describe creation/annihilation of massless particles with zero 4-momentum. Since, in the Hermitian scalar case, the 4-momentum and mass are the only characteristics of the field's quanta, the particles corresponding to

$$\varphi_0^{\pm}(\boldsymbol{k}) \qquad \text{with } m = 0 \text{ and } \boldsymbol{k} = \boldsymbol{0} \tag{7.27}$$

are unphysical as they cannot lead to some observable consequences. The operators (7.27) are special kind of the solutions (4.3) of the Klein-Gordon equation and, consequently, can be interpreted as absence of the field under consideration. Besides, as we proved above under the hypothesis (7.14), the only restrictions to which $\varphi_0^{\pm}(\boldsymbol{0})$ with $m = 0$ should be subjected are the conditions (7.14) with $\boldsymbol{k} = \boldsymbol{0}$, arbitrary $\boldsymbol{q}$, and any (generalized) functions $\alpha^{\pm}$ and $\beta^{\pm}$. Thus, to ensure a continuous limit when $(m, \boldsymbol{k}) \to (0, \boldsymbol{0})$, we, *by convention*, choose $\alpha^{\pm}(\boldsymbol{0},\boldsymbol{q})$ and $\beta^{\pm}(\boldsymbol{0},\boldsymbol{q})$ to be given by (7.26) with $\boldsymbol{k} = \boldsymbol{0}$.[15]

So, we have obtained the next solution of the problem 6.1. In momentum picture, the Klein-Gordon equation (3.8) admits a solution (6.10), i.e.

$$\varphi_0 = \int \Big(2c(2\pi\hbar)^3\sqrt{m^2c^2 + \boldsymbol{k}^2}\Big)^{-1/2} (\varphi_0^{+}(\boldsymbol{k}) + \varphi_0^{-}(\boldsymbol{k})) \,\mathrm{d}^3\boldsymbol{k},$$

[15] In this way we exclude from the theory a special kind of 'absent' (unphysical) field described by $m = 0$ and $\varphi_0 = 0$ or $\varphi_0^{\pm}(\boldsymbol{k}) = 0$.

in which the creation/annihilation operators $\varphi_0^{\pm}(\boldsymbol{k})$ satisfy only the commutation relations

$$[\varphi_0^{\pm}(\boldsymbol{k}), \varphi_0^{\pm}(\boldsymbol{q})]_{\_} = 0 \qquad [\varphi_0^{\mp}(\boldsymbol{k}), \varphi_0^{\pm}(\boldsymbol{q})]_{\_} = \pm\delta^3(\boldsymbol{k}-\boldsymbol{q})\,\mathsf{id}_{\mathcal{F}}. \tag{7.28}$$

Now, it is a trivial exercise to be verified that, in view of (6.5) and (7.28), the equality (6.11) is identically valid.

We would like to remark, in the above considerations the massless case, i.e. $m = 0$, is not neglected. However, obviously, the commutation relations (7.28) exclude the degenerate solution (7.11) or, equivalently, (7.20) or (7.12).

More generally, one can look for solutions of the tri-linear (para?)'commutation' relation (6.13), under the condition (6.14) which do *not* satisfy the additional conditions (7.1). But this is out of the aims of this work. [16]

As we have noted several times above, the concepts of a distribution (generalized function) and operator-valued distribution appear during the derivation of the commutation relations (7.28). We first met them in the tri-linear relations (6.13). In particular, the canonical commutation relations (7.28) have a sense iff $[\varphi_0^{\mp}(\boldsymbol{k}), \varphi_0^{\pm}(\boldsymbol{k})]_{\_}$ is an operator-valued distribution (proportional to $\mathsf{id}_{\mathcal{F}}$), which is *not* the case if the field φ_0 (or $\tilde{\varphi}_0$) is an ordinary operator acting on $\mathcal{F}$. These facts point to inherent contradiction of quantum field theory if the field variables are considered as operators acting on a Hilbert space. The rigorous mathematical setting requires the fields variables to be regarded as operator-valued distributions. However, such a setting is out of the scope of the present work and the reader is referred to books like [9,10,24,25] for more details and realization of that program. In what follows, the distribution character of the quantum fields will be encoded in the Dirac's delta function, which will appear in relations like (6.13) and (7.28).

Ending the discussion of the commutation relations for a free Hermitian scalar field, we would like to note that the commutation, not anticommutation, relations for it were derived directly from the Klein-Gordon equation (3.8) without involving the spin-statistics theorem, as it is done everywhere in the literature [3, 5]. In fact, this theorem is practically derived here in the special case under consideration. Besides, we saw that the commutation relations can be regarded as additional restrictions, postulated for the field operators as stated, e.g., in [5, pp. 59–60], which must be compatible with the equations of motion. In fact, as we proved, these relations are, under some assumptions, equivalent to the equations of motion, i.e. to the Klein-Gordon equation in our case. Said differently, the commutation relations convert the field equation(s) into identity (identities) and, in this sense are their solutions. An alternative viewpoint is the commutation relations (7.28) to be considered as field equations (under the conditions specified above) with respect to the creation and annihilation operators as field operators (variables).

[16] Tri-linear relations, like (6.13), are known as paracommutation relations and were discovered in [19] (See also [20, 21]). However, it seems that at present are not indications that solutions of (6.13), which do not satisfy (7.28), may describe actually existing physical objects or phenomena [10, 22, 23]. This is one of the reasons the quantum field theory to deal with (7.28) instead of (6.13) (or the equivalent to it Klein-Gordon equation (3.8) (in momentum picture) or (3.9) (in Heisenberg picture). Elsewhere we shall demonstrate how the parabose-commutation relations for a free scalar field can be derived from (6.13).

To close this section, we have to make the general remark that the tri-linear relations (6.13) (together with (6.14)) are equivalent to the initial Klein-Gordon equation (in terms of creation/annihilation operators) and all efforts for the establishment of the commutation relations (7.28) reflect, first of all, the fact of extraction of physically essential solutions of these equations.[17] In this sense, we can say that the commutation relations (7.28) are a reduction of the initial Klein-Gordon equation (3.8) (in momentum picture) or (3.9) (in Heisenberg picture), under the conditions (7.1) and the assumption that (7.24) hold for any $\varphi_0^{\pm}(\boldsymbol{q})$.

8 The vacuum and normal ordering

The vacuum of a free Hermitian scalar field φ_0 is a particular its state, described by a state vector $\mathcal{X}_0$ which carries no energy-momentum and, correspondingly, it is characterized by a constant (in spacetime) state vector, i.e.

$$\mathcal{P}_\mu(\tilde{\mathcal{X}}_0(x)) = 0 \tag{8.1}$$

$$\tilde{\mathcal{X}}_0(x) = \tilde{\mathcal{X}}_0(x_0) = \mathcal{X}_0 \tag{8.2}$$

where $\tilde{\mathcal{X}}_0$ and $\mathcal{X}_0$ are the vacua in Heisenberg and momentum pictures respectively. Equation (8.1) can be taken as a 'macroscopic' definition of the vacuum state vector $\mathcal{X}_0$. Since, 'microscopically', the field is considered as a collection of particles (see Sect. 5), the vacuum should be considered as a vector characterizing a state with no particles in it. Recalling the interpretation of creation, $\varphi_0^+(\boldsymbol{k})$, and annihilation, $\varphi_0^-(\boldsymbol{k})$, operators from Sect. 5, we can make the definition (8.1) more precise by demanding

$$\varphi_0^-(\boldsymbol{k})(\mathcal{X}_0) = 0 \qquad \mathcal{X}_0 \neq 0. \tag{8.3}$$

This is the everywhere accepted definition of a vacuum for a free Hermitian scalar field. However, it does not agree with the expression (6.5) for the momentum operator and the commutation relations (7.28). In fact, commuting $\varphi_0^+(\boldsymbol{k})$ and $\varphi_0^-(\boldsymbol{k})$, according to (7.28), in the second term in the integrand in (6.5) and using (8.3), we get

$$\mathcal{P}_\mu(\mathcal{X}_0) = \frac{1}{2}\int k_\mu \delta^3(\mathbf{0})\,\mathrm{d}^3\boldsymbol{k}\,\mathcal{X}_0 = \mathcal{X}_0 \times \delta^3(\mathbf{0}) \times \begin{cases} \infty^4 & \text{for } \mu = 0 \\ \infty^2(\infty^2 - \infty^2) & \text{for } \mu = 1,2,3 \end{cases}. \tag{8.4}$$

Of course, this is a nonsense which must be corrected. The problem can be solved by 'repairing' the r.h.s. of (6.5), by replacing the commutation relations (7.28) with other relations (compatible with (6.13) and (6.14)), or by some combination of these possibilities. At this point, we agree with the established procedure for removing (8.4) from the theory. If one accepts *not to change the logical structure of the theory*, the only possibility is a change

[17] One may recognize in (6.13) a kind of paracommutation relations which are typical for the so-called parastatistics [19–21, 26].

in the Lagrangian from which all follows. Since in (8.4) the infinities come from the term $\varphi_0^-(\boldsymbol{k}) \circ \varphi_0^+(\boldsymbol{k})$ in (6.5), it should be eliminated somehow. The known and, it seems, well working procedure for doing this, which we accept, is the following one. At first the Lagrangian and the dynamical variables, obtained from it and containing the field φ_0, should be written, by means of (5.1)–(5.3) in terms of creation, $\varphi_0^+(\boldsymbol{k})$, and annihilation, $\varphi_0^-(\boldsymbol{k})$ operators. Then, any composition (product) of these operators, possibly appearing under some integral sign, must be change so that all creation operators to stand to the left relative to all annihilation operators.[18] The described procedure for transforming compositions of creation and annihilation operators is known as *normal ordering* and the result of it is called *normal product* of the corresponding operators. This item is discussed at length in the literature to which the reader is referred for details [3–5, 27].

The mapping assigning to a composition of creation/annihilation operators their normal product will be denoted by $\mathcal{N}$ and called normal ordering operator. The action of $\mathcal{N}$ on polynomials or convergent power series of creation/annihilation operators is defined by extending it by linearity; the resulting mapping being denoted by $\mathcal{N}$ too.

Since, evidently, $\mathcal{N}\big(\varphi_0^{\pm}(\boldsymbol{k}) \circ \varphi_0^{\mp}(\boldsymbol{k})\big) = \varphi_0^+(\boldsymbol{k}) \circ \varphi_0^-(\boldsymbol{k})$, the representation (6.5) of the momentum operator changes, after normal ordering, into

$$\mathcal{P}_\mu = \int \mathrm{d}^s \boldsymbol{k} k_\mu \big|_{k_0=\sqrt{m^2c^2+\boldsymbol{k}^2}} \varphi_0^+(\boldsymbol{k}) \circ \varphi_0^-(\boldsymbol{k}). \tag{8.5}$$

(Notice, after normal ordering, we retain the notation $\mathcal{P}_\mu$ for the object resulting from (6.5). This is an everywhere accepted system of notation in the literature and it is applied to all similar situations, e.g. for the Lagrangian $\mathcal{L}$ or energy-momentum operator $\mathcal{T}^{\mu\nu}$. After some experience with such a system of doubling the meaning of the symbols, one finds it useful and harmless.) Now the equality (8.1) is a trivial corollary of (8.5) and (8.3).

As $\mathcal{X}_0 \neq 0$, we shall assume that the vacuum $\mathcal{X}_0$ can be normalized to unity, viz.

$$\langle \mathcal{X}_0 | \mathcal{X}_0 \rangle = 1, \tag{8.6}$$

where $\langle\cdot|\cdot\rangle : \mathcal{F} \times \mathcal{F} \to \mathbb{C}$ is the Hermitian scalar product of the Hilbert space $\mathcal{F}$ of states. In fact, the value $\langle \mathcal{X}_0 | \mathcal{X}_0 \rangle$ is insignificant and its choice as the number 1 is of technical character. In this way, in many calculations, disappears the coefficient $\langle \mathcal{X}_0 | \mathcal{X}_0 \rangle$. *Prima facie* one can loosen (8.6) by demanding $\mathcal{X}_0$ to have a finite norm, but this only adds to the theory the insignificant constant $\langle \mathcal{X}_0 | \mathcal{X}_0 \rangle$ which can be eliminated by a rescaling of $\mathcal{X}_0$.[19]

Let us summarize the above discussion. The vacuum of a free scalar field is its physical state which does not contains any particles and has zero energy and 3-momentum. It is described by a state vector, denoted by $\mathcal{X}_0$ (in momentum picture) and also called the

[18] The so-formulated rule is valid only for integer spin particles/fields. By virtue of (7.28), the order of the different creation/annihilation operators relative to each other is insignificant, i.e. it does not influence the result of described procedure.

[19] If $\mathcal{X}_0$ has an infinite norm, so is the situation with any other state vector obtained from $\mathcal{X}_0$ via action with creation operators, which makes the theory almost useless.

vacuum of the field, such that:

$$\mathcal{X}_0 \neq 0 \tag{8.7a}$$
$$\mathcal{X}_0 = \tilde{\mathcal{X}}_0 \tag{8.7b}$$
$$\varphi_0^-(\boldsymbol{k})(\mathcal{X}_0) = 0 \tag{8.7c}$$
$$\langle \mathcal{X}_0 | \mathcal{X}_0 \rangle = 1 \tag{8.7d}$$

for any 3-momentum $\boldsymbol{k}$. Since the existence of the vacuum $\tilde{\mathcal{X}}_0$ in the Heisenberg picture is a known theorem, the condition (8.7b), expressing the coincidence of 'Heisenberg vacuum' and 'momentum vacuum', ensures the existence of the vacuum $\mathcal{X}_0$ in momentum picture. Besides, to make the theory sensible, we have assumed normal ordering of the creation/annihilation operators in the Lagrangian and all observables derived from it.

The normal ordering of products changes the field equations (6.13) into

$$[\varphi_0^{\pm}(\boldsymbol{k}), \varphi_0^{+}(\boldsymbol{q}) \circ \varphi_0^{-}(\boldsymbol{q})]_{\_} \pm \varphi_0^{\pm}(\boldsymbol{k})\delta^3(\boldsymbol{k}-\boldsymbol{q}) = \frac{1}{2} f^{\pm}(\boldsymbol{k},\boldsymbol{q}) \tag{8.8}$$

as the anticommutator in (6.13) originates from the expression (6.5) for the momentum operator (before normal ordering). The conditions (6.14) remains unchanged. However, by means of (7.4) with $\varepsilon = -1$ and the commutation relations (7.28), one can verify that (8.8) and (6.14) are identically valid. This means that, in fact, the commutation relations (7.28) play a role of field equations under the hypotheses made.

9 State vectors and transitions between them

According to the general theory of Sect. 2, the general form of a state vector $\mathcal{X}(x)$ of a free Hermitian scalar field in momentum picture is

$$\mathcal{X}(x) = \mathcal{U}(x, x_0)(\mathcal{X}(x_0)) = \mathrm{e}^{\frac{1}{\mathrm{i}\hbar}(x^\mu - x_0^\mu)\mathcal{P}_\mu}(\mathcal{X}(x_0)), \tag{9.1}$$

where $x_0 \in M$ is an arbitrarily fixed point in the Minkowski spacetime M, $\mathcal{P}_\mu$ is given via (8.5), and the initial value $\mathcal{X}(x_0)$ of $\mathcal{X}$ at x_0 is identical with the (constant) state vector $\tilde{\mathcal{X}}$ representing the same state as $\mathcal{X}(x)$ but in Heisenberg picture, i.e.

$$\mathcal{X}(x_0) = \tilde{\mathcal{X}}. \tag{9.2}$$

In particular, if $\mathcal{X}_p$ is a state vector at x_0 with fixed 4-momentum p_μ, i.e.

$$\mathcal{P}_\mu(\mathcal{X}_p) = p_\mu \mathcal{X}_p, \tag{9.3}$$

then its general form at a point x is

$$\mathcal{X}_p(x) = \mathrm{e}^{\frac{1}{\mathrm{i}\hbar}(x^\mu - x_0^\mu)p_\mu} \mathcal{X}_p \tag{9.4}$$

and $\mathcal{P}_\mu(\mathcal{X}_p(x)) = p_\mu \mathcal{X}_p(x)$

From the vacuum $\mathcal{X}_0$ can be constructed a base for the system's Hilbert space $\mathcal{F}$, called the Fock base. A general s-particle state containing s particles with momenta $k_1 \dots, k_s$ (some of these vectors may be identical) of a scalar field φ_0 has the form

$$\mathcal{X}(k_1, \dots, k_s) = f_s(k_1, \dots, k_s)\big(\varphi_0^+(k_1) \circ \dots \circ \varphi_0^+(k_s)\big)(\mathcal{X}_0) \qquad (9.5)$$

for some function f_s characterizing the distribution of the particles.[20] Notice, by virtue (4.9), the 4-momenta $k_1, \dots, k_s$ are subjected to the conditions $k_a^2 = m^2c^2$, $a = 1, \dots, s$, with m being the mass of the quanta of the field φ_0. An arbitrary state, described via the Klein-Gordon equation (3.8) or its version expressed by (4.8) and (4.9), can be presented as a superposition of all possible states like (9.5), viz.

$$\mathcal{X} = \sum_{s\geq 0} \int \mathrm{d}k_1 \dots \int \mathrm{d}k_s f_s(k_1, \dots, k_s)\big(\varphi_0^+(k_1) \circ \dots \circ \varphi_0^+(k_s)\big)(\mathcal{X}_0). \qquad (9.6)$$

The above results, concerning free Hermitian scalar field, are identical with similar ones in the momentum representation in ordinary quantum field theory (in Heisenberg picture); the difference being that now $\varphi_0(k)$ is the field operator in the *momentum picture*, which, as we proved, are identical with the Fourier images of the field operators in Heisenberg picture. So, the Fock base goes without changes from Heisenberg into momentum picture.

One of the main problems in quantum field theory is to find the amplitude for a transition from some initial state $\mathcal{X}_i(x_i)$ into a final state $\mathcal{X}_f(x_f)$, i.e. the quantities

$$S_{fi}(x_f, x_i) := \langle \mathcal{X}_f(x_f) | \mathcal{X}_i(x_i) \rangle \qquad (9.7)$$

called elements of the so-called S-matrix (scattering matrix). Ordinary one considers the limits of (9.7) with $x_f^0 \to +\infty$ and $x_i^0 \to -\infty$ or, more generally, $x_f^\mu \to +\infty$ and $x_i^\mu \to -\infty$. These cases are important in the scattering theory but not for the general theory, described here, and, respectively, will not be discussed in our work. If we know $\mathcal{X}_f$ and $\mathcal{X}_i$ at some points $x_f^{(0)}$ and $x_i^{(0)}$, respectively, then, combining (9.1) and (9.7), we get

$$S_{fi}(x_f, x_i) = \langle \mathcal{X}_f(x_f^{(0)}) | \mathrm{e}^{\frac{1}{\mathrm{i}\hbar}(x_i^\mu - x_f^\mu)\mathcal{P}_\mu}(\mathcal{X}_i(x_i^{(0)})) \rangle$$
$$= \langle \mathcal{X}_f(x_f^{(0)}) | \mathcal{U}(x_i, x_f)(\mathcal{X}_i(x_i^{(0)})) \rangle. \qquad (9.8)$$

Consequently (cf. [11, § 107]), the operator $(\mathcal{U}(x_f, x_i))^\dagger = \mathcal{U}^{-1}(x_f, x_i) = \mathcal{U}(x_i, x_f)$, where $\dagger$ means (Hermitian) conjugation, has to be identified with the S-operator (often called also S-matrix). To continue the analogy with the S-matrix theory, we can expand the exponent in (9.8) into a power series. This yields (see (8.5))

$$\mathcal{U}(x_i, x_f) = \mathsf{id}_{\mathcal{F}} + \sum_{n=1}^{\infty} \mathcal{U}^{(n)}(x_i, x_f) \qquad (9.9)$$

[20] In (9.5) we have omit a spacetime dependent factor which the reader may recover, using (9.4); the vector (9.5) corresponds to the vector $\mathcal{X}_p$ in (9.4) in a case of s-particle state.

$$\mathcal{U}^{(n)}(x_i,x_f) := \frac{1}{n!}\frac{1}{(\mathrm{i}\hbar)^n}(x_i^{\mu_1}-x_f^{\mu_1})\dots(x_i^{\mu_n}-x_f^{\mu_n}) \\ \times \int \mathrm{d}^3\boldsymbol{k}^{(1)}\dots\mathrm{d}^3\boldsymbol{k}^{(n)} k_{\mu_1}^{(1)}\dots k_{\mu_n}^{(n)} \varphi_0^+(\boldsymbol{k}^{(1)})\circ\varphi_0^-(\boldsymbol{k}^{(1)})\circ\dots\circ\varphi_0^+(\boldsymbol{k}^{(n)})\circ\varphi_0^-(\boldsymbol{k}^{(n)}) \tag{9.10}$$

where $k_0^{(a)} = \sqrt{m^2c^2 + (\boldsymbol{k}^{(a)})^2}$, $a = 1,\dots,n$. This expression is extremely useful in 'scattering theory' when one deals with states having a fixed number of particles.[21]

The first thing one notices, is that the vacuum, defined via (8.7), cannot be changed, viz.

$$\mathcal{U}(x_i,x_f)(\mathcal{X}_0) \equiv \mathcal{X}_0, \tag{9.11}$$

and if $\mathcal{X}_{\geq 1}(x)$ is a state vector of a state containing at least one particle, then

$$\langle\, \mathcal{X}_{\geq 1}(x) |\, \mathcal{X}_0\rangle \equiv 0 \tag{9.12}$$

This simple result means that the only non-forbidden transition from the vacuum is into itself, i.e.

$$\langle\, \mathcal{X}_0 |\, \mathcal{X}_0\rangle = 1 \neq 0. \tag{9.13}$$

The results just obtained are known as the *stability of the vacuum*.

In accord with (9.4), (8.5) and (7.28), the vector

$$\mathcal{X}(x,p) = \mathrm{e}^{\frac{1}{\mathrm{i}\hbar}(x^\mu - x_0^\mu)p_\mu} \varphi_0^+(\boldsymbol{p})(\mathcal{X}_0) \tag{9.14}$$

describes a particle at a point $x \in M$ with 4-momentum p. Similarly, an n-particle state, $n \geq 1$, in which the ith particle is at a point x_i with 4-momentum p_i, $i = 1,\dots,n$, is represented by[22]

$$\mathcal{X}(x_1,p_1;\dots;x_n,p_n) = \frac{1}{\sqrt{n!}} \exp\Big\{\frac{1}{\mathrm{i}\hbar}\sum_{i=1}^{n}(x_i^\mu - x_0^\mu)(p_i)_\mu\Big\} (\varphi_0^+(\boldsymbol{p}_1)\circ\dots\circ\varphi_0^+(\boldsymbol{p}_n))(\mathcal{X}_0). \tag{9.15}$$

After some simple algebra with creation and annihilation operators, which uses (7.28), (6.7) and (8.7c), one finds the following transition amplitude from m-particle state into n-particle state, $m,n \in \mathbb{N}$:

$$\langle\, \mathcal{X}(y_1,q_1;\dots;y_n,q_n) |\, \mathcal{X}(x_1,p_1;\dots;x_m,p_m)\rangle = \frac{1}{n!}\delta_{mn} \exp\Big\{\frac{1}{\mathrm{i}\hbar}\sum_{i=1}^{n}(x_i^\mu - y_i^\mu)(p_i)_\mu\Big\} \\ \times \sum_{(i_1,\dots,i_n)} \delta^3(\boldsymbol{p}_n - \boldsymbol{q}_{i_1})\delta^3(\boldsymbol{p}_{n-1} - \boldsymbol{q}_{i_2})\dots\delta^3(\boldsymbol{p}_1 - \boldsymbol{q}_{i_n}), \tag{9.16}$$

---

[21] Since we are dealing with a free field, there is no interaction between its quanta (particles) and, hence, there is no real scattering. However, the method, we present below, is of quite general nature and can be applied in real scattering problems. This will be illustrated in a separate paper.

[22] Since the vacuum and creation/annihilation operators in Heisenberg and momentum pictures coincide, we use the usual Fock base to expand the state vectors. The spacetime depending factor comes from (9.4).

where δ_{mn} is the Kronecker δ-symbol, i.e. $\delta_{mn} = 1$ for $m = n$ and $\delta_{mn} = 0$ for $m \neq n$, and the summation is over all permutations $(i_1, \dots, i_n)$ of $(1, \dots, n)$. The presence of δ_{mn} in (9.16) means that an n-particle state can be transformed only into an n-particle state; all other transitions are forbidden. Besides, the δ-functions in (9.16) say that if the 4-momentum of a particle changes, the transition is also forbidden. So, the only change an n-particle state can experience is the change in the coordinates of the particles it contains. All these results are quite understandable (and trivial too) since we are dealing with a *free* field whose quanta move completely independent of each other, without any interactions between them.

Notice, if in (9.16) we set $m = n$ and integrate over all momenta, we get a pure phase factor, equal to $\exp\left\{\frac{1}{i\hbar}\sum_{i=1}^{n}(x_i^\mu - y_i^\mu)(p_i)_\mu\right\}$. Since, in this case, the module of the square of (9.16) is interpreted as a probability for the transition between the corresponding states, this means that the transition between two n-particle states is completely sure, i.e. with 100% probability.

At the end of this section, we remark that the states (9.15) are normalized to unity,

$$\int \mathrm{d}^3\boldsymbol{q}_1 \dots \mathrm{d}^3\boldsymbol{q}_n \langle\, \mathcal{X}(x_1, q_1; \dots; x_n, q_n) |\, \mathcal{X}(x_1, p_1; \dots; x_m, p_m)\rangle = 1, \qquad (9.17)$$

due to (8.7d). However, the norm $\langle\, \mathcal{X}(x_1, p_1; \dots; x_n, p_n) |\, \mathcal{X}(x_1, p_1; \dots; x_m, p_m)\rangle$ is infinity as it is proportional to $(\delta^3(0))^n$, due to (9.16). If one works with a vacuum not normalized to unity, in (9.15) the factor $\langle\, \mathcal{X}_0 |\, \mathcal{X}_0\rangle^{-1/2}$ will appear. This will change (9.16) with the factor $\langle\, \mathcal{X}_0 |\, \mathcal{X}_0\rangle^{-1}$.

Part B

Free arbitrary scalar field

Until now the case of free Hermitian (neutral) scalar field was explored. In the present, second, part of the present investigation, the results obtained for such a field will be transferred to the general case of free arbitrary, Hermitian (real, neutral, uncharged) or non-Hermitian (complex, charged), scalar field.[23]

As we shall see, there are two essential peculiarities in the non-Hermitian case. On one hand, the field operator and its Hermitian conjugate are so 'mixed' in the momentum operator that one cannot write (in momentum picture) separate field equations for them. On the other hand, a non-Hermitian field carries a charge. These facts will later be reflected in the corresponding commutation relations.

[23] A classical complex field, after quantization, becomes a non-Hermitian operator acting on the system's (field's) Hilbert space of states. That is why the quantum analogue of a classical complex scalar field is called non-Hermitian scalar field. However, it is an accepted common practice such a field to be called (also) a complex scalar field. In this sense, the terms complex scalar field and non-Hermitian scalar field are equivalent and, hence, interchangeable. Besides, since a complex (classical or quantum) scalar field carries a charge, it is called also charged scalar field. Cf. footnote 4.

10 Description of free scalar field

In Heisenberg picture a free arbitrary, Hermitian or non-Hermitian, scalar field is described via a field operator $\tilde{\varphi}(x)$, which may be Hermitian,

$$\tilde{\varphi}^{\dagger}(x) = \tilde{\varphi}(x) \tag{10.1a}$$

or non-Hermitian,

$$\tilde{\varphi}^{\dagger}(x) \neq \tilde{\varphi}(x). \tag{10.1b}$$

The properties of a free non-Hermitian scalar field are, usually [3–5, 28], encoded in the Lagrangian

$$\tilde{\mathcal{L}} := -m^2c^4\,\tilde{\varphi}^{\dagger}(x)\circ\tilde{\varphi}(x) + c^2\hbar^2(\partial_\mu\tilde{\varphi}^{\dagger}(x))\circ(\partial^\mu\tilde{\varphi}(x)), \tag{10.2}$$

which in momentum picture, according to the general rules of Sect. 2 (see equation (2.16)), reads

$$\mathcal{L} = -m^2c^4\varphi_0^{\dagger}\circ\varphi_0 - c^2[\varphi_0^{\dagger}, \mathcal{P}_\mu]_{\_}\circ[\varphi_0, \mathcal{P}^\mu]_{\_}, \tag{10.3}$$

where (see (2.15) and cf. (3.4))

$$\varphi(x) = \mathcal{U}(x,x_0)\circ\tilde{\varphi}(x)\circ\mathcal{U}^{-1}(x,x_0) = \varphi(x_0) = \tilde{\varphi}(x_0) =: \varphi_0 \tag{10.4a}$$

$$\varphi^{\dagger}(x) = \mathcal{U}(x,x_0)\circ\tilde{\varphi}^{\dagger}(x)\circ\mathcal{U}^{-1}(x,x_0) = \varphi^{\dagger}(x_0) = \tilde{\varphi}^{\dagger}(x_0) =: \varphi_0^{\dagger} \tag{10.4b}$$

are the corresponding to $\tilde{\varphi}(x)$ and $\tilde{\varphi}^{\dagger}(x)$, respectively, constant field operators in momentum picture. In general, the operator φ_0 can be Hermitian,

$$\varphi_0^{\dagger}(x) = \varphi_0 \tag{10.5a}$$

or non-Hermitian,

$$\varphi_0^{\dagger} \neq \varphi_0. \tag{10.5b}$$

as a result of (10.1) and the unitarity of $\mathcal{U}(x,x_0)$.

Defining

$$\tau(\tilde{\varphi}) := \begin{cases} 1 & \text{for } \tilde{\varphi}^{\dagger} = \tilde{\varphi} \text{ (Hermitian (neutral) field)} \\ 0 & \text{for } \tilde{\varphi}^{\dagger} \neq \tilde{\varphi} \text{ (non-Hermitian (charged) field)} \end{cases}, \tag{10.6}$$

we can unify the Lagrangians (10.2) and (3.2) by writing

$${}'\tilde{\mathcal{L}} := -\frac{1}{1+\tau(\tilde{\varphi})}m^2c^4\,\tilde{\varphi}^{\dagger}(x)\circ\tilde{\varphi}(x) + \frac{1}{1+\tau(\tilde{\varphi})}c^2\hbar^2(\partial_\mu\tilde{\varphi}^{\dagger}(x))\circ(\partial^\mu\tilde{\varphi}(x)). \tag{10.7}$$

As an alternative to (10.7), one may also put

$$
{}^{\prime\prime}\tilde{\mathcal{L}} := -\frac{1}{1+\tau(\tilde{\varphi})} m^2 c^4\, \tilde{\varphi}(x) \circ \tilde{\varphi}^\dagger(x) + \frac{1}{1+\tau(\tilde{\varphi})} c^2 \hbar^2 (\partial_\mu \tilde{\varphi}(x)) \circ (\partial^\mu \tilde{\varphi}^\dagger(x)) \tag{10.8}
$$

There is also one more candidate for a Lagrangian for a free arbitrary scalar field. Since such a field $\tilde{\varphi}$ is equivalent to two independent free Hermitian scalar fields $\tilde{\varphi}_1 = \tilde{\varphi}_1^\dagger$ and $\tilde{\varphi}_2 = \tilde{\varphi}_2^\dagger$ with masses equal to the one of $\tilde{\varphi}$ and such that $\tilde{\varphi} = \tilde{\varphi}_1 + \mathrm{i}\,\tilde{\varphi}_2$, i being the imaginary unit, we can set ${}^{\prime\prime\prime}\tilde{\mathcal{L}} = \mathcal{L}_0(\tilde{\varphi}_1) + \mathcal{L}_0(\tilde{\varphi}_2)$ with $\mathcal{L}_0$ defined by (3.2). Taking into account that $\tilde{\varphi}^\dagger = \tilde{\varphi}_1 - \mathrm{i}\,\tilde{\varphi}_2$, one can transform the last Lagrangian into the form

$$
\begin{aligned}
{}^{\prime\prime\prime}\tilde{\mathcal{L}} :=& -\frac{1}{2(1+\tau(\tilde{\varphi}))} m^2 c^4 \big(\tilde{\varphi}^\dagger(x) \circ \tilde{\varphi}(x) + \tilde{\varphi}(x) \circ \tilde{\varphi}^\dagger(x) \big) \\
&+ \frac{1}{2(1+\tau(\tilde{\varphi}))} c^2 \hbar^2 \big((\partial_\mu \tilde{\varphi}^\dagger(x)) \circ (\partial^\mu \tilde{\varphi}(x)) + (\partial_\mu \tilde{\varphi}(x)) \circ (\partial^\mu \tilde{\varphi}^\dagger(x)) \big).
\end{aligned} \tag{10.9}
$$

This Lagrangian, which is the half of the sum of (10.7) and (10.8), also reduces to (3.2) in the Hermitian case $\tilde{\varphi}^\dagger = \tilde{\varphi}$ (or $\tilde{\varphi}_2 = 0$ in terms of the Hermitian fields $\tilde{\varphi}_1$ and $\tilde{\varphi}_2$). Evidently, the Lagrangian (10.9) is a 'symmetrization' of the r.h.s. of (10.7) or (10.8) relative to $\tilde{\varphi}$ and $\tilde{\varphi}^\dagger$ with coefficient $\frac{1}{2}$. The advantage of (10.9) is that in it the field $\tilde{\varphi}$ and its Hermitian conjugate $\tilde{\varphi}^\dagger$ enter in a symmetric way, which cannot be said relative to (10.2), (10.7) and (10.8).

Going some steps ahead, the consequences of the Lagrangians $\tilde{\mathcal{L}}$, ${}^{\prime}\tilde{\mathcal{L}}$, ${}^{\prime\prime}\tilde{\mathcal{L}}$, and ${}^{\prime\prime\prime}\tilde{\mathcal{L}}$ can be summarized as follows: (i) All of these Lagrangians lead to identical (Klein-Gordon) field equations for $\tilde{\varphi}$ and $\tilde{\varphi}^\dagger$; (ii) The energy-momentum, momentum and charge operators generated by these Lagrangians are, generally, different; (iii) After the establishment of the commutation relations and a normal ordering of products (compositions), the momentum and charge operators generated by ${}^{\prime}\tilde{\mathcal{L}}$, ${}^{\prime\prime}\tilde{\mathcal{L}}$, and ${}^{\prime\prime\prime}\tilde{\mathcal{L}}$ become identical and equal to one half of the ones induced by $\mathcal{L}$. Therefore, in view of these assertions, all of the Lagrangians given above can be considered as equivalent.[24]

In momentum picture, by virtue of (2.16), the Lagrangians (10.7), (10.8) and (10.9) are:

$$
{}^{\prime}\tilde{\mathcal{L}} = -\frac{1}{1+\tau(\varphi)} m^2 c^4 \varphi_0^\dagger \circ \varphi_0 - \frac{1}{1+\tau(\varphi)} c^2 [\varphi_0^\dagger, \mathcal{P}_\mu]_{\_} \circ [\varphi_0, \mathcal{P}^\mu]_{\_} \tag{10.10}
$$

$$
{}^{\prime\prime}\tilde{\mathcal{L}} = -\frac{1}{1+\tau(\varphi)} m^2 c^4 \varphi_0 \circ \varphi_0^\dagger - \frac{1}{1+\tau(\varphi)} c^2 [\varphi_0, \mathcal{P}_\mu]_{\_} \circ [\varphi_0^\dagger, \mathcal{P}^\mu]_{\_} \tag{10.11}
$$

$$
\begin{aligned}
{}^{\prime\prime\prime}\tilde{\mathcal{L}} =& -\frac{1}{2(1+\tau(\varphi))} m^2 c^4 \big(\varphi_0^\dagger \circ \varphi_0 + \varphi_0 \circ \varphi_0^\dagger \big) \\
&- \frac{1}{2(1+\tau(\varphi))} c^2 \big([\varphi_0^\dagger, \mathcal{P}_\mu]_{\_} \circ [\varphi_0, \mathcal{P}^\mu]_{\_} + [\varphi_0, \mathcal{P}_\mu]_{\_} \circ [\varphi_0^\dagger, \mathcal{P}^\mu]_{\_} \big),
\end{aligned} \tag{10.12}
$$

[24] However, in Sect. 15, we shall see that the Lagrangian (10.9) carries more information than (10.7), (10.8) and (10.2). In this sense, it is the 'best' one.

where (cf. (10.6))

$$\tau(\varphi_0) := \begin{cases} 1 & \text{for } \varphi_0^\dagger = \varphi_0 \text{ (Hermitian (neutral) field)} \\ 0 & \text{for } \varphi_0^\dagger \neq \varphi_0 \text{ (non-Hermitian (charged) field)} \end{cases} = \tau(\tilde{\varphi}). \tag{10.13}$$

From here, we derive:

$$\frac{\partial\, {}^a\mathcal{L}}{\partial \varphi_0} = \frac{\partial\, \tilde{\mathcal{L}}}{\partial \varphi_0} = -m^2c^4\varphi_0^\dagger \qquad \frac{\partial\, {}^a\mathcal{L}}{\partial \varphi_0^\dagger} = \frac{\partial\, \tilde{\mathcal{L}}}{\partial \varphi_0^\dagger} = -m^2c^4\varphi_0 \tag{10.14}$$

$$\pi^\mu := \frac{\partial\, {}^a\mathcal{L}}{\partial y_\mu} = -\mathrm{i}\hbar c^2[\varphi_0^\dagger, \mathcal{P}^\mu]_{\_} \quad \pi^{\dagger\,\mu} := \frac{\partial\, {}^a\mathcal{L}}{\partial y_\mu^\dagger} = -\mathrm{i}\hbar c^2[\varphi_0, \mathcal{P}^\mu]_{\_} \tag{10.15}$$

where $a = I, II, III$, $y_\mu := \frac{1}{\mathrm{i}\hbar}[\varphi_0, \mathcal{P}_\mu]_{\_}$, $y_\mu^\dagger := \frac{1}{\mathrm{i}\hbar}[\varphi_0^\dagger, \mathcal{P}_\mu]_{\_}$ and we have followed the differentiation rules of classical analysis of commuting variables. At this point, all remarks, made in Sect. 3 in a similar situation, are completely valid too. For a rigorous derivation of the field equations (10.16) and energy-momentum tensors (10.21) below, the reader is referred to [14].

By means of the above equalities, from (2.17), we get the field equations for φ_0 and $\varphi_0^\dagger$:

$$m^2c^2\varphi_0 - [[\varphi_0, \mathcal{P}_\mu]_{\_}, \mathcal{P}^\mu]_{\_} = 0 \tag{10.16a}$$

$$m^2c^2\varphi_0^\dagger - [[\varphi_0^\dagger, \mathcal{P}_\mu]_{\_}, \mathcal{P}^\mu]_{\_} = 0. \tag{10.16b}$$

So, regardless of the Lagrangians one starts, the fields φ_0 and $\varphi_0^\dagger$ satisfy one and the same Klein-Gordon equation. However, in contrast to the Heisenberg picture, in momentum picture these equations are not independent as the momentum operator $\mathcal{P}_\mu$, appearing in (10.16) and given via (2.1) or (2.18), also depends on φ_0 and $\varphi_0^\dagger$ through the energy-momentum operator $\mathcal{T}_{\mu\nu}$. Hence, to determine φ_0, $\varphi_0^\dagger$ and $\mathcal{P}_\mu$, we need an explicit expression for $\mathcal{T}_{\mu\nu}$ as a function of φ_0 and $\varphi_0^\dagger$.

If $\tilde{\varphi}$ was a classical complex/real field, we would have

$$\tilde{\mathcal{T}}_{\mu\nu} = \frac{1}{1+\tau(\tilde{\varphi})}\{\,\tilde{\pi}_\mu(\partial_\nu\,\tilde{\varphi}) + \tilde{\pi}_\mu^*(\partial_\nu\,\tilde{\varphi}^*)\} - \eta_{\mu\nu}\,\tilde{\mathcal{L}}$$

where the $*$ means complex conjugation. The straightforward transferring of this expression in the quantum case results in

$$\tilde{\mathcal{T}}_{\mu\nu}^{(1)} = \frac{1}{1+\tau(\tilde{\varphi})}\{\,\tilde{\pi}_\mu\circ(\partial_\nu\,\tilde{\varphi}) + \tilde{\pi}_\mu^\dagger\circ(\partial_\nu\,\tilde{\varphi}^\dagger)\} - \eta_{\mu\nu}\,\tilde{\mathcal{L}}. \tag{10.17}$$

However, if $\tilde{\pi}_\mu$ and $\partial_\nu\,\tilde{\varphi}$ and $\tilde{\pi}_\mu^\dagger$ and $\partial_\nu\,\tilde{\varphi}^\dagger$ do not commute, this $\tilde{\mathcal{T}}_{\mu\nu}$ is non-Hermitian, $\tilde{\mathcal{T}}_{\mu\nu}^\dagger \neq \tilde{\mathcal{T}}_{\mu\nu}$. This situation can be corrected by a 'Hermitian symmetrization' of the first two terms in (10.17), which gives

$$\tilde{\mathcal{T}}_{\mu\nu}^{(2)} = \frac{1}{2(1+\tau(\tilde{\varphi}))}\{\,\tilde{\pi}_\mu\circ(\partial_\nu\,\tilde{\varphi}) + (\partial_\nu\,\tilde{\varphi}^\dagger)\circ\tilde{\pi}_\mu^\dagger + \tilde{\pi}_\mu^\dagger\circ(\partial_\nu\,\tilde{\varphi}^\dagger) + (\partial_\nu\,\tilde{\varphi})\circ\tilde{\pi}_\mu\} - \eta_{\mu\nu}\,\tilde{\mathcal{L}}. \tag{10.18}$$

Evidently, if $\tilde{\varphi}^\dagger = \tilde{\varphi}$, and the Lagrangians (10.7) and (10.8) are employed, the equations (10.17) and (10.18) reduce to (3.10a) and (3.10b), respectively. But these are not the only possibilities for the energy-momentum operator. Often (see, e.g., [3, eq. (3.34)], or [5, eq. (2-151)], or [28, eq. (6)]), one writes it in the form

$$\tilde{\mathcal{T}}^{(3)}_{\mu\nu} = \frac{1}{1+\tau(\tilde{\varphi})} \{ \tilde{\pi}_\mu \circ (\partial_\nu \tilde{\varphi}) + \tilde{\pi}_\nu \circ (\partial_\mu \tilde{\varphi}) \} - \eta_{\mu\nu} \tilde{\mathcal{L}}. \tag{10.19}$$

As an alternative, we may also choose

$$\tilde{\mathcal{T}}^{(4)}_{\mu\nu} = \frac{1}{1+\tau(\tilde{\varphi})} \{ \tilde{\pi}^\dagger_\mu \circ (\partial_\nu \tilde{\varphi}^\dagger) + \tilde{\pi}^\dagger_\nu \circ (\partial_\mu \tilde{\varphi}^\dagger) \} - \eta_{\mu\nu} \tilde{\mathcal{L}}. \tag{10.20}$$

The last two expressions are suitable as $\tilde{\pi}_\mu$ and $\tilde{\pi}^\dagger_\mu$ are proportional to $\partial_\mu \tilde{\varphi}^\dagger$ and $\partial_\mu \tilde{\varphi}$ respectively.

Partial discussion of the problem how should be defined the quantum energy-momentum tensorial operator $\mathcal{T}_{\mu\nu}$ and a similar one for the current (see below), the reader can find in [28, § 2], where a reference to an early work of B. W. Gordon in Z. Phys. (vol. 40, p. 117. 1926) is given.

From the view-point of symmetry, $\mathcal{T}_{\mu\nu} = \mathcal{T}_{\nu\mu}$, and Hermiticity $\mathcal{T}^\dagger_{\mu\nu} = \mathcal{T}_{\mu\nu}$, the energy-momentum operators (10.18)–(10.20) are indistinguishable (if one and the same Lagrangian is used in them).

So, if we want to explore all possibilities, we have to look for the consequences of the four energy-momentum operators (10.17)–(10.20) for any one of the three Lagrangians (10.7)–(10.9). However, instead of investigating these 12 cases, we shall study only 3 of them. The reason is that in [14] we have proved that for a given Lagrangian, from the Schwinger's action principle [5, 29], follow, between other things, also *unique expressions for all conserved quantities in terms of the field operators* . In particular, it implies unique energy-momentum and current operators. These operators, for the Lagrangians (10.7)–(10.9) will be pointed below. Since the discussion of the way of their selection is out of the range of the present work, the reader may: (i) take this by faith; (ii) consider it as a lucky choice; (iii) look on it as an additional hypothesis/postulate; (iv) explore the consequences of the other 8 cases to see that they lead to contradictions in the theory;[25] (v) apply the results obtained in [14].

The correct energy-momentum operators for the Lagrangians (10.7)–(10.9) are respec-

[25] For instance, for them, generally, there are not one particle states with fixed energy, i.e. there are not one particle eigenvectors of the zeroth component of the momentum operator.

tively (10.19), (10.20) and (10.18).[26] Explicitly, in view of (10.15), we have

$$'\tilde{\mathcal{T}}^{(3)}_{\mu\nu} = \frac{1}{1+\tau(\tilde{\varphi})} c^2\hbar^2 \{ (\partial_\mu \tilde{\varphi}^\dagger) \circ (\partial_\nu \tilde{\varphi}) + (\partial_\nu \tilde{\varphi}^\dagger) \circ (\partial_\mu \tilde{\varphi}) \} - \eta_{\mu\nu}\, '\tilde{\mathcal{L}} \tag{10.21a}$$

$$''\tilde{\mathcal{T}}^{(4)}_{\mu\nu} = \frac{1}{1+\tau(\tilde{\varphi})} c^2\hbar^2 \{ (\partial_\mu \tilde{\varphi}) \circ (\partial_\nu \tilde{\varphi}^\dagger) + (\partial_\nu \tilde{\varphi}) \circ (\partial_\mu \tilde{\varphi}^\dagger) \} - \eta_{\mu\nu}\, ''\tilde{\mathcal{L}} \tag{10.21b}$$

$$\begin{aligned} '''\tilde{\mathcal{T}}^{(2)}_{\mu\nu} = \frac{1}{2(1+\tau(\tilde{\varphi}))} c^2\hbar^2 \{ & (\partial_\mu \tilde{\varphi}^\dagger) \circ (\partial_\nu \tilde{\varphi}) + (\partial_\nu \tilde{\varphi}^\dagger) \circ (\partial_\mu \tilde{\varphi}) \\ & + (\partial_\mu \tilde{\varphi}) \circ (\partial_\nu \tilde{\varphi}^\dagger) + (\partial_\nu \tilde{\varphi}) \circ (\partial_\mu \tilde{\varphi}^\dagger) \} - \eta_{\mu\nu}\, '''\tilde{\mathcal{L}}. \end{aligned} \tag{10.21c}$$

In momentum picture, these operators read (see (10.10)–(10.15)):

$$\begin{aligned} '\mathcal{T}^{(3)}_{\mu\nu} = & - \frac{1}{1+\tau(\varphi_0)} c^2 \{ [\varphi_0^\dagger, \mathcal{P}_\mu]_- \circ [\varphi_0, \mathcal{P}_\nu]_- + [\varphi_0^\dagger, \mathcal{P}_\nu]_- \circ [\varphi_0, \mathcal{P}_\mu]_- \} \\ & + \eta_{\mu\nu} \frac{1}{1+\tau(\varphi_0)} c^2 \{ m^2c^2 \varphi_0^\dagger \circ \varphi_0 + [\varphi_0^\dagger, \mathcal{P}_\lambda]_- \circ [\varphi_0, \mathcal{P}^\lambda]_- \} \end{aligned} \tag{10.22a}$$

$$\begin{aligned} ''\mathcal{T}^{(4)}_{\mu\nu} = & - \frac{1}{1+\tau(\varphi_0)} c^2 \{ [\varphi_0, \mathcal{P}_\mu]_- \circ [\varphi_0^\dagger, \mathcal{P}_\nu]_- + [\varphi_0, \mathcal{P}_\nu]_- \circ [\varphi_0^\dagger, \mathcal{P}_\mu]_- \} \\ & + \eta_{\mu\nu} \frac{1}{1+\tau(\varphi_0)} c^2 \{ m^2c^2 \varphi_0 \circ \varphi_0^\dagger + [\varphi_0, \mathcal{P}_\lambda]_- \circ [\varphi_0^\dagger, \mathcal{P}^\lambda]_- \} \end{aligned} \tag{10.22b}$$

$$\begin{aligned} '''\mathcal{T}^{(2)}_{\mu\nu} = & - \frac{1}{2(1+\tau(\varphi_0))} c^2 \{ [\varphi_0^\dagger, \mathcal{P}_\mu]_- \circ [\varphi_0, \mathcal{P}_\nu]_- + [\varphi_0^\dagger, \mathcal{P}_\nu]_- \circ [\varphi_0, \mathcal{P}_\mu]_- \\ & + [\varphi_0, \mathcal{P}_\mu]_- \circ [\varphi_0^\dagger, \mathcal{P}_\nu]_- + [\varphi_0, \mathcal{P}_\nu]_- \circ [\varphi_0^\dagger, \mathcal{P}_\mu]_- \} \\ & + \eta_{\mu\nu} \frac{1}{2(1+\tau(\varphi_0))} c^2 \{ m^2c^2 \varphi_0^\dagger \circ \varphi_0 + m^2c^2 \varphi_0 \circ \varphi_0^\dagger \\ & + [\varphi_0^\dagger, \mathcal{P}_\lambda]_- \circ [\varphi_0, \mathcal{P}^\lambda]_- + [\varphi_0, \mathcal{P}_\lambda]_- \circ [\varphi_0^\dagger, \mathcal{P}^\lambda]_- \}. \end{aligned} \tag{10.22c}$$

Any one of the equations (10.22), together with (10.16), (2.18) and (2.2) form a complete system of equations for explicit determination of φ, $\varphi^\dagger$ and $\mathcal{P}_\mu$. It will be analyzed in the subsequent sections.

Since the Lagrangians of a free general scalar field are invariant under (constant) phase transformations, such a field carries a, possibly vanishing, charge (see, e.g., [3, 5]. The (total) charge operator $\tilde{\mathcal{Q}}$ is defined by

$$\tilde{\mathcal{Q}} := \frac{1}{c} \int\limits_{x^0=\text{const}} \tilde{\mathcal{J}}_0(x)\, \mathrm{d}^3\boldsymbol{x} \tag{10.23}$$

where $\tilde{\mathcal{J}}_\mu(x)$ is a Hermitian operator,

$$\tilde{\mathcal{J}}_\mu^\dagger(x) = \tilde{\mathcal{J}}_\mu(x), \tag{10.24}$$

[26] Since (10.2) and (10.7) are proportional, all results for (10.7) can trivially be formulated for (10.2).

describing the field's current considered a little below. Since $\tilde{\mathcal{Q}}$ and $\tilde{\mathcal{J}}_\mu$ are conserved quantities, viz. they satisfy the equivalent conservation laws

$$\frac{\mathrm{d}\,\tilde{\mathcal{Q}}}{\mathrm{d}x^0} = 0 \qquad \partial^\mu\,\tilde{\mathcal{J}}_\mu = 0, \tag{10.25}$$

and $\partial_a\,\tilde{\mathcal{Q}} \equiv 0$ for $a = 1, 2, 3$, due to (10.23), we can write

$$\partial_\mu\,\tilde{\mathcal{Q}} = 0. \tag{10.26}$$

The consideration of $\tilde{\mathcal{Q}}$ as a generator of (constant) phase transformations [3, 5] leads to the following (Heisenberg) equations/relations [27]

$$[\tilde{\varphi},\,\tilde{\mathcal{Q}}]_{\_} = q\,\tilde{\varphi} \qquad [\tilde{\varphi}^\dagger,\,\tilde{\mathcal{Q}}]_{\_} = -q\,\tilde{\varphi}^\dagger \tag{10.27}$$

where q is a constant, equal to the opposite charge of the particles (quanta) of $\tilde{\varphi}$ (see below Sect. 12), such that

$$q = 0 \qquad \text{for } \tilde{\varphi}^\dagger = \tilde{\varphi}. \tag{10.28}$$

The charge operator $\tilde{\mathcal{Q}}$ is Hermitian, i.e.

$$\tilde{\mathcal{Q}}^\dagger = \tilde{\mathcal{Q}} \tag{10.29}$$

and commutes with the momentum operator $\tilde{\mathcal{P}}_\mu$,

$$[\,\tilde{\mathcal{Q}},\,\tilde{\mathcal{P}}_\mu]_{\_} = 0. \tag{10.30}$$

As a consequence of (10.30) and (2.2), the charge operator commutes with the (evolution) operator $\mathcal{U}(x, x_0)$ responsible to the transition from Heisenberg picture to momentum one,

$$[\,\tilde{\mathcal{Q}},\,\mathcal{U}(x, x_0)]_{\_} = 0. \tag{10.31}$$

Combining this with (2.4), we get

$$\mathcal{Q}(x) = \tilde{\mathcal{Q}} =:\ \mathcal{Q}, \tag{10.32}$$

that is the charge operators in Heisenberg and momentum pictures coincide. [28]

In momentum picture, the equations (10.27) and (10.29), evidently, read:

$$[\varphi,\,\mathcal{Q}]_{\_} = q\,\varphi \qquad [\varphi^\dagger,\,\mathcal{Q}]_{\_} = -q\,\varphi^\dagger \tag{10.33}$$

$$\mathcal{Q}^\dagger = \mathcal{Q}. \tag{10.34}$$

---

[27] The equations (10.27) follow from the transformation properties of $\tilde{\varphi}$ and $\tilde{\varphi}^\dagger$ too.

[28] Obviously, (10.31) and (10.32) are valid for any operator $\tilde{\mathcal{Q}}$ commuting with the momentum operator.

In this picture the equality (10.23) is convenient to be rewritten as (see (2.4))

$$\mathcal{Q} = \frac{1}{c} \int\limits_{x^0 = x_0^0} \mathcal{U}^{-1}(x, x_0) \circ \mathcal{J}_0(x) \circ \mathcal{U}(x, x_0) \, \mathrm{d}^3 \boldsymbol{x}. \tag{10.35}$$

The only thing, we need for a complete determination of $\mathcal{Q}$, is the explicit definition of the (quantum) current $\mathcal{J}_\mu$. If $\tilde{\varphi}$ was a free classical arbitrary, real or complex, scalar field, we would have

$$\tilde{\mathcal{J}}_\mu(x) = \frac{q}{\mathrm{i}\hbar} (\, \tilde{\pi}_\mu(x) \, \tilde{\varphi}(x) - \, \tilde{\pi}_\mu^*(x) \, \tilde{\varphi}^*(x)). \tag{10.36}$$

The straightforward transferring of this result into the quantum case gives

$$\tilde{\mathcal{J}}_\mu^{(1)}(x) = \frac{q}{\mathrm{i}\hbar} \{ \, \tilde{\pi}_\mu(x) \circ \tilde{\varphi}(x) - \, \tilde{\pi}_\mu^\dagger(x) \circ \tilde{\varphi}^\dagger(x) \}. \tag{10.37a}$$

But, since the current operator must satisfy (10.24), the quantities (10.37a) are not suitable for components of a current operator if $[\, \tilde{\pi}_\mu, \tilde{\varphi}]_{\_} \neq 0$ and/or $[\, \tilde{\pi}_\mu^\dagger, \tilde{\varphi}^\dagger]_{\_} \neq 0$. Evidently, here the situation is quite similar to the one with the definition of the energy-momentum operator considered above. So, without going into details, we shall write here is a list of three admissible candidates for a current operator:[29]

$$\tilde{\mathcal{J}}_\mu^{(2)} = \frac{q}{2\mathrm{i}\hbar} (\, \tilde{\pi}_\mu \circ \tilde{\varphi} - \, \tilde{\pi}_\mu^\dagger \circ \tilde{\varphi}^\dagger - \tilde{\varphi}^\dagger \circ \tilde{\pi}_\mu^\dagger + \tilde{\varphi} \circ \tilde{\pi}_\mu) \tag{10.37b}$$

$$\tilde{\mathcal{J}}_\mu^{(3)} = \frac{q}{\mathrm{i}\hbar} (\, \tilde{\pi}_\mu \circ \tilde{\varphi} - \tilde{\varphi}^\dagger \circ \tilde{\pi}_\mu^\dagger) \tag{10.37c}$$

$$\tilde{\mathcal{J}}_\mu^{(4)} = \frac{q}{\mathrm{i}\hbar} (\, \tilde{\varphi} \circ \tilde{\pi}_\mu - \, \tilde{\pi}_\mu^\dagger \circ \tilde{\varphi}^\dagger). \tag{10.37d}$$

Similarly to the case of energy-momentum operator, to any one of the Lagrangians (10.7)–(10.9), there corresponds a unique current operator. These operators are as follows (see [14]):

$${}'\tilde{\mathcal{J}}_\mu^{(3)} = \frac{q}{\mathrm{i}\hbar} ({}'\tilde{\pi}_\mu \circ \tilde{\varphi} - \tilde{\varphi}^\dagger \circ {}'\tilde{\pi}_\mu^\dagger) \tag{10.38a}$$

$${}''\tilde{\mathcal{J}}_\mu^{(4)} = \frac{q}{\mathrm{i}\hbar} (\tilde{\varphi} \circ {}''\tilde{\pi}_\mu - {}''\tilde{\pi}_\mu^\dagger \circ \tilde{\varphi}^\dagger) \tag{10.38b}$$

$${}'''\tilde{\mathcal{J}}_\mu^{(2)} = \frac{q}{2\mathrm{i}\hbar} ({}'''\tilde{\pi}_\mu \circ \tilde{\varphi} + \tilde{\varphi} \circ {}'''\tilde{\pi}_\mu - {}'''\tilde{\pi}_\mu^\dagger \circ \tilde{\varphi}^\dagger - \tilde{\varphi}^\dagger \circ {}'''\tilde{\pi}_\mu^\dagger). \tag{10.38c}$$

As a consequence of (10.15), these current operators in momentum picture read respec-

[29] For a partial discussion of the problem, see [28, § 2]. The expression (10.37c) is the one most often used in the literature [3, 11, 28]; however, the definition (10.37a) is utilized too, for instance, in [5, p. 99].

tively:

$$'\mathcal{J}^{(3)}_{\mu} = \frac{1}{2} q c^2 \big(\varphi_0^\dagger \circ [\varphi_0,\, \mathcal{P}_\mu]_- - [\varphi_0^\dagger,\, \mathcal{P}_\mu]_- \circ \varphi_0 \big) \tag{10.39a}$$

$$''\mathcal{J}^{(4)}_{\mu} = \frac{1}{2} q c^2 \big([\varphi_0,\, \mathcal{P}_\mu]_- \circ \varphi_0^\dagger - \varphi_0 \circ [\varphi_0^\dagger,\, \mathcal{P}_\mu]_- \big) \tag{10.39b}$$

$$'''\mathcal{J}^{(2)}_{\mu} = \frac{1}{4} q c^2 \big(\varphi_0^\dagger \circ [\varphi_0,\, \mathcal{P}_\mu]_- + [\varphi_0,\, \mathcal{P}_\mu]_- \circ \varphi_0^\dagger - [\varphi_0^\dagger,\, \mathcal{P}_\mu]_- \circ \varphi_0 - \varphi_0 \circ [\varphi_0^\dagger,\, \mathcal{P}_\mu]_- \big). \tag{10.39c}$$

A free scalar field has no spin angular momentum and possesses a, generally, non-vanishing orbital angular momentum, as described in Sect. 3 (in particular, see equations (3.12)–(3.16)). It will be explored in Sect. 14 directly in terms of creation and annihilation operators.

According to the Klein-Gordon equations (10.16), the field operators φ_0 and $\varphi_0^\dagger$ are eigen-operators for the mapping (3.17) with eigenvalues equal to the square m^2 of the mass (parameter) m of the field (more precisely, of its quanta). Therefore the interpretation of the operator (3.17) as a square-of-mass operator of the field is preserved also in the case of free arbitrary, Hermitian of non-Hermitian, scalar field. At the same time, the square of the momentum operator, $\frac{1}{c^2}\,\mathcal{P}_\mu \circ \mathcal{P}^\mu$, has an interpretation of a square of mass operator for the solutions of the field equations, i.e. for the *field's states*.

11 Analysis of the field equations

As we know, the field operator φ_0 and its Hermitian conjugate $\varphi_0^\dagger$ satisfy the Klein-Gordon equations (10.16) which are 'mixed' through the momentum operator $\mathcal{P}_\mu$, due to the simultaneous presentation of φ_0 and $\varphi_0^\dagger$ in the energy-momentum operator(s) (10.22). However, for φ_0 and $\varphi_0^\dagger$ are completely valid all of the results of Sect. 4 as in it is used only the Klein-Gordon equation (in momentum picture for φ_0) and it does not utilize any hypotheses about the concrete form of the momentum operator $\mathcal{P}_\mu$. Let us formulate the main of them.

Proposition 11.1. *The solutions φ_0 and $\varphi_0^\dagger$ of* (10.16) *can be written as*

$$\varphi_0 = \int \mathrm{d}^3\boldsymbol{k} \{ f_+(\boldsymbol{k}) \varphi_0(k) \big|_{k_0=+\sqrt{m^2c^2+\boldsymbol{k}^2}} + f_-(\boldsymbol{k}) \varphi_0(k) \big|_{k_0=-\sqrt{m^2c^2+\boldsymbol{k}^2}} \} \tag{11.1a}$$

$$\varphi_0^\dagger = \int \mathrm{d}^3\boldsymbol{k} \{ f_+^\dagger(\boldsymbol{k}) \varphi_0^\dagger(k) \big|_{k_0=+\sqrt{m^2c^2+\boldsymbol{k}^2}} + f_-^\dagger(\boldsymbol{k}) \varphi_0^\dagger(k) \big|_{k_0=-\sqrt{m^2c^2+\boldsymbol{k}^2}} \}, \tag{11.1b}$$

where $\varphi_0(k), \varphi_0^\dagger(k) \colon \mathcal{F} \to \mathcal{F}$ are solutions of

$$[\varphi_0(k),\, \mathcal{P}_\mu]_- = -k_\mu \varphi_0(k) \qquad [\varphi_0^\dagger(k),\, \mathcal{P}_\mu]_- = -k_\mu \varphi_0^\dagger(k) \tag{11.2}$$

and, for solutions different from the 'degenerate' solutions

$$[\varphi_0,\, \mathcal{P}_\mu]_- = 0 \quad [\varphi_0^\dagger,\, \mathcal{P}_\mu]_- = 0 \qquad \text{for } m = 0 \tag{11.3}$$

or, in Heisenberg picture,

$$\tilde{\varphi}(x) = \tilde{\varphi}(x_0) = \varphi_0 \quad \tilde{\varphi}^\dagger(x) = \tilde{\varphi}^\dagger(x_0) = \varphi_0^\dagger \quad \tilde{\mathcal{P}}_\mu = \mathcal{P}_\mu = 0 \qquad \text{for } m = 0, \quad (11.3')$$

the symbols $f_\pm$ and $f_\pm^\dagger$ denote complex-valued functions of $\mathbf{k}$ and for the solutions (11.3) *they stand for some distributions of $\mathbf{k}$.*

Notice, as a result of the restriction $k_0 = \pm\sqrt{m^2c^2 + \boldsymbol{k}^2}$ in (11.1), only the solutions of (11.2) for which

$$k^2 = k_0^2 - \boldsymbol{k}^2 = m^2c^2 \tag{11.4}$$

are significant.

It should be emphasized, the operator $\varphi_0^\dagger(k)$ in (11.1) is *not* the Hermitian conjugate of $\varphi_0(k)$. In fact, the reader can verify that (11.1) imply the equalities (cf. (4.12))

$$\begin{aligned}
\big(f_\pm(\boldsymbol{k})\varphi_0(k)\big|_{k_0=\pm\sqrt{m^2c^2+\boldsymbol{k}^2}}\big)^\dagger &= -f_\mp^\dagger(-\boldsymbol{k})\varphi_0^\dagger(-k)\big|_{k_0=\mp\sqrt{m^2c^2+\boldsymbol{k}^2}} \\
\big(f_\pm^\dagger(\boldsymbol{k})\varphi_0^\dagger(k)\big|_{k_0=\pm\sqrt{m^2c^2+\boldsymbol{k}^2}}\big)^\dagger &= -f_\mp(-\boldsymbol{k})\varphi_0(-k)\big|_{k_0=\mp\sqrt{m^2c^2+\boldsymbol{k}^2}}.
\end{aligned} \tag{11.5}$$

However, in the Hermitian case, i.e. for $\varphi_0^\dagger = \varphi_0$, the equations (11.1a) and (11.1b) must be identical and, consequently, we have

$$f_\pm^\dagger(\boldsymbol{k}) = f_\pm(\boldsymbol{k}) \quad \varphi_0^\dagger(k) = \varphi_0(k) \qquad \text{for } \varphi_0^\dagger = \varphi_0. \tag{11.6}$$

In this case, the equations (11.5) reduce to (4.12).

Proposition 11.2. *The solutions of* (10.16) *have the representations*

$$\varphi_0 = \int \delta(k^2 - m^2c^2)\underline{\varphi_0}(k)\,\mathrm{d}^4k \qquad \varphi_0^\dagger = \int \delta(k^2 - m^2c^2)\underline{\varphi_0^\dagger}(k)\,\mathrm{d}^4k \tag{11.7}$$

where $\underline{\varphi_0}(k)$ and $\underline{\varphi_0^\dagger}(k)$ are suitably normalized solutions of (11.2) *which, up to a phase factor equal to $\mathrm{e}^{\frac{1}{\mathrm{i}\hbar}x_0^\mu k_\mu}$, coincide with the Fourier coefficients of $\tilde{\varphi}_0(x)$ and $\tilde{\varphi}_0^\dagger(x)$ (in Heisenberg picture for solutions different from* (11.3)*).*

It should be emphasized, the solutions (11.3) are completely 'unphysical' as they have zero (energy-)momentum operator (see (10.22) and (2.18)), zero total charge (see (10.39)) and zero orbital angular momentum (see (3.14)) and, consequently, they cannot lead to some physically predictable consequences.

12 Frequency decompositions and their physical meaning

The presented in Sect. 5 frequency decompositions of a free Hermitian scalar field are based on the Klein-Gordon equation, or, more precisely, on (4.6) and (4.8), and do not rely on a concrete representation of the energy-momentum operator. Hence they can *mutatis mutandis* be transferred in the general case of Hermitian or non-Hermitian scalar field. The basic moments of that procedure are as follows.

Let us put

$$\varphi_0^{\pm}(k) := \begin{cases} f_{\pm}(\pm\boldsymbol{k})\varphi_0(\pm k) & \text{for } k_0 \geq 0 \\ 0 & \text{for } k_0 < 0 \end{cases}$$
$$\varphi_0^{\dagger\pm}(k) := \begin{cases} f_{\pm}^{\dagger}((\pm\boldsymbol{k})\varphi_0^{\dagger}(\pm k) & \text{for } k_0 \geq 0 \\ 0 & \text{for } k_0 < 0 \end{cases} \tag{12.1}$$

As an evident consequence of (11.5), we have the equalities

$$\left(\varphi_0^{\pm}(k)\right)^{\dagger} = \varphi_0^{\dagger\mp}(k) \quad \left(\varphi_0^{\dagger\pm}(k)\right)^{\dagger} = \varphi_0^{\mp}(k) \tag{12.2}$$

which mean that the operators $\varphi_0^{\dagger\pm}(k)$ are *not* the Hermitian conjugate of $\varphi_0^{\pm}(k)$. In the Hermitian case, $\varphi_0^{\dagger} = \varphi_0$, (12.1) reduce to (5.1) due to (11.6).

In view of (11.1) and (11.2), we have:

$$\varphi_0 = \varphi_0^{+} + \varphi_0^{-} \qquad \varphi_0^{\dagger} = \varphi_0^{\dagger+} + \varphi_0^{\dagger-} \tag{12.3}$$
$$\varphi_0^{\pm} = \int \mathrm{d}^3\boldsymbol{k}\varphi_0^{\pm}(k)|_{k_0=\sqrt{m^2c^2+\boldsymbol{k}^2}} \qquad \varphi_0^{\dagger\pm} = \int \mathrm{d}^3\boldsymbol{k}\varphi_0^{\dagger\pm}(k)|_{k_0=\sqrt{m^2c^2+\boldsymbol{k}^2}} \tag{12.4}$$
$$[\varphi_0^{\pm}(k), \mathcal{P}_\mu]_{\_} = \mp k_\mu \varphi_0^{\pm}(k) \qquad [\varphi_0^{\dagger\pm}(k), \mathcal{P}_\mu]_{\_} = \mp k_\mu \varphi_0^{\dagger\pm}(k) \qquad k_0 = \sqrt{m^2c^2 + \boldsymbol{k}^2} \tag{12.5}$$

$$[\varphi_0^{\pm}(k), \mathcal{Q}]_{\_} = q\varphi_0^{\pm}(k) \quad [\varphi_0^{\dagger\pm}(k), \mathcal{Q}]_{\_} = -q\varphi_0^{\dagger\pm}(k)$$
$$[\varphi_0^{\pm}, \mathcal{Q}]_{\_} = q\varphi_0^{\pm} \quad [\varphi_0^{\dagger\pm}, \mathcal{Q}]_{\_} = -q\varphi_0^{\dagger\pm}. \tag{12.6}$$

If $\mathcal{X}_p$ is a state vector characterizing a state with 4-momentum p (see equation (5.6)), then (12.5) entail

$$\mathcal{P}_\mu(\varphi_0^{\pm}(k)(\mathcal{X}_p)) = (p_\mu \pm k_\mu)\varphi_0^{\pm}(k)(\mathcal{X}_p) \qquad k_0 = \sqrt{m^2c^2 + \boldsymbol{k}^2}$$
$$\mathcal{P}_\mu(\varphi_0^{\dagger\pm}(k)(\mathcal{X}_p)) = (p_\mu \pm k_\mu)\varphi_0^{\dagger\pm}(k)(\mathcal{X}_p) \qquad k_0 = \sqrt{m^2c^2 + \boldsymbol{k}^2}. \tag{12.7}$$

So, φ_0^{+} and $\varphi_0^{\dagger+}$ create particles with 4-momentum k, while φ_0^{-} and $\varphi_0^{\dagger-}$ annihilate such particles. If $\varphi^{\dagger} = \varphi$, the operators $\varphi_0^{\pm}$ and $\varphi_0^{\dagger\pm}$ coincide, while for $\varphi^{\dagger} \neq \varphi$ they are different. In the last case the difference comes from the existence of non-zero charge operator (10.23) for which the (Heisenberg equations/)relations (10.27) hold. If $\mathcal{X}_e$ is a state vector corresponding to a state with total charge e, i.e.

$$\mathcal{Q}(\mathcal{X}_e) = e\,\mathcal{X}_e, \tag{12.8}$$

then, from (10.33) and (12.6), we get:[30]

$$\begin{gathered}\mathcal{Q}(\varphi_0(\mathcal{X}_e)) = (e-q)\varphi_0(\mathcal{X}_e) \quad \mathcal{Q}(\varphi_0^\dagger(\mathcal{X}_e)) = (e+q)\varphi_0^\dagger(\mathcal{X}_e)\\ \mathcal{Q}(\varphi_0^\pm(\mathcal{X}_e)) = (e-q)\varphi_0^\pm(\mathcal{X}_e) \quad \mathcal{Q}(\varphi_0^{\dagger\pm}(\mathcal{X}_e)) = (e+q)\varphi_0^{\dagger\pm}(\mathcal{X}_e).\\ \mathcal{Q}(\varphi_0^\pm(\boldsymbol{k})(\mathcal{X}_e)) = (e-q)\varphi_0^\pm(\boldsymbol{k})(\mathcal{X}_e) \quad \mathcal{Q}(\varphi_0^{\dagger\pm}(\boldsymbol{k})(\mathcal{X}_e)) = (e+q)\varphi_0^{\dagger\pm}(\boldsymbol{k})(\mathcal{X}_e).\end{gathered} \tag{12.9}$$

Therefore φ_0, $\varphi_0^\pm$ and $\varphi_0^\pm(\boldsymbol{k})$ decrease the field's charge by q, while $\varphi_0^\dagger$, $\varphi_0^{\dagger\pm}$ and $\varphi_0^{\dagger\pm}(\boldsymbol{k})$ increase it by the same quantity. So, in a summary, $\varphi_0^+(\boldsymbol{k})$ and $\varphi_0^{\dagger+}(\boldsymbol{k})$ create particles with 4-momentum $(\sqrt{m^2c^2+\boldsymbol{k}^2}, \boldsymbol{k})$ and charges $(-q)$ and $(+q)$, respectively, while $\varphi_0^-(\boldsymbol{k})$ and $\varphi_0^{\dagger-}(\boldsymbol{k})$ annihilate particles with 4-momentum $(\sqrt{m^2c^2+\boldsymbol{k}^2}, \boldsymbol{k})$ and charges $(+q)$ and $(-q)$, respectively.[31, 32]

13 The field equations in terms of creation and annihilation operators

If one wants to obtain from (10.16) a system of equations for the momentum and field operators, an explicit expression for $\mathcal{P}_\mu$, as a function (functional) of the field operators φ_0 and $\varphi_0^\dagger$, is required. To find it, we shall proceed as in Sect. 6, when the Hermitian case, $\varphi_0^\dagger = \varphi_0$, was investigated.

Since (12.3)–(12.5) imply

$$\begin{aligned}[\varphi_0, \mathcal{P}_\mu]_- &= \int \{k_\mu(-\varphi_0^+(k) + \varphi_0^-(k))\}|_{k_0=\sqrt{m^2c^2+\boldsymbol{k}^2}}\,\mathrm{d}^3\boldsymbol{k}\\ [\varphi_0^\dagger, \mathcal{P}_\mu]_- &= \int \{k_\mu(-\varphi_0^{\dagger+}(k) + \varphi_0^{\dagger-}(k))\}|_{k_0=\sqrt{m^2c^2+\boldsymbol{k}^2}}\,\mathrm{d}^3\boldsymbol{k},\end{aligned} \tag{13.1}$$

the energy-momentum operators (10.22), in view of (12.4), can be written as:

$$\begin{aligned}{}'\mathcal{T}_{\mu\nu}^{(3)} =& \frac{1}{1+\tau(\varphi_0)} c^2 \int \mathrm{d}^3\boldsymbol{k}\,\mathrm{d}^3\boldsymbol{k}' \{(-k_\mu k'_\nu - k_\nu k'_\mu + \eta_{\mu\nu} k_\lambda k'^\lambda)\\ &\times(-\varphi_0^{\dagger+}(k) + \varphi_0^{\dagger-}(k))\circ(-\varphi_0^+(k') + \varphi_0^-(k'))\\ &+ \eta_{\mu\nu} m^2c^2 (\varphi_0^{\dagger+}(k) + \varphi_0^{\dagger-}(k))\circ(\varphi_0^+(k') + \varphi_0^-(k'))\}\end{aligned} \tag{13.2a}$$

$$\begin{aligned}{}''\mathcal{T}_{\mu\nu}^{(4)} =& \frac{1}{1+\tau(\varphi_0)} c^2 \int \mathrm{d}^3\boldsymbol{k}\,\mathrm{d}^3\boldsymbol{k}' \{(-k_\mu k'_\nu - k_\nu k'_\mu + \eta_{\mu\nu} k_\lambda k'^\lambda)\\ &\times(-\varphi_0^+(k) + \varphi_0^-(k))\circ(-\varphi_0^{\dagger+}(k') + \varphi_0^{\dagger-}(k'))\\ &+ \eta_{\mu\nu} m^2c^2 (\varphi_0^+(k) + \varphi_0^-(k))\circ(\varphi_0^{\dagger+}(k') + \varphi_0^{\dagger-}(k'))\}\end{aligned} \tag{13.2b}$$

[30] These considerations do not use concrete forms, like (10.39), of the current operator $\mathcal{J}_\mu$.

[31] By convention, the particles created by φ_0^+ or annihilated by $\varphi_0^{\dagger-}(\boldsymbol{k})$ are called 'particles', while the ones created by $\varphi_0^{\dagger+}(\boldsymbol{k})$ or annihilated by $\varphi_0^-(\boldsymbol{k})$ are called 'antiparticles'.

[32] Since (12.9) originates from the equation (10.27), which is external to the Lagrangian formalism, one should accept the given interpretation of $\varphi_0^\pm(\boldsymbol{k})$ and $\varphi_0^{\dagger\pm}(\boldsymbol{k})$ by some reserve. However, this interpretation is confirmed in the later development of the theory on the base of a notion of n-particle, $n \in \mathbb{N}$, states (see Sect. 17).

$$
\begin{aligned}
{}'''\mathcal{T}^{(2)}_{\mu\nu} =& \frac{1}{2(1+\tau(\varphi_0))} c^2 \int \mathrm{d}^3\boldsymbol{k}\,\mathrm{d}^3\boldsymbol{k}' \{ (-k_\mu k'_\nu - k_\nu k'_\mu + \eta_{\mu\nu} k_\lambda k'^\lambda) \\
& \times (-\varphi_0^{\dagger\,+}(k) + \varphi_0^{\dagger\,-}(k)) \circ (-\varphi_0^{+}(k') + \varphi_0^{-}(k')) \\
& + (-k_\mu k'_\nu - k_\nu k'_\mu + \eta_{\mu\nu} k_\lambda k'^\lambda) \\
& \times (-\varphi_0^{+}(k) + \varphi_0^{-}(k)) \circ (-\varphi_0^{\dagger\,+}(k') + \varphi_0^{\dagger\,-}(k')) \\
& + \eta_{\mu\nu} m^2 c^2 (\varphi_0^{\dagger\,+}(k) + \varphi_0^{\dagger\,-}(k)) \circ (\varphi_0^{+}(k') + \varphi_0^{-}(k')) \\
& + \eta_{\mu\nu} m^2 c^2 (\varphi_0^{+}(k) + \varphi_0^{-}(k)) \circ (\varphi_0^{\dagger\,+}(k') + \varphi_0^{\dagger\,-}(k')) \}
\end{aligned}
\tag{13.2c}
$$

where $k_0 = \sqrt{m^2c^2 + \boldsymbol{k}^2}$ and $k'_0 = \sqrt{m^2c^2 + \boldsymbol{k}'^2}$.

Performing with these expressions the same manipulations as the ones leading from (6.1) to (6.5), we derive the following expressions for the momentum operator:[33, 34]

$$
{}'\mathcal{P}^{(3)}_{\mu} = \frac{1}{1+\tau(\varphi_0)} \int k_\mu|_{k_0=\sqrt{m^2c^2+\boldsymbol{k}^2}} \{ \varphi_0^{\dagger\,+}(\boldsymbol{k}) \circ \varphi_0^{-}(\boldsymbol{k}) + \varphi_0^{\dagger\,-}(\boldsymbol{k}) \circ \varphi_0^{+}(\boldsymbol{k}) \}\,\mathrm{d}^3\boldsymbol{k}
\tag{13.3a}
$$

$$
{}''\mathcal{P}^{(4)}_{\mu} = \frac{1}{1+\tau(\varphi_0)} \int k_\mu|_{k_0=\sqrt{m^2c^2+\boldsymbol{k}^2}} \{ \varphi_0^{+}(\boldsymbol{k}) \circ \varphi_0^{\dagger\,-}(\boldsymbol{k}) + \varphi_0^{-}(\boldsymbol{k}) \circ \varphi_0^{\dagger\,+}(\boldsymbol{k}) \}\,\mathrm{d}^3\boldsymbol{k}
\tag{13.3b}
$$

$$
\begin{aligned}
{}'''\mathcal{P}^{(2)}_{\mu} = \frac{1}{2(1+\tau(\varphi_0))} \int k_\mu|_{k_0=\sqrt{m^2c^2+\boldsymbol{k}^2}} \{ & \varphi_0^{\dagger\,+}(\boldsymbol{k}) \circ \varphi_0^{-}(\boldsymbol{k}) + \varphi_0^{\dagger\,-}(\boldsymbol{k}) \circ \varphi_0^{+}(\boldsymbol{k}) \\
& + \varphi_0^{+}(\boldsymbol{k}) \circ \varphi_0^{\dagger\,-}(\boldsymbol{k}) + \varphi_0^{-}(\boldsymbol{k}) \circ \varphi_0^{\dagger\,+}(\boldsymbol{k}) \}\,\mathrm{d}^3\boldsymbol{k}.
\end{aligned}
\tag{13.3c}
$$

Here $\tau(\varphi_0)$ is defined by (10.13) and the following shortcuts are introduced:

$$
\begin{aligned}
\varphi_0^{\pm}(\boldsymbol{k}) &:= \{ \big(2c(2\pi\hbar)^3 k_0\big)^{1/2} \varphi_0^{\pm}(k) \}|_{k_0=\sqrt{m^2c^2+\boldsymbol{k}^2}} \\
\varphi_0^{\dagger\,\pm}(\boldsymbol{k}) &:= \{ \big(2c(2\pi\hbar)^3 k_0\big)^{1/2} \varphi_0^{\dagger\,\pm}(k) \}|_{k_0=\sqrt{m^2c^2+\boldsymbol{k}^2}} \ .
\end{aligned}
\tag{13.4}
$$

The operators $\varphi_0^{+}(\boldsymbol{k})$ and $\varphi_0^{\dagger\,+}(\boldsymbol{k})$ (resp. $\varphi_0^{-}(\boldsymbol{k})$ and $\varphi_0^{\dagger\,-}(\boldsymbol{k})$) are called the *creation* (resp. *annihilation*) operators (of the field (field's particles)).

Obviously, for a Hermitian field, $\varphi_0^{\dagger} = \varphi_0$, all of the three expressions in (13.3) reduce to the 'right Hermitian' result (6.5); besides, the '3-dimensional' creation/annihilation operators (13.4) reduce to (6.6), as one should expect. In the non-Hermitian case, $\varphi_0^{\dagger} \neq \varphi_0$, the operator (13.3b), as a function of the creation/annihilation operators (13.4), formally

[33] Notice, the equalities (6.4) remain valid in the general case. Besides, these equations hold if in them some or all of the operators $\varphi_0^{\pm}(k)$ and $\varphi_0^{\pm}(k')$ are replaced with $\varphi_0^{\dagger\,\pm}(k)$ and $\varphi_0^{\dagger\,\pm}(k')$, respectively.

[34] For the other 8 combinations of the Lagrangians (10.7)–(10.9) and energy-momentum operators (10.17)–(10.20), in the integrands in the r.h.s. of (13.3) terms proportional to $\varphi_0^{\pm}(k) \circ \varphi_0^{\dagger\,\pm}(k_0, -\boldsymbol{k})$ and $\varphi_0^{\dagger\,\pm}(k) \circ \varphi_0^{\pm}(k_0, -\boldsymbol{k})$ will appear. They are responsible for the contradictions mentioned in Sect. 10 (see, in particular, footnote 25).

coincides with the momentum operator obtained from the Lagrangian (10.2) in the literature [3, eq. (3.39)]. However, it should be remarked, our creation and annihilation operators for the Lagrangian (10.2) with $\varphi_0^\dagger \neq \varphi_0$ differ by a phase factor from the ones in Heisenberg picture used in the literature (see below equations (13.5)). Generally, the three momentum operators (13.3) are different, but, after normal ordering, they result into one and the same momentum operator (see Sect. 16, equation (16.2)).

For a comparison with expressions in (the momentum representation of) Heisenberg picture, it is worth to be noticed that, due to proposition 11.2, the creation/annihilation operators $\tilde{\varphi}^\pm(\boldsymbol{k})$ and $\tilde{\varphi}^{\dagger\pm}(\boldsymbol{k})$ in (the momentum representation of) Heisenberg picture are (cf. (6.8))

$$\tilde{\varphi}^\pm(\boldsymbol{k}) = \mathrm{e}^{\pm\frac{1}{\mathrm{i}\hbar}x_0^\mu k_\mu}\Big|_{k_0=\sqrt{m^2c^2+\boldsymbol{k}^2}}\varphi_0^\pm \qquad \tilde{\varphi}^{\dagger\pm}(\boldsymbol{k}) = \mathrm{e}^{\pm\frac{1}{\mathrm{i}\hbar}x_0^\mu k_\mu}\Big|_{k_0=\sqrt{m^2c^2+\boldsymbol{k}^2}}\varphi_0^{\dagger\pm}. \tag{13.5}$$

(Relations like (6.9) are, of course, also valid; (13.5) is a consequence from them for $x^\mu = x_0^\mu$.) Therefore, quadratic expressions, like the ones in the integrands in (13.3), look in one and the same way in momentum and Heisenberg pictures.

Now we are ready to obtain the field equations in terms of creation and annihilation operators. Since (12.3)–(12.5) are equivalent to (10.16), the equations, we want to derive, are (12.5) with $\mathcal{P}_\mu$ given via (13.3). At this stage of the development of the theory, we will get *three*, generally different, systems of equations, corresponding to the three Lagrangians, (10.7), (10.8) and (10.9), we started off. But, as after normal ordering the three momentum operators (13.3) become identical, these systems of equations will turn to be identical after normal ordering.

In terms of the operators (13.4), the equations (12.3)–(12.5) can equivalently be rewritten as:

$$\begin{aligned}\varphi_0 &= \int \big(2c(2\pi\hbar)^3 k_0\big)^{-1/2}(\varphi_0^+(\boldsymbol{k}) + \varphi_0^-(\boldsymbol{k}))\,\mathrm{d}^3\boldsymbol{k}\\ \varphi_0^\dagger &= \int \big(2c(2\pi\hbar)^3 k_0\big)^{-1/2}(\varphi_0^{\dagger+}(\boldsymbol{k}) + \varphi_0^{\dagger-}(\boldsymbol{k}))\,\mathrm{d}^3\boldsymbol{k}\end{aligned} \tag{13.6}$$

$$[\varphi_0^\pm(\boldsymbol{k}), \mathcal{P}_\mu]_{\_} = \mp k_\mu \varphi_0^\pm(\boldsymbol{k}) \quad [\varphi_0^{\dagger\pm}(\boldsymbol{k}), \mathcal{P}_\mu]_{\_} = \mp k_\mu \varphi_0^{\dagger\pm}(\boldsymbol{k}) \qquad k_0 = \sqrt{m^2c^2+\boldsymbol{k}^2}\,. \tag{13.7}$$

Inserting the equalities (with $k_0 = \sqrt{m^2c^2+\boldsymbol{k}^2}$ and $q_0 = \sqrt{m^2c^2+\boldsymbol{q}^2}$)

$$\begin{aligned}\mp k_\mu \varphi_0^\pm(\boldsymbol{k}) &= \int \mp q_\mu \varphi_0^\pm(\boldsymbol{k})\delta^3(\boldsymbol{q}-\boldsymbol{k})\,\mathrm{d}^3\boldsymbol{q}\\ \mp k_\mu \varphi_0^{\dagger\pm}(\boldsymbol{k}) &= \int \mp q_\mu \varphi_0^{\dagger\pm}(\boldsymbol{k})\delta^3(\boldsymbol{q}-\boldsymbol{k})\,\mathrm{d}^3\boldsymbol{q}\end{aligned}$$

and (13.3) into (13.7), we, after some algebra, obtain the next variants of the systems of field equations for an arbitrary scalar field in terms of creation and annihilation operators:

$$\begin{aligned}\int q_\mu\big|_{q_0=\sqrt{m^2c^2+\boldsymbol{q}^2}}\big\{[\varphi_0^{\pm}(\boldsymbol{k}),\varphi_0^{\dagger +}(\boldsymbol{q})\circ\varphi_0^{-}(\boldsymbol{q})+\varphi_0^{\dagger -}(\boldsymbol{q})\circ\varphi_0^{+}(\boldsymbol{q})]_{\_}\\ \pm(1+\tau(\varphi_0))\varphi_0^{\pm}(\boldsymbol{k})\delta^3(\boldsymbol{q}-\boldsymbol{k})\big\}\,\mathrm{d}^3\boldsymbol{q}=0\end{aligned}\tag{13.8a}$$

$$\begin{aligned}\int q_\mu\big|_{q_0=\sqrt{m^2c^2+\boldsymbol{q}^2}}\big\{[\varphi_0^{\dagger\pm}(\boldsymbol{k}),\varphi_0^{\dagger +}(\boldsymbol{q})\circ\varphi_0^{-}(\boldsymbol{q})+\varphi_0^{\dagger -}(\boldsymbol{q})\circ\varphi_0^{+}(\boldsymbol{q})]_{\_}\\ \pm(1+\tau(\varphi_0))\varphi_0^{\dagger\pm}(\boldsymbol{k})\delta^3(\boldsymbol{q}-\boldsymbol{k})\big\}\,\mathrm{d}^3\boldsymbol{q}=0\end{aligned}\tag{13.8b}$$

$$\begin{aligned}\int q_\mu\big|_{q_0=\sqrt{m^2c^2+\boldsymbol{q}^2}}\big\{[\varphi_0^{\pm}(\boldsymbol{k}),\varphi_0^{+}(\boldsymbol{q})\circ\varphi_0^{\dagger -}(\boldsymbol{q})+\varphi_0^{-}(\boldsymbol{q})\circ\varphi_0^{\dagger +}(\boldsymbol{q})]_{\_}\\ \pm(1+\tau(\varphi_0))\varphi_0^{\pm}(\boldsymbol{k})\delta^3(\boldsymbol{q}-\boldsymbol{k})\big\}\,\mathrm{d}^3\boldsymbol{q}=0\end{aligned}\tag{13.9a}$$

$$\begin{aligned}\int q_\mu\big|_{q_0=\sqrt{m^2c^2+\boldsymbol{q}^2}}\big\{[\varphi_0^{\dagger\pm}(\boldsymbol{k}),\varphi_0^{+}(\boldsymbol{q})\circ\varphi_0^{\dagger -}(\boldsymbol{q})+\varphi_0^{-}(\boldsymbol{q})\circ\varphi_0^{\dagger +}(\boldsymbol{q})]_{\_}\\ \pm(1+\tau(\varphi_0))\varphi_0^{\dagger\pm}(\boldsymbol{k})\delta^3(\boldsymbol{q}-\boldsymbol{k})\big\}\,\mathrm{d}^3\boldsymbol{q}=0\end{aligned}\tag{13.9b}$$

$$\begin{aligned}\int q_\mu\big|_{q_0=\sqrt{m^2c^2+\boldsymbol{q}^2}}\big\{[\varphi_0^{\pm}(\boldsymbol{k}),[\varphi_0^{\dagger +}(\boldsymbol{q}),\varphi_0^{-}(\boldsymbol{q})]_{+}+[\varphi_0^{+}(\boldsymbol{q}),\varphi_0^{\dagger -}(\boldsymbol{q})]_{+}]_{\_}\\ \pm 2(1+\tau(\varphi_0))\varphi_0^{\pm}(\boldsymbol{k})\delta^3(\boldsymbol{q}-\boldsymbol{k})\big\}\,\mathrm{d}^3\boldsymbol{q}=0\end{aligned}\tag{13.10a}$$

$$\begin{aligned}\int q_\mu\big|_{q_0=\sqrt{m^2c^2+\boldsymbol{q}^2}}\big\{[\varphi_0^{\dagger\pm}(\boldsymbol{k}),[\varphi_0^{\dagger +}(\boldsymbol{q}),\varphi_0^{-}(\boldsymbol{q})]_{+}+[\varphi_0^{+}(\boldsymbol{q}),\varphi_0^{\dagger -}(\boldsymbol{q})]_{+}]_{\_}\\ \pm 2(1+\tau(\varphi_0))\varphi_0^{\dagger\pm}(\boldsymbol{k})\delta^3(\boldsymbol{q}-\boldsymbol{k})\big\}\,\mathrm{d}^3\boldsymbol{q}=0.\end{aligned}\tag{13.10b}$$

Consequently, to the Lagrangians (10.7)–(10.9) correspond respectively the following three systems of equations for $\varphi_0^{\pm}$ and $\varphi_0^{\dagger\pm}$:

$$\begin{aligned}[\varphi_0^{\pm}(\boldsymbol{k}),\varphi_0^{\dagger +}(\boldsymbol{q})\circ\varphi_0^{-}(\boldsymbol{q})+\varphi_0^{\dagger -}(\boldsymbol{q})\circ\varphi_0^{+}(\boldsymbol{q})]_{\_}\\ \pm(1+\tau(\varphi_0))\varphi_0^{\pm}(\boldsymbol{k})\delta^3(\boldsymbol{q}-\boldsymbol{k})={}'f^{\pm}(\boldsymbol{k},\boldsymbol{q})\end{aligned}\tag{13.11a}$$

$$\begin{aligned}[\varphi_0^{\dagger\pm}(\boldsymbol{k}),\varphi_0^{\dagger +}(\boldsymbol{q})\circ\varphi_0^{-}(\boldsymbol{q})+\varphi_0^{\dagger -}(\boldsymbol{q})\circ\varphi_0^{+}(\boldsymbol{q})]_{\_}\\ \pm(1+\tau(\varphi_0))\varphi_0^{\dagger\pm}(\boldsymbol{k})\delta^3(\boldsymbol{q}-\boldsymbol{k})={}'f^{\dagger\pm}(\boldsymbol{k},\boldsymbol{q})\end{aligned}\tag{13.11b}$$

$$\begin{aligned}[\varphi_0^{\pm}(\boldsymbol{k}),\varphi_0^{+}(\boldsymbol{q})\circ\varphi_0^{\dagger -}(\boldsymbol{q})+\varphi_0^{-}(\boldsymbol{q})\circ\varphi_0^{\dagger +}(\boldsymbol{q})]_{\_}\\ \pm(1+\tau(\varphi_0))\varphi_0^{\pm}(\boldsymbol{k})\delta^3(\boldsymbol{q}-\boldsymbol{k})={}''f^{\pm}(\boldsymbol{k},\boldsymbol{q})\end{aligned}\tag{13.12a}$$

$$\begin{aligned}[\varphi_0^{\dagger\pm}(\boldsymbol{k}),\varphi_0^{+}(\boldsymbol{q})\circ\varphi_0^{\dagger -}(\boldsymbol{q})+\varphi_0^{-}(\boldsymbol{q})\circ\varphi_0^{\dagger +}(\boldsymbol{q})]_{\_}\\ \pm(1+\tau(\varphi_0))\varphi_0^{\dagger\pm}(\boldsymbol{k})\delta^3(\boldsymbol{q}-\boldsymbol{k})={}''f^{\dagger\pm}(\boldsymbol{k},\boldsymbol{q})\end{aligned}\tag{13.12b}$$

$$[\varphi_0^{\pm}(\boldsymbol{k}), [\varphi_0^{\dagger +}(\boldsymbol{q}), \varphi_0^{-}(\boldsymbol{q})]_+ + [\varphi_0^{+}(\boldsymbol{q}), \varphi_0^{\dagger -}(\boldsymbol{q})]_+]_- \\ \pm 2(1+\tau(\varphi_0))\varphi_0^{\pm}(\boldsymbol{k})\delta^3(\boldsymbol{q}-\boldsymbol{k}) = {}'''f^{\pm}(\boldsymbol{k},\boldsymbol{q}) \tag{13.13a}$$

$$[\varphi_0^{\dagger\pm}(\boldsymbol{k}), [\varphi_0^{\dagger +}(\boldsymbol{q}), \varphi_0^{-}(\boldsymbol{q})]_+ + [\varphi_0^{+}(\boldsymbol{q}), \varphi_0^{\dagger -}(\boldsymbol{q})]_+]_- \\ \pm 2(1+\tau(\varphi_0))\varphi_0^{\dagger\pm}(\boldsymbol{k})\delta^3(\boldsymbol{q}-\boldsymbol{k}) = {}'''f^{\dagger\pm}(\boldsymbol{k},\boldsymbol{q}), \tag{13.13b}$$

where the operator-valued (generalized) functions ${}^{a}f^{\pm}(\boldsymbol{k},\boldsymbol{q})$ and ${}^{a}f^{\dagger\pm}(\boldsymbol{k},\boldsymbol{q})$ with $a = {}', {}'', {}'''$ must be such that

$$\int q_\mu|_{q_0=\sqrt{m^2c^2+\boldsymbol{q}^2}} {}^{a}f^{\pm}(\boldsymbol{k},\boldsymbol{q})\,\mathrm{d}^3\boldsymbol{q} = \int q_\mu|_{q_0=\sqrt{m^2c^2+\boldsymbol{q}^2}} {}^{a}f^{\dagger\pm}(\boldsymbol{k},\boldsymbol{q})\,\mathrm{d}^3\boldsymbol{q} = 0. \tag{13.14}$$

Generally the systems of equations (13.11), (13.12) and (13.13) are different. They will become equivalent after normal ordering, when the equations in them will turn to be identical. From the derivation of (13.11)–(13.14), it is clear that these systems of equations are equivalent to the initial system of Klein-Gordon equations (10.16). Thus, we can say that these systems represent the field equations in terms of creation and annihilation operators.

As a verification of the self-consistence of the theory, one can prove the commutativity between the components of any one of the momentum operators (13.3), i.e.

$$[\mathcal{P}_\mu, \mathcal{P}_\nu]_- = 0, \tag{13.15}$$

where $\mathcal{P}_\mu = {}'\mathcal{P}^{(3)}_\mu, {}''\mathcal{P}^{(4)}_\mu, {}'''\mathcal{P}^{(2)}_\mu$, is a consequence of (13.3), (13.11)–(13.13) and the identity (7.4) with $\varepsilon = -1$.

14 The charge and orbital angular momentum operators

In Sect. 10, we introduced the charge operator (10.23) (see also (10.35)) and pointed to different possible definitions of the defining it current operator. In particular, to the Lagrangians (10.7)–(10.9) correspond respectively the current operators (10.39a)–(10.39c) in momentum picture. Below we shall express the charge operator $\mathcal{Q}$ through the creation and annihilation operators (12.1).

Substituting (12.3), (12.4) and (13.1) into (10.39), we get: [35]

$$ {}'\mathcal{J}^{(3)}_\mu = \frac{1}{2}qc^2 \int \mathrm{d}^3\boldsymbol{k}\,\mathrm{d}^3\boldsymbol{k}' \{k'_\mu(\varphi_0^{\dagger +}(\boldsymbol{k}) + \varphi_0^{\dagger -}(\boldsymbol{k})) \circ (-\varphi_0^{+}(\boldsymbol{k}') + \varphi_0^{-}(\boldsymbol{k}')) \\ - k_\mu(-\varphi_0^{\dagger +}(\boldsymbol{k}) + \varphi_0^{\dagger -}(\boldsymbol{k})) \circ (\varphi_0^{+}(\boldsymbol{k}') + \varphi_0^{-}(\boldsymbol{k}'))\} \tag{14.1a}$$

[35] Since we apply only results based on the general properties of the momentum operator, the below obtained equalities for the current and charge operators are independent of the concrete choice of energy-momentum operator, like (10.17)–(10.20), and, consequently, of the particular form of the momentum operator, like (13.3). However, they depend on the Lagrangians (10.7)–(10.9) from which the theory is derived.

$$''\mathcal{J}_\mu^{(4)} = \frac{1}{2} qc^2 \int \mathrm{d}^3\boldsymbol{k}\, \mathrm{d}^3\boldsymbol{k}' \{ k_\mu (-\varphi_0^+(\boldsymbol{k}) + \varphi_0^-(\boldsymbol{k})) \circ (\varphi_0^{\dagger +}(\boldsymbol{k}') + \varphi_0^{\dagger -}(\boldsymbol{k}')) \\ - k'_\mu (\varphi_0^+(\boldsymbol{k}) + \varphi_0^-(\boldsymbol{k})) \circ (-\varphi_0^{\dagger +}(\boldsymbol{k}') + \varphi_0^{\dagger -}(\boldsymbol{k}')) \} \quad (14.1\text{b})$$

$$'''\mathcal{J}_\mu^{(2)} = \frac{1}{4} qc^2 \int \mathrm{d}^3\boldsymbol{k}\, \mathrm{d}^3\boldsymbol{k}' \{ k'_\mu (\varphi_0^{\dagger +}(\boldsymbol{k}) + \varphi_0^{\dagger -}(\boldsymbol{k})) \circ (-\varphi_0^+(\boldsymbol{k}') + \varphi_0^-(\boldsymbol{k}')) \\ + k_\mu (-\varphi_0^+(\boldsymbol{k}) + \varphi_0^-(\boldsymbol{k})) \circ (\varphi_0^{\dagger +}(\boldsymbol{k}') + \varphi_0^{\dagger -}(\boldsymbol{k}')) \\ - k_\mu (-\varphi_0^{\dagger +}(\boldsymbol{k}) + \varphi_0^{\dagger -}(\boldsymbol{k})) \circ (\varphi_0^+(\boldsymbol{k}') + \varphi_0^-(\boldsymbol{k}')) \\ - k'_\mu (\varphi_0^+(\boldsymbol{k}) + \varphi_0^-(\boldsymbol{k})) \circ (-\varphi_0^{\dagger +}(\boldsymbol{k}') + \varphi_0^{\dagger -}(\boldsymbol{k}')) \} . \quad (14.1\text{c})$$

Now we have to perform the following three steps: (i) insert these expressions with $\mu = 0$ into (10.23); (ii) apply (6.4), possibly with $\varphi_0^{\dagger \pm}(\boldsymbol{k})$ and/or $\varphi_0^{\dagger \pm}(\boldsymbol{k}')$ for $\varphi_0^{\pm}(\boldsymbol{k})$ and/or $\varphi_0^{\pm}(\boldsymbol{k}')$; (iii) integrate over $\boldsymbol{x}$, which gives $(2\pi\hbar)^3\delta^3(\boldsymbol{k}+\boldsymbol{k}')$ for products of equal-frequency operators and $(2\pi\hbar)^3\delta^3(\boldsymbol{k}-\boldsymbol{k}')$ for products of different-frequency operators. As a result of these steps, we obtain:[36]

$$'\tilde{\mathcal{Q}}^{(3)} = q \int \mathrm{d}^3\boldsymbol{k} \{ \varphi_0^{\dagger +}(\boldsymbol{k}) \circ \varphi_0^-(\boldsymbol{k}) - \varphi_0^{\dagger -}(\boldsymbol{k}) \circ \varphi_0^+(\boldsymbol{k}) \} \quad (14.2\text{a})$$

$$''\tilde{\mathcal{Q}}^{(4)} = -q \int \mathrm{d}^3\boldsymbol{k} \{ \varphi_0^+(\boldsymbol{k}) \circ \varphi_0^{\dagger -}(\boldsymbol{k}) - \varphi_0^-(\boldsymbol{k}) \circ \varphi_0^{\dagger +}(\boldsymbol{k}) \} \quad (14.2\text{b})$$

$$'''\tilde{\mathcal{Q}}^{(2)} = \frac{1}{2} q \int \mathrm{d}^3\boldsymbol{k} \{ \varphi_0^{\dagger +}(\boldsymbol{k}) \circ \varphi_0^-(\boldsymbol{k}) - \varphi_0^+(\boldsymbol{k}) \circ \varphi_0^{\dagger -}(\boldsymbol{k}) \\ + \varphi_0^-(\boldsymbol{k}) \circ \varphi_0^{\dagger +}(\boldsymbol{k}) - \varphi_0^{\dagger -}(\boldsymbol{k}) \circ \varphi_0^+(\boldsymbol{k}) \}. \quad (14.2\text{c})$$

Recall, here the '3-dimensional' creation/annihilation operators are defined via (13.4). Notice, if $\varphi_0^\dagger = \varphi_0$, the charges (14.2a) and (14.2b), as well as the defining them respective current operators (10.39a) and (10.39b), vanish as $q = 0$ in this case, while the charge (14.2c) and the defining it current operator (10.39c) vanish for *two* reasons, if $\varphi_0^\dagger = \varphi_0$: due to $q = 0$ and due to the vanishment of the integrand in (14.2c) or the expression in parentheses in (10.39c).

Generally, the three charge operators (14.2a)–(14.2c), originating respectively from the Lagrangians (10.7)–(10.9), are different, but they become identical after normal ordering (see Sect. 16).

Let us turn our attention now to the orbital angular momentum operator of free scalar field. In Heisenberg picture, it is given via (3.14) To obtain an explicit expression for the orbital angular momentum operator $\tilde{\mathcal{L}}_{\mu\nu}$ (in Heisenberg picture) through the creation and annihilation operators $\varphi_0^{\pm}(\boldsymbol{k})$ and $\varphi_0^{\dagger \pm}(\boldsymbol{k})$ (see (13.4)), we have to do the following: substitute each of the equalities in (13.2) into the last equality in (3.14), to apply (6.4) to all terms in the obtained equation, then to integrate over x, which results in δ-function terms,

[36] When deriving (14.2), one gets the equalities in it with $\frac{q}{1+\tau(\varphi_0)}$ for q with $\tau(\varphi_0)$ defined by (10.13). Since $q = 0$ for $\varphi_0^\dagger = \varphi_0$ and $\tau(\varphi_0) = 0$ for $\varphi_0^\dagger \neq \varphi_0$, we have $\frac{q}{1+\tau(\varphi_0)} \equiv q$ in all cases.

and, at last, to perform the integration over $\boldsymbol{k}'$ by means of the arising δ-functions.[37] This procedure results in:

$$
\begin{aligned}
{}'\tilde{\mathcal{L}}^{(3)}_{\mu\nu} &= x_{0\,\mu}\,{}'\mathcal{P}^{(3)}_{\nu} - x_{0\,\nu}\,{}'\mathcal{P}^{(3)}_{\mu} \\
&\quad + \frac{\mathrm{i}\hbar}{2(1+\tau(\varphi_0))}\int \mathrm{d}^3\boldsymbol{k}\Big\{ \varphi_0^{\dagger\,+}(\boldsymbol{k})\Big(k_\mu \overleftrightarrow{\frac{\partial}{\partial k^\nu}} - k_\nu \overleftrightarrow{\frac{\partial}{\partial k^\mu}}\Big)\circ\varphi_0^{-}(\boldsymbol{k}) \\
&\qquad - \varphi_0^{\dagger\,-}(\boldsymbol{k})\Big(k_\mu \overleftrightarrow{\frac{\partial}{\partial k^\nu}} - k_\nu \overleftrightarrow{\frac{\partial}{\partial k^\mu}}\Big)\circ\varphi_0^{+}(\boldsymbol{k})\Big\}\Big|_{k_0=\sqrt{m^2c^2+\boldsymbol{k}^2}}
\end{aligned}
\tag{14.5a}
$$

$$
\begin{aligned}
{}''\tilde{\mathcal{L}}^{(4)}_{\mu\nu} &= x_{0\,\mu}\,{}''\mathcal{P}^{(4)}_{\nu} - x_{0\,\nu}\,{}''\mathcal{P}^{(4)}_{\mu} \\
&\quad + \frac{\mathrm{i}\hbar}{2(1+\tau(\varphi_0))}\int \mathrm{d}^3\boldsymbol{k}\Big\{ \varphi_0^{+}(\boldsymbol{k})\Big(k_\mu \overleftrightarrow{\frac{\partial}{\partial k^\nu}} - k_\nu \overleftrightarrow{\frac{\partial}{\partial k^\mu}}\Big)\circ\varphi_0^{\dagger\,-}(\boldsymbol{k}) \\
&\qquad - \varphi_0^{-}(\boldsymbol{k})\Big(k_\mu \overleftrightarrow{\frac{\partial}{\partial k^\nu}} - k_\nu \overleftrightarrow{\frac{\partial}{\partial k^\mu}}\Big)\circ\varphi_0^{\dagger\,+}(\boldsymbol{k})\Big\}\Big|_{k_0=\sqrt{m^2c^2+\boldsymbol{k}^2}}
\end{aligned}
\tag{14.5b}
$$

---

[37] The integrals, one has to calculate, are of the type

$$
\begin{aligned}
J &= \sum_{\alpha}\sum_{\varepsilon,\varepsilon'=+,-}\int \mathrm{d}^3\boldsymbol{x}\int \mathrm{d}^3\boldsymbol{k}\,\mathrm{d}^3\boldsymbol{k}'\,x_a\,\mathcal{U}^{-1}(x,x_0)\circ\{\varphi_0^{\dagger\,\varepsilon}(\boldsymbol{k})A^{\alpha}_{\varepsilon\varepsilon'}(\boldsymbol{k},\boldsymbol{k}')\circ\varphi_0^{\varepsilon'}(\boldsymbol{k}')\}\circ\mathcal{U}(x,x_0) \\
&= \sum_{\alpha}\sum_{\varepsilon,\varepsilon'=+,-}\int \mathrm{d}^3\boldsymbol{x}\int \mathrm{d}^3\boldsymbol{k}\,\mathrm{d}^3\boldsymbol{k}'\{\varphi_0^{\dagger\,\varepsilon}(\boldsymbol{k})A^{\alpha}_{\varepsilon\varepsilon'}(\boldsymbol{k},\boldsymbol{k}')\circ\varphi_{s'}^{\varepsilon'}(\boldsymbol{k}')\}x_a\mathrm{e}^{-\frac{1}{\mathrm{i}\hbar}(x^\lambda-x_0^\lambda)(\varepsilon k_\lambda+\varepsilon' k'_\lambda)},
\end{aligned}
\tag{14.3}
$$

where $a = 1,2,3$, $A^{\alpha}_{\varepsilon\varepsilon'}(\boldsymbol{k},\boldsymbol{k}')$, $\alpha = 1,2,\dots$, are some functions, $k_0 = \sqrt{m^2c^2+\boldsymbol{k}^2}$, and $k'_0 = \sqrt{m^2c^2+\boldsymbol{k}'^2}$. The integration over x results in $(2\pi\hbar)^3\Big(-\mathrm{i}\hbar\frac{\partial}{\partial(\varepsilon k^a+\varepsilon' k'^a)}\Big)\delta^3(\varepsilon\boldsymbol{k}+\varepsilon'\boldsymbol{k}')$. Simple manipulations with the remaining terms, by invoking the equality $f(y)\frac{\partial\delta(y)}{\partial y} = -\frac{\partial f(y)}{\partial y}\delta(y)$ in the form

$$
\begin{aligned}
\int \mathrm{d}^3\boldsymbol{y}\,\mathrm{d}^3\boldsymbol{z}\,f(\boldsymbol{y},\boldsymbol{z})\frac{\partial\delta^3(\boldsymbol{y}-\boldsymbol{z})}{\partial(y^a-z^a)} &= \int \mathrm{d}^3\boldsymbol{y}\,\mathrm{d}^3\boldsymbol{z}\frac{1}{2}(f(\boldsymbol{y},\boldsymbol{z})-f(\boldsymbol{z},\boldsymbol{y}))\frac{\partial\delta^3(\boldsymbol{y}-\boldsymbol{z})}{\partial(y^a-z^a)} \\
&= -\frac{1}{2}\int \mathrm{d}^3\boldsymbol{y}\,\mathrm{d}^3\boldsymbol{z}\,\delta^3(\boldsymbol{y}-\boldsymbol{z})\Big(\frac{\partial}{\partial y^a}-\frac{\partial}{\partial z^a}\Big)f(\boldsymbol{y},\boldsymbol{z}),
\end{aligned}
$$

gives the following result:

$$
\begin{aligned}
J &= (2\pi\hbar)^3\sum_{\alpha}\sum_{\varepsilon,\varepsilon'=+,-}\int \mathrm{d}^3\boldsymbol{k}\,\mathrm{d}^3\boldsymbol{k}'\,\delta^3(\varepsilon\boldsymbol{k}+\varepsilon'\boldsymbol{k}')\mathrm{e}^{-\frac{1}{\mathrm{i}\hbar}(x^0-x_0^0)k_0(\varepsilon 1+\varepsilon' 1)} \\
&\times\Big\{(x^0-x_0^0)\frac{1}{2}\Big(\frac{k_a}{k_0}+\frac{k'_a}{k_0}\Big)+x_{0a}+\frac{1}{2}\mathrm{i}\hbar\Big(\varepsilon\frac{\partial}{\partial k^a}+\varepsilon'\frac{\partial}{\partial k'^a}\Big)\Big\}\{\varphi_0^{\dagger\,\varepsilon}(\boldsymbol{k})A^{\alpha}_{\varepsilon\varepsilon'}(\boldsymbol{k},\boldsymbol{k}')\circ\varphi_0^{\varepsilon'}(\boldsymbol{k}')\}.
\end{aligned}
\tag{14.4}
$$

The particular form of $A^{\alpha}_{\varepsilon\varepsilon'}(\boldsymbol{k},\boldsymbol{k}')$ is clear from (3.14) and (10.22). So, applying several times (14.4), calculating the appearing derivatives, and, at last, performing the trivial integration over $\boldsymbol{k}$ or $\boldsymbol{k}'$ by means of $\delta^3(\varepsilon\boldsymbol{k}+\varepsilon'\boldsymbol{k}')$, one can derive (14.5) after simple, but lengthy and tedious algebraic manipulations.

$$
\begin{aligned}
{}^{\prime\prime\prime}\tilde{\mathcal{L}}^{(2)}_{\mu\nu} &= x_{0\,\mu}\,{}^{\prime\prime}\mathcal{P}^{(2)}_{\nu} - x_{0\,\nu}\,{}^{\prime\prime}\mathcal{P}^{(2)}_{\mu} \\
&+ \frac{\mathrm{i}\hbar}{4(1+\tau(\varphi_0))}\int \mathrm{d}^3\boldsymbol{k}\Big\{\varphi_0^{\dagger\,+}(\boldsymbol{k})\Big(k_\mu\overleftrightarrow{\frac{\partial}{\partial k^\nu}} - k_\nu\overleftrightarrow{\frac{\partial}{\partial k^\mu}}\Big)\circ\varphi_0^{-}(\boldsymbol{k}) \\
&+ \varphi_0^{+}(\boldsymbol{k})\Big(k_\mu\overleftrightarrow{\frac{\partial}{\partial k^\nu}} - k_\nu\overleftrightarrow{\frac{\partial}{\partial k^\mu}}\Big)\circ\varphi_0^{\dagger\,-}(\boldsymbol{k}) - \varphi_0^{\dagger\,-}(\boldsymbol{k})\Big(k_\mu\overleftrightarrow{\frac{\partial}{\partial k^\nu}} - k_\nu\overleftrightarrow{\frac{\partial}{\partial k^\mu}}\Big)\circ\varphi_0^{+}(\boldsymbol{k}) \\
&- \varphi_0^{-}(\boldsymbol{k})\Big(k_\mu\overleftrightarrow{\frac{\partial}{\partial k^\nu}} - k_\nu\overleftrightarrow{\frac{\partial}{\partial k^\mu}}\Big)\circ\varphi_0^{\dagger\,+}(\boldsymbol{k})\Big\}\Big|_{k_0=\sqrt{m^2c^2+\boldsymbol{k}^2}}\,. \qquad (14.5\text{c})
\end{aligned}
$$

Here the derivatives with respect to k_0, like $\frac{\partial}{\partial k^0}\varphi_0^{\pm}(\boldsymbol{k})$, must be set equal to zero, and[38]

$$
\begin{aligned}
A(\boldsymbol{k})k_\mu\overleftrightarrow{\frac{\partial}{\partial k^\nu}}\circ B(\boldsymbol{k}) &:= -\Big(k_\mu\frac{\partial A(\boldsymbol{k})}{\partial k^\nu}\Big)\circ B(\boldsymbol{k}) + \Big(A(\boldsymbol{k})\circ k_\mu\frac{\partial B(\boldsymbol{k})}{\partial k^\nu}\Big) \\
&= k_\mu\Big(A(\boldsymbol{k})\overleftrightarrow{\frac{\partial}{\partial k^\nu}}\circ B(\boldsymbol{k})\Big) \qquad (14.6)
\end{aligned}
$$

for operators $A(\boldsymbol{k})$ and $B(\boldsymbol{k})$ having C^1 dependence on $\boldsymbol{k}$. If the operators $A(\boldsymbol{k})$ and $B(\boldsymbol{k})$ tend to zero sufficiently fast at spacial infinity, then, by integration by parts, one can prove the equality

$$
\begin{aligned}
&\int \mathrm{d}^3\boldsymbol{k}\Big\{A(\boldsymbol{k})\Big(k_\mu\overleftrightarrow{\frac{\partial}{\partial k^\nu}} - k_\nu\overleftrightarrow{\frac{\partial}{\partial k^\mu}}\Big)\circ B(\boldsymbol{k})\Big\}\Big|_{k_0=\sqrt{m^2c^2+\boldsymbol{k}^2}} \\
&\quad = 2\int \mathrm{d}^3\boldsymbol{k}\Big\{A(\boldsymbol{k})\circ\Big(k_\mu\frac{\partial}{\partial k^\nu} - k_\nu\frac{\partial}{\partial k^\mu}\Big)B(\boldsymbol{k})\Big\}\Big|_{k_0=\sqrt{m^2c^2+\boldsymbol{k}^2}} \\
&\quad = -2\int \mathrm{d}^3\boldsymbol{k}\Big\{\Big(\Big(k_\mu\frac{\partial}{\partial k^\nu} - k_\nu\frac{\partial}{\partial k^\mu}\Big)A(\boldsymbol{k})\Big)\circ B(\boldsymbol{k})\Big\}\Big|_{k_0=\sqrt{m^2c^2+\boldsymbol{k}^2}}\,. \qquad (14.7)
\end{aligned}
$$

By means of these equations, one can reduce (two times) the number of terms in (14.5), but we prefer to retain the 'more (anti)symmetric' form of the results by invoking the operation introduced via (14.6).

Since for a neutral scalar field $\varphi_0^\dagger = \varphi_0$ and $\tau(\varphi_0) = 1$, in this case the three operators (14.5) reduce to

$$
\begin{aligned}
{}^{0}\tilde{\mathcal{L}}_{\mu\nu} &= x_{0\,\mu}\mathcal{P}_\nu - x_{0\,\nu}\mathcal{P}_\mu + \frac{\mathrm{i}\hbar}{4}\int \mathrm{d}^3\boldsymbol{k}\Big\{\varphi_0^{+}(\boldsymbol{k})\Big(k_\mu\overleftrightarrow{\frac{\partial}{\partial k^\nu}} - k_\nu\overleftrightarrow{\frac{\partial}{\partial k^\mu}}\Big)\circ\varphi_0^{-}(\boldsymbol{k}) \\
&- \varphi_0^{-}(\boldsymbol{k})\Big(k_\mu\overleftrightarrow{\frac{\partial}{\partial k^\nu}} - k_\nu\overleftrightarrow{\frac{\partial}{\partial k^\mu}}\Big)\circ\varphi_0^{+}(\boldsymbol{k})\Big\}\Big|_{k_0=\sqrt{m^2c^2+\boldsymbol{k}^2}} \qquad (14.8)
\end{aligned}
$$

[38] More generally, if $\omega\colon \{\mathcal{F}\to\mathcal{F}\}\to\{\mathcal{F}\to\mathcal{F}\}$ is a mapping on the operator space over the system's Hilbert space, we put $A\overleftrightarrow{\omega}\circ B := -\omega(A)\circ B + A\circ\omega(B)$ for any $A, B\colon \mathcal{F}\to\mathcal{F}$. Usually [4, 12], this notation is used for $\omega = \partial_\mu$.

with $\mathcal{P}_\mu$ given by (6.5). The reader may verify that the equality (14.8) holds for any one of the energy-momentum operators (3.11) (or (3.10)) for the Lagrangian (3.3) (or (3.2)).

It is a trivial calculation to be shown that in terms of the operators (13.5), representing the creation/annihilation operators in (momentum representation of) Heisenberg picture, in the equations (14.5) and (14.8) the first two terms, proportional to the momentum operator, should be deleted and tildes over all creation and annihilation operators must be added.

Using the explicit formulae (13.3), (14.2) and (14.5), by means of the identity (7.4), with $\varepsilon = -1$, and the field equations (13.11)–(13.13), one can verify the equations:

$$[\tilde{\mathcal{Q}}, \mathcal{P}_\lambda] = 0 \tag{14.9}$$

$$[\tilde{\mathcal{L}}_{\mu\nu}, \mathcal{P}_\lambda] = -\mathrm{i}\hbar(\eta_{\lambda\mu}\mathcal{P}_\nu - \eta_{\lambda\nu}\mathcal{P}_\mu), \tag{14.10}$$

where $\tilde{\mathcal{L}}_{\mu\nu}$ (resp. $\tilde{\mathcal{Q}}$) denotes any one of the orbital momentum operators in (14.5) (resp. charge operators in (15.21)). The first of these equalities confirms the validity of the (external to the Lagrangian formalism) equation (10.30). We emphasize on the sign before $\mathrm{i}\hbar$ in the r.h.s. of (14.10), which is opposite to the one usually assumed in the literature, for instance in [5, p. 77, eq. (2-87)] or in [6, eq. (2.187)].[39]

From (14.9) and (2.2), we get

$$[\tilde{\mathcal{Q}}, \mathcal{U}(x, x_0)]_{\_} = 0 \tag{14.11}$$

and, hence,

$$\mathcal{Q} = \tilde{\mathcal{Q}}, \tag{14.12}$$

due to (2.4). Therefore the *charge operator is one and the same in momentum and Heisenberg pictures.*

Applying (14.10), we get the orbital angular momentum of a scalar field in *momentum picture* as

$$\begin{aligned} \mathcal{L}_{\mu\nu} &= \mathcal{U}(x, x_0) \circ \tilde{\mathcal{L}}_{\mu\nu} \circ \mathcal{U}^{-1}(x, x_0) = \tilde{\mathcal{L}}_{\mu\nu} + [\mathcal{U}(x, x_0), \tilde{\mathcal{L}}_{\mu\nu}]_{\_} \circ \mathcal{U}^{-1}(x, x_0) \\ &= \tilde{\mathcal{L}}_{\mu\nu} + (x_\mu - x_{0\,\mu})\mathcal{P}_\nu - (x_\nu - x_{0\,\nu})\mathcal{P}_\mu, \end{aligned} \tag{14.13}$$

due to the equality

$$[\tilde{\mathcal{L}}_{\mu\nu}, \mathcal{U}(x, x_0)]_{\_} = -\{(x_\mu - x_{0\,\mu})\tilde{\mathcal{P}}_\nu - (x_\nu - x_{0\,\nu})\tilde{\mathcal{P}}_\mu\} \circ \mathcal{U}(x, x_0). \tag{14.14}$$

[39] Equation (14.10) with $+\mathrm{i}\hbar$ for $-\mathrm{i}\hbar$ in its r.h.s. is part of the commutation relations for the Lie algebra of the Poincaré group – see, e.g., [9, pp.143–147] or [10, sec. 7.1]. However, such a change of the sign in the r.h.s. of (14.10) contradicts to the results and the physical interpretation of the creation and annihilation operators – *vide infra*.

which is a consequence of (14.10) and (2.2).[40] Thus, in momentum picture, the equations (14.5) read:

$$
\begin{aligned}
{}'\mathcal{L}^{(3)}_{\mu\nu} &= x_\mu \, {}'\mathcal{P}^{(3)}_{\nu} - x_\nu \, {}'\mathcal{P}^{(3)}_{\mu} \\
&\quad + \frac{\mathrm{i}\hbar}{2(1+\tau(\varphi_0))} \int \mathrm{d}^3\boldsymbol{k} \Big\{ \varphi_0^{\dagger +}(\boldsymbol{k}) \Big(k_\mu \overleftrightarrow{\frac{\partial}{\partial k^\nu}} - k_\nu \overleftrightarrow{\frac{\partial}{\partial k^\mu}} \Big) \circ \varphi_0^{-}(\boldsymbol{k}) \\
&\qquad - \varphi_0^{\dagger -}(\boldsymbol{k}) \Big(k_\mu \overleftrightarrow{\frac{\partial}{\partial k^\nu}} - k_\nu \overleftrightarrow{\frac{\partial}{\partial k^\mu}} \Big) \circ \varphi_0^{+}(\boldsymbol{k}) \Big\} \Big|_{k_0=\sqrt{m^2c^2+\boldsymbol{k}^2}}
\end{aligned}
\tag{14.15a}
$$

$$
\begin{aligned}
{}''\mathcal{L}^{(4)}_{\mu\nu} &= x_\mu \, {}''\mathcal{P}^{(4)}_{\nu} - x_\nu \, {}''\mathcal{P}^{(4)}_{\mu} \\
&\quad + \frac{\mathrm{i}\hbar}{2(1+\tau(\varphi_0))} \int \mathrm{d}^3\boldsymbol{k} \Big\{ \varphi_0^{+}(\boldsymbol{k}) \Big(k_\mu \overleftrightarrow{\frac{\partial}{\partial k^\nu}} - k_\nu \overleftrightarrow{\frac{\partial}{\partial k^\mu}} \Big) \circ \varphi_0^{\dagger -}(\boldsymbol{k}) \\
&\qquad - \varphi_0^{-}(\boldsymbol{k}) \Big(k_\mu \overleftrightarrow{\frac{\partial}{\partial k^\nu}} - k_\nu \overleftrightarrow{\frac{\partial}{\partial k^\mu}} \Big) \circ \varphi_0^{\dagger +}(\boldsymbol{k}) \Big\} \Big|_{k_0=\sqrt{m^2c^2+\boldsymbol{k}^2}}
\end{aligned}
\tag{14.15b}
$$

$$
\begin{aligned}
{}'''\mathcal{L}^{(2)}_{\mu\nu} &= x_\mu \, {}'''\mathcal{P}^{(2)}_{\nu} - x_\nu \, {}'''\mathcal{P}^{(2)}_{\mu} \\
&\quad + \frac{\mathrm{i}\hbar}{4(1+\tau(\varphi_0))} \int \mathrm{d}^3\boldsymbol{k} \Big\{ \varphi_0^{\dagger +}(\boldsymbol{k}) \Big(k_\mu \overleftrightarrow{\frac{\partial}{\partial k^\nu}} - k_\nu \overleftrightarrow{\frac{\partial}{\partial k^\mu}} \Big) \circ \varphi_0^{-}(\boldsymbol{k}) \\
&+ \varphi_0^{+}(\boldsymbol{k}) \Big(k_\mu \overleftrightarrow{\frac{\partial}{\partial k^\nu}} - k_\nu \overleftrightarrow{\frac{\partial}{\partial k^\mu}} \Big) \circ \varphi_0^{\dagger -}(\boldsymbol{k}) - \varphi_0^{\dagger -}(\boldsymbol{k}) \Big(k_\mu \overleftrightarrow{\frac{\partial}{\partial k^\nu}} - k_\nu \overleftrightarrow{\frac{\partial}{\partial k^\mu}} \Big) \circ \varphi_0^{+}(\boldsymbol{k}) \\
&\qquad - \varphi_0^{-}(\boldsymbol{k}) \Big(k_\mu \overleftrightarrow{\frac{\partial}{\partial k^\nu}} - k_\nu \overleftrightarrow{\frac{\partial}{\partial k^\mu}} \Big) \circ \varphi_0^{\dagger +}(\boldsymbol{k}) \Big\} \Big|_{k_0=\sqrt{m^2c^2+\boldsymbol{k}^2}} .
\end{aligned}
\tag{14.15c}
$$

These three angular momentum operators are different but, after normal ordering, they will be mapped into one and the same operator (see Sect. 16).

15 The commutation relations

The trilinear systems of equations (13.11)–(13.13) are similar to the (system of) Klein-Gordon equation(s) (6.13) and, correspondingly, will be treated in an analogous way.

[40] To derive equation (14.14), notice that (14.10) implies $[\tilde{\mathcal{L}}_{\mu\nu}, \tilde{\mathcal{P}}_{\mu_1} \circ \dots \circ \tilde{\mathcal{P}}_{\mu_n}]_{\_} = -\sum_{i=1}^{n} (\eta_{\mu\mu_i} \tilde{\mathcal{P}}_\nu - \eta_{\nu\mu_i} \tilde{\mathcal{P}}_\mu) \tilde{\mathcal{P}}_{\mu_1} \circ \dots \circ \tilde{\mathcal{P}}_{\mu_{i-1}} \circ \tilde{\mathcal{P}}_{\mu_{i+1}} \circ \dots \circ \tilde{\mathcal{P}}_{\mu_n}$, due to $[A, B \circ C]_{\_} = [A,B]_{\_} \circ C + B \circ [A,C]_{\_}$, and expand the exponent in (2.2) into a power series. More generally, if $[A(x), \tilde{\mathcal{P}}_\mu]_{\_} = B_\mu(x)$ with $[B_\mu(x), \tilde{\mathcal{P}}_\nu]_{\_} = 0$, then $[A(x), \mathcal{U}(x,x_0)]_{\_} = \frac{1}{\mathrm{i}\hbar}(x^\mu - x_0^\mu) B_\mu(x) \mathcal{U}(x,x_0)$; in particular, $[A(x), \tilde{\mathcal{P}}_\mu]_{\_} = 0$ implies $[A(x), \mathcal{U}(x,x_0)]_{\_} = 0$. Notice, we consider $(x^\mu - x_0^\mu)$ as a real parameter by which the corresponding operators are multiplied and which operators are supposed to be linear in it.

Since the equations (13.11b), (13.12b), and (13.13b) can be obtained from (13.11a), (13.12a), and (13.13a) by replacing $\varphi_0^{\pm}(\boldsymbol{k})$ with $\varphi_0^{\dagger\pm}(\boldsymbol{k})$ and ${}^a f^{\pm}(\boldsymbol{k},\boldsymbol{q})$ with ${}^a f^{\dagger\pm}(\boldsymbol{k},\boldsymbol{q})$, respectively, all of the next 'intermediate' considerations will be done only for the former set of equations; only the more essential and final results will be doubled, i.e. written for $\varphi_0^{\pm}(\boldsymbol{k})$ and $\varphi_0^{\dagger\pm}(\boldsymbol{k})$.

First of all, applying the identity (7.4) several times, we rewrite (13.11a), (13.12a), and (13.13a) respectively as (recall, $\varepsilon = \pm 1$)

$$\begin{aligned}
&[\varphi_0^{\pm}(\boldsymbol{k}), \varphi_0^{\dagger +}(\boldsymbol{q})]_{\varepsilon} \circ \varphi_0^{-}(\boldsymbol{q}) - \varepsilon \varphi_0^{\dagger +}(\boldsymbol{q}) \circ [\varphi_0^{\pm}(\boldsymbol{k}), \varphi_0^{-}(\boldsymbol{q})]_{\varepsilon} \\
&+[\varphi_0^{\pm}(\boldsymbol{k}), \varphi_0^{\dagger -}(\boldsymbol{q})]_{\varepsilon} \circ \varphi_0^{+}(\boldsymbol{q}) - \varepsilon \varphi_0^{\dagger -}(\boldsymbol{q}) \circ [\varphi_0^{\pm}(\boldsymbol{k}), \varphi_0^{+}(\boldsymbol{q})]_{\varepsilon} \\
&\qquad \pm (1+\tau(\varphi_0))\varphi_0^{\pm}(\boldsymbol{k})\delta^3(\boldsymbol{k}-\boldsymbol{q}) = {}'f^{\pm}(\boldsymbol{k},\boldsymbol{q})
\end{aligned} \tag{15.1}$$

$$\begin{aligned}
&[\varphi_0^{\pm}(\boldsymbol{k}), \varphi_0^{+}(\boldsymbol{q})]_{\varepsilon} \circ \varphi_0^{\dagger -}(\boldsymbol{q}) - \varepsilon \varphi_0^{+}(\boldsymbol{q}) \circ [\varphi_0^{\pm}(\boldsymbol{k}), \varphi_0^{\dagger -}(\boldsymbol{q})]_{\varepsilon} \\
&+[\varphi_0^{\pm}(\boldsymbol{k}), \varphi_0^{-}(\boldsymbol{q})]_{\varepsilon} \circ \varphi_0^{\dagger +}(\boldsymbol{q}) - \varepsilon \varphi_0^{-}(\boldsymbol{q}) \circ [\varphi_0^{\pm}(\boldsymbol{k}), \varphi_0^{\dagger +}(\boldsymbol{q})]_{\varepsilon} \\
&\qquad \pm (1+\tau(\varphi_0))\varphi_0^{\pm}(\boldsymbol{k})\delta^3(\boldsymbol{k}-\boldsymbol{q}) = {}''f^{\pm}(\boldsymbol{k},\boldsymbol{q})
\end{aligned} \tag{15.2}$$

$$\begin{aligned}
&[\varphi_0^{\pm}(\boldsymbol{k}), \varphi_0^{\dagger +}(\boldsymbol{q})]_{\varepsilon} \circ \varphi_0^{-}(\boldsymbol{q}) - \varepsilon \varphi_0^{\dagger +}(\boldsymbol{q}) \circ [\varphi_0^{\pm}(\boldsymbol{k}), \varphi_0^{-}(\boldsymbol{q})]_{\varepsilon} \\
&+[\varphi_0^{\pm}(\boldsymbol{k}), \varphi_0^{-}(\boldsymbol{q})]_{\varepsilon} \circ \varphi_0^{\dagger +}(\boldsymbol{q}) - \varepsilon \varphi_0^{-}(\boldsymbol{q}) \circ [\varphi_0^{\pm}(\boldsymbol{k}), \varphi_0^{\dagger +}(\boldsymbol{q})]_{\varepsilon} \\
&+[\varphi_0^{\pm}(\boldsymbol{k}), \varphi_0^{+}(\boldsymbol{q})]_{\varepsilon} \circ \varphi_0^{\dagger -}(\boldsymbol{q}) - \varepsilon \varphi_0^{+}(\boldsymbol{q}) \circ [\varphi_0^{\pm}(\boldsymbol{k}), \varphi_0^{\dagger -}(\boldsymbol{q})]_{\varepsilon} \\
&+[\varphi_0^{\pm}(\boldsymbol{k}), \varphi_0^{\dagger -}(\boldsymbol{q})]_{\varepsilon} \circ \varphi_0^{+}(\boldsymbol{q}) - \varepsilon \varphi_0^{\dagger -}(\boldsymbol{q}) \circ [\varphi_0^{\pm}(\boldsymbol{k}), \varphi_0^{+}(\boldsymbol{q})]_{\varepsilon} \\
&\qquad \pm 2(1+\tau(\varphi_0))\varphi_0^{\pm}(\boldsymbol{k})\delta^3(\boldsymbol{k}-\boldsymbol{q}) = {}'''f^{\pm}(\boldsymbol{k},\boldsymbol{q}).
\end{aligned} \tag{15.3}$$

Now, following the know argumentation [3–5], we shall impose an *additional condition* saying that the commutators, $\varepsilon = -1$, or anticommutators, $\varepsilon = +1$, of all combinations of creation and/or annihilation operators should be proportional to the identity operator $\mathsf{id}_{\mathcal{F}}$ of the Hilbert space $\mathcal{F}$ of the considered free arbitrary scalar field.

It is easily seen, the equations (15.1) and (15.2) (and similar ones obtained from them with $\varphi_0^{\dagger\pm}(\boldsymbol{k})$ for $\varphi_0^{\pm}(\boldsymbol{k})$) do not make any difference between the choices $\varepsilon = -1$ and $\varepsilon = +1$. But, for equation (15.3), the situation is completely different. Indeed, for $\varepsilon = +1$, which corresponds to quantization of a scalar field by anticommutators, equation (15.3) reduces to $\pm 2(1+\tau(\varphi_0))\varphi_0^{\pm}\delta^3(\boldsymbol{k}-\boldsymbol{q}) = {}'''f^{\pm}(\boldsymbol{k},\boldsymbol{q})$ which, when inserted in (13.14), entails $k_\mu|_{k_0=\sqrt{m^2c^2+\boldsymbol{k}^2}}\varphi^{\pm}(\boldsymbol{k}) = 0$ for any $\boldsymbol{k}$; a similar result follows from (13.13b), i.e. we have

$$k_\mu|_{k_0=\sqrt{m^2c^2+\boldsymbol{k}^2}}\varphi_0^{\pm}(\boldsymbol{k}) = 0 \quad k_\mu|_{k_0=\sqrt{m^2c^2+\boldsymbol{k}^2}}\varphi_0^{\dagger\pm}(\boldsymbol{k}) = 0 \qquad \text{for } \varepsilon = +1 \tag{15.4}$$

which, by (13.3c), implies

$$'''\mathcal{P}_\mu^{(2)} = 0. \tag{15.5}$$

Consequently, since (15.5) and the Klein-Gordon equations (10.16) imply

$$m^2c^2\varphi_0 = 0 \qquad m^2c^2\varphi_0^\dagger = 0, \tag{15.6}$$

the choice $\varepsilon = +1$ for (15.3) is possible only for the degenerate (unphysical) solutions (11.3) (or (11.3′) in Heisenberg picture) and for the solution

$$\varphi_0 = 0 \quad \varphi_0^\dagger = 0 \qquad \text{for } m \neq 0, \tag{15.7}$$

the last of which is equivalent to

$$\varphi_0^\pm(\boldsymbol{k}) = 0 \quad \varphi_0^{\dagger\pm}(\boldsymbol{k}) = 0 \qquad \text{for } m \neq 0. \tag{15.8}$$

According to equations (10.37) and (15.5), the degenerate solutions (11.3) and (15.7) carry no 4-momentum and charge and, hence, cannot be detected. So, these solutions should be interpreted as an absence of the scalar field and, if one starts from the Lagrangian (10.9), they are the only ones that can be quantized by anticommutators.[41]

Let us return to the consideration of equations (15.1)–(15.3) and similar ones with $\varphi_0^{\dagger\pm}(\boldsymbol{k})$ for $\varphi_0^\pm(\boldsymbol{k})$ having in mind that $\varepsilon = -1$ for (15.3). Writing explicitly them for the upper, "+", and lower, "−", signs, we see that they can equivalently be represented respectively in the forms:

$$\begin{aligned}
&[\varphi_0^\pm(\boldsymbol{k}), \varphi_0^{\dagger\pm}(\boldsymbol{q})]_\varepsilon \circ \varphi_0^\mp(\boldsymbol{q}) - \varepsilon\varphi_0^{\dagger\mp}(\boldsymbol{q}) \circ [\varphi_0^\pm(\boldsymbol{k}), \varphi_0^\pm(\boldsymbol{q})]_\varepsilon \\
&+[\varphi_0^\pm(\boldsymbol{k}), \varphi_0^{\dagger\mp}(\boldsymbol{q})]_\varepsilon \circ \varphi_0^\pm(\boldsymbol{q}) - \varepsilon\varphi_0^{\dagger\pm}(\boldsymbol{q}) \circ [\varphi_0^\pm(\boldsymbol{k}), \varphi_0^\mp(\boldsymbol{q})]_\varepsilon \\
&\qquad\qquad \pm(1+\tau(\varphi_0))\varphi_0^\pm(\boldsymbol{k})\delta^3(\boldsymbol{k}-\boldsymbol{q}) = {}'f^\pm(\boldsymbol{k},\boldsymbol{q})
\end{aligned} \tag{15.9}$$

$$\begin{aligned}
&[\varphi_0^\pm(\boldsymbol{k}), \varphi_0^\pm(\boldsymbol{q})]_\varepsilon \circ \varphi_0^{\dagger\mp}(\boldsymbol{q}) - \varepsilon\varphi_0^\mp(\boldsymbol{q}) \circ [\varphi_0^\pm(\boldsymbol{k}), \varphi_0^{\dagger\pm}(\boldsymbol{q})]_\varepsilon \\
&+[\varphi_0^\pm(\boldsymbol{k}), \varphi_0^\mp(\boldsymbol{q})]_\varepsilon \circ \varphi_0^{\dagger\pm}(\boldsymbol{q}) - \varepsilon\varphi_0^\pm(\boldsymbol{q}) \circ [\varphi_0^\pm(\boldsymbol{k}), \varphi_0^{\dagger\mp}(\boldsymbol{q})]_\varepsilon \\
&\qquad\qquad \pm(1+\tau(\varphi_0))\varphi_0^\pm(\boldsymbol{k})\delta^3(\boldsymbol{k}-\boldsymbol{q}) = {}''f^\pm(\boldsymbol{k},\boldsymbol{q})
\end{aligned} \tag{15.10}$$

$$\begin{aligned}
&\varphi_0^{\dagger\mp}(\boldsymbol{q}) \circ [\varphi_0^\pm(\boldsymbol{k}), \varphi_0^\pm(\boldsymbol{q})]_\varepsilon + \varphi_0^\mp(\boldsymbol{q}) \circ [\varphi_0^\pm(\boldsymbol{k}), \varphi_0^{\dagger\pm}(\boldsymbol{q})]_\varepsilon \\
&\varphi_0^{\dagger\pm}(\boldsymbol{q}) \circ [\varphi_0^\pm(\boldsymbol{k}), \varphi_0^\mp(\boldsymbol{q})]_\varepsilon + \varphi_0^\pm(\boldsymbol{q}) \circ [\varphi_0^\pm(\boldsymbol{k}), \varphi_0^{\dagger\mp}(\boldsymbol{q})]_\varepsilon \\
&\qquad\qquad \pm(1+\tau(\varphi_0))\varphi_0^\pm(\boldsymbol{k})\delta^3(\boldsymbol{k}-\boldsymbol{q}) = \frac{1}{2}\,{}'''f^\pm(\boldsymbol{k},\boldsymbol{q}).
\end{aligned} \tag{15.11}$$

Let us write explicitly the above-stated *additional condition* concerning the (anti)commutators of creation and annihilation operators. We have (cf. equations (7.1)):

$$\begin{aligned}
&[\varphi_0^\pm(\boldsymbol{k}), \varphi_0^\pm(\boldsymbol{q})]_\varepsilon = a_\varepsilon^\pm(\boldsymbol{k},\boldsymbol{q})\,\mathsf{id}_\mathcal{F} &\quad& [\varphi_0^{\dagger\pm}(\boldsymbol{k}), \varphi_0^{\dagger\pm}(\boldsymbol{q})]_\varepsilon = a_\varepsilon^{\dagger\pm}(\boldsymbol{k},\boldsymbol{q})\,\mathsf{id}_\mathcal{F} \\
&[\varphi_0^\mp(\boldsymbol{k}), \varphi_0^\pm(\boldsymbol{q})]_\varepsilon = b_\varepsilon^\pm(\boldsymbol{k},\boldsymbol{q})\,\mathsf{id}_\mathcal{F} && [\varphi_0^{\dagger\mp}(\boldsymbol{k}), \varphi_0^{\dagger\pm}(\boldsymbol{q})]_\varepsilon = b_\varepsilon^{\dagger\pm}(\boldsymbol{k},\boldsymbol{q})\,\mathsf{id}_\mathcal{F} \\
&[\varphi_0^\pm(\boldsymbol{k}), \varphi_0^{\dagger\pm}(\boldsymbol{q})]_\varepsilon = d_\varepsilon^\pm(\boldsymbol{k},\boldsymbol{q})\,\mathsf{id}_\mathcal{F} && [\varphi_0^{\dagger\pm}(\boldsymbol{k}), \varphi_0^\pm(\boldsymbol{q})]_\varepsilon = \varepsilon d_\varepsilon^\pm(\boldsymbol{q},\boldsymbol{k})\,\mathsf{id}_\mathcal{F} \\
&[\varphi_0^\mp(\boldsymbol{k}), \varphi_0^{\dagger\pm}(\boldsymbol{q})]_\varepsilon = e_\varepsilon^\pm(\boldsymbol{k},\boldsymbol{q})\,\mathsf{id}_\mathcal{F} && [\varphi_0^{\dagger\mp}(\boldsymbol{k}), \varphi_0^\pm(\boldsymbol{q})]_\varepsilon = \varepsilon e_\varepsilon^\mp(\boldsymbol{q},\boldsymbol{k})\,\mathsf{id}_\mathcal{F}
\end{aligned} \tag{15.12}$$

[41] In fact, the last assertion completes the proof of spin-statistics theorem for free arbitrary scalar field. Notice, in this proof we have not used any additional hypotheses, like charge conjugation/symmetry or positivity of the Hilbert space metric (cf. [3, sec. 10.2]).

where $\varepsilon = \pm 1$ for (15.1) and (15.2), $\varepsilon = -1$ for (15.3), and $a_\varepsilon^\pm$, $a_\varepsilon^{\dagger\pm}$, ..., $e_\varepsilon^\pm$ are some complex-valued (generalized) functions, which we have to determine. These last functions are subjected to a number of restrictions which can be derived in the same way as (7.18) and (7.19) in the Hermitian case.[42] One can easily verify that these restrictions are:

$$(\boldsymbol{k}+\boldsymbol{q})a_\varepsilon^\pm(\boldsymbol{k},\boldsymbol{q}) = 0 \quad (\boldsymbol{k}+\boldsymbol{q})a_\varepsilon^{\dagger\pm}(\boldsymbol{k},\boldsymbol{q}) = 0 \quad (\boldsymbol{k}+\boldsymbol{q})d_\varepsilon^\pm(\boldsymbol{k},\boldsymbol{q}) = 0 \tag{15.13a}$$

$$(\boldsymbol{k}-\boldsymbol{q})b_\varepsilon^\pm(\boldsymbol{k},\boldsymbol{q}) = 0 \quad (\boldsymbol{k}-\boldsymbol{q})b_\varepsilon^{\dagger\pm}(\boldsymbol{k},\boldsymbol{q}) = 0 \quad (\boldsymbol{k}-\boldsymbol{q})e_\varepsilon^\pm(\boldsymbol{k},\boldsymbol{q}) = 0 \tag{15.13b}$$

$$\big(\sqrt{m^2c^2+\boldsymbol{k}^2}+\sqrt{m^2c^2+\boldsymbol{q}^2}\big)\alpha(\boldsymbol{k},\boldsymbol{q}) = 0 \qquad \text{for } \alpha = a_\varepsilon^\pm, a_\varepsilon^{\dagger\pm}, d_\varepsilon^\pm \tag{15.14a}$$

$$\big(\sqrt{m^2c^2+\boldsymbol{k}^2}-\sqrt{m^2c^2+\boldsymbol{q}^2}\big)\beta(\boldsymbol{k},\boldsymbol{q}) = 0 \qquad \text{for } \beta = b_\varepsilon^\pm, b_\varepsilon^{\dagger\pm}, e_\varepsilon^\pm. \tag{15.14b}$$

Regarding $a_\varepsilon^\pm$, $a_\varepsilon^{\dagger\pm}$, ...,$e_\varepsilon^\pm$ as distributions, from (15.13), we derive (cf. (7.21)):

$$f(\boldsymbol{q})\alpha(\boldsymbol{k},\boldsymbol{q}) = f(-\boldsymbol{k})\alpha(\boldsymbol{k},\boldsymbol{q}) \qquad \text{for } \alpha = a_\varepsilon^\pm, a_\varepsilon^{\dagger\pm}, d_\varepsilon^\pm \tag{15.15a}$$

$$f(\boldsymbol{q})\beta(\boldsymbol{k},\boldsymbol{q}) = f(+\boldsymbol{k})\beta(\boldsymbol{k},\boldsymbol{q}) \qquad \text{for } \beta = b_\varepsilon^\pm, b_\varepsilon^{\dagger\pm}, e_\varepsilon^\pm \tag{15.15b}$$

for any function f which is polynomial or convergent power series. In view of (15.15), the equalities (15.14b) are identically satisfied, while (15.14a) are equivalent to the equations

$$\sqrt{m^2c^2+\boldsymbol{k}^2}\,\alpha(\boldsymbol{k},\boldsymbol{q}) = 0 \qquad \text{for } \alpha = a_\varepsilon^\pm, a_\varepsilon^{\dagger\pm}, d_\varepsilon^\pm. \tag{15.16}$$

Substituting the equalities (15.12) into equations (15.9)–(15.11) and similar ones with $\varphi_0^{\dagger\pm}(\boldsymbol{k})$ for $\varphi_0^\pm(\boldsymbol{k})$, we see that the restrictions (13.14), in view of (15.15), give the next systems of equations for the unknown (generalized) functions $a_\varepsilon^\pm$, $a_\varepsilon^{\dagger\pm}$, ..., $e_\varepsilon^\pm$:

$$\begin{gathered} k_a \int \mathrm{d}^3\boldsymbol{q}\{\varepsilon\varphi_0^{\dagger\mp}(\boldsymbol{q})a_\varepsilon^\pm(\boldsymbol{k},\boldsymbol{q}) - \varphi_0^\mp(\boldsymbol{q})d_\varepsilon^\pm(\boldsymbol{k},\boldsymbol{q}) - \varepsilon\varphi_0^{\dagger\pm}(\boldsymbol{q})b_\varepsilon^\mp(\boldsymbol{k},\boldsymbol{q}) \\ +\varphi_0^\pm(\boldsymbol{q})\big(e_\varepsilon^\mp(\boldsymbol{k},\boldsymbol{q}) \pm \sigma(1+\tau(\varphi_0))\delta^3(\boldsymbol{k}-\boldsymbol{q})\big)\} = 0 \end{gathered} \tag{15.17a}$$

$$\begin{gathered} \sqrt{m^2c^2+\boldsymbol{k}^2} \int \mathrm{d}^3\boldsymbol{q}\{-\varepsilon\varphi_0^{\dagger\mp}(\boldsymbol{q})a_\varepsilon^\pm(\boldsymbol{k},\boldsymbol{q}) + \varphi_0^\mp(\boldsymbol{q})d_\varepsilon^\pm(\boldsymbol{k},\boldsymbol{q}) \\ -\varepsilon\varphi_0^\pm(\boldsymbol{q})b_\varepsilon^\mp(\boldsymbol{k},\boldsymbol{q}) + \varphi_0^{\dagger\pm}(\boldsymbol{q})\big(e_\varepsilon^\mp(\boldsymbol{k},\boldsymbol{q}) \pm \sigma(1+\tau(\varphi_0))\delta^3(\boldsymbol{k}-\boldsymbol{q})\big)\} = 0 \end{gathered} \tag{15.17b}$$

$$\begin{gathered} k_a \int \mathrm{d}^3\boldsymbol{q}\{\varphi_0^{\dagger\mp}(\boldsymbol{q})d_\varepsilon^\pm(\boldsymbol{q},\boldsymbol{k}) - \varphi_0^\mp(\boldsymbol{q})a_\varepsilon^{\dagger\pm}(\boldsymbol{k},\boldsymbol{q}) + \varphi_0^\pm(\boldsymbol{q})b_\varepsilon^{\dagger\mp}(\boldsymbol{k},\boldsymbol{q}) \\ +\varphi_0^{\dagger\pm}(\boldsymbol{q})\big(-e_\varepsilon^\pm(\boldsymbol{q},\boldsymbol{k}) \pm \sigma(1+\tau(\varphi_0))\delta^3(\boldsymbol{k}-\boldsymbol{q})\big)\} = 0 \end{gathered} \tag{15.17c}$$

$$\begin{gathered} \sqrt{m^2c^2+\boldsymbol{k}^2} \int \mathrm{d}^3\boldsymbol{q}\{-\varphi_0^{\dagger\mp}(\boldsymbol{q})d_\varepsilon^\pm(\boldsymbol{q},\boldsymbol{k}) + \varphi_0^\mp(\boldsymbol{q})a_\varepsilon^{\dagger\pm}(\boldsymbol{k},\boldsymbol{q}) \\ +\varphi_0^\pm(\boldsymbol{q})b_\varepsilon^{\dagger\mp}(\boldsymbol{k},\boldsymbol{q}) + \varphi_0^{\dagger\pm}(\boldsymbol{q})\big(-e_\varepsilon^\pm(\boldsymbol{q},\boldsymbol{k}) \pm \sigma(1+\tau(\varphi_0))\delta^3(\boldsymbol{k}-\boldsymbol{q})\big)\} = 0. \end{gathered} \tag{15.17d}$$

[42] Notice, (7.15)–(7.17) remain valid if we replace in them $\varphi_0^\pm(\boldsymbol{k})$ and/or $\varphi_0^\pm(\boldsymbol{q})$ with $\varphi_0^{\dagger\pm}(\boldsymbol{k})$ and/or $\varphi_0^{\dagger\pm}(\boldsymbol{q})$ respectively; see (12.7).

Here: $a = 1, 2, 3$, $\sigma = -\varepsilon$ for (15.10) and $\sigma = 1$ for (15.9) and (15.11), $\varepsilon = \pm 1$ for (15.9) and (15.10), and $\varepsilon = -1$ for (15.11) (*vide supra*). Notice, (15.17a) and (15.17b) correspond to (15.9)–(15.11), while (15.17c) and (15.17d) correspond to the same equations with $\varphi_0^{\dagger\pm}(\boldsymbol{k})$ for $\varphi_0^{\pm}(\boldsymbol{k})$.

If we impose a *second*, after (15.12), *additional condition*, namely that equation (15.17) to be valid for arbitrary $\varphi_0^{\pm}(\boldsymbol{q})$ and $\varphi_0^{\dagger\pm}(\boldsymbol{q})$, we see that, if $(m, \boldsymbol{k}) \neq (0, \boldsymbol{0})$, the only solution of (15.17) relative to $a_\varepsilon^{\pm}$, $a_\varepsilon^{\dagger\pm}$, ..., $e_\varepsilon^{\pm}$ is:

$$a_{\varepsilon(\varphi_0)}^{\pm}(\boldsymbol{k}, \boldsymbol{q}) = a_{\varepsilon(\varphi_0)}^{\dagger\pm}(\boldsymbol{k}, \boldsymbol{q}) = d_{\varepsilon(\varphi_0)}^{\pm}(\boldsymbol{k}, \boldsymbol{q}) = 0 \tag{15.18a}$$

$$b_{\varepsilon(\varphi_0)}^{\pm}(\boldsymbol{k}, \boldsymbol{q}) = b_{\varepsilon(\varphi_0)}^{\dagger\pm}(\boldsymbol{k}, \boldsymbol{q}) = \pm\tau(\varphi_0)\delta^3(\boldsymbol{k} - \boldsymbol{q}) \tag{15.18b}$$

$$e_{\varepsilon(\varphi_0)}^{\pm}(\boldsymbol{k}, \boldsymbol{q}) = \pm\sigma(\varphi_0)\delta^3(\boldsymbol{k} - \boldsymbol{q}), \tag{15.18c}$$

where $\tau(\varphi_0)$ is defined via (10.13) and:

$$\varepsilon(\varphi_0) = \begin{cases} -1 & \text{for equation (15.11) with any } \varphi_0 \\ & \text{and for equations (15.9) and (15.10) with } \varphi_0^\dagger = \varphi_0 \\ \pm 1 & \text{for equations (15.9) and (15.10) with } \varphi_0^\dagger \neq \varphi_0 \end{cases}$$
$$\sigma(\varphi_0) = \begin{cases} -\varepsilon(\varphi_0) & \text{for equation (15.10)} \\ +1 & \text{for equations (15.9) and (15.11)} \end{cases} \tag{15.19}$$

Evidently, (15.18a) converts (15.16) into identity and, consequently, under the hypotheses made, (15.18) is the general solution of our problem.

It should be emphasized on the fact that the function $\tau(\varphi_0)$ in (15.18) takes care of what is the field φ_0, Hermitian or non-Hermitian, while the functions $\varepsilon(\varphi_0)$ and $\sigma(\varphi_0)$ take care of from what Lagrangian, (10.7)–(10.9), we have started off.

Before commenting on the solutions (15.18), we want to say some words on the case $m = 0$ and $\boldsymbol{k} = \boldsymbol{0}$ for which the equations (15.17) and (15.16) take the form of the identity $0 = 0$ and, consequently, no information can be extracted from them. The above analysis reveals that, under the additional conditions (15.12), the field equations do not impose some restrictions on the operators

$$\varphi_0^{\pm}(\boldsymbol{k}) \text{ and } \varphi_0^{\dagger\pm}(\boldsymbol{k}) \qquad \text{for } m = 0 \text{ and } \boldsymbol{k} = \boldsymbol{0}, \tag{15.20}$$

i.e. these operators must satisfy (15.12) with $m = 0$ and $\boldsymbol{k} = \boldsymbol{0}$ and arbitrary $a_\varepsilon^{\pm}(\boldsymbol{0}, \boldsymbol{q})$, $a_\varepsilon^{\dagger\pm}(\boldsymbol{0}, \boldsymbol{q})$, ..., $e_\varepsilon^{\pm}(\boldsymbol{0}, \boldsymbol{q})$ (with $\varepsilon = \pm 1$ for (15.1) and (15.2) and $\varepsilon = -1$ for (15.3)). To ensure a continuous limit $(m, \boldsymbol{k}) \to (0, \boldsymbol{0})$, we shall assume *by convention* that $a_\varepsilon^{\pm}(\boldsymbol{0}, \boldsymbol{q})$, $a_\varepsilon^{\dagger\pm}(\boldsymbol{0}, \boldsymbol{q})$, ..., $e_\varepsilon^{\pm}(\boldsymbol{0}, \boldsymbol{q})$ are given via (15.18) with $\boldsymbol{k} = \boldsymbol{0}$ (and $m = 0$). From physical point of view (see Sect. 12), the operators (15.20) describe creation/annihilation of massless particles with vanishing 4-momentum and charge $\pm q$, which is zero for a Hermitian (neutral) filed and non-zero for a non-Hermitian (charged) one. Consequently, *in the non-Hermitian case, the theory admits existence of free, charged, massless scalar particles with vanishing 4-momentum*, which are quanta of free, charged, massless scalar field. As far as the author of these lines knows, such particles/fields have not been observed until now. In the Hermitian case, as we pointed in Sect. 7, the operators (15.20) reduce to (7.27) and describe unphysical particles/fields which are experimentally unobservable.

Since the (anti)commutation relations (15.12) are extremely important for quantum field theory, we shall write them explicitly for the obtained solutions (15.18). As the three versions of some equations, like (15.17), (15.1)–(15.3), (13.11)–(13.13), (13.3), etc., originate from the Lagrangians (10.7)–(10.9) we have started off, we shall associate the found (anti)commutation relations with the initial Lagrangians rather than with the particular equations utilized in their derivation.

Since equations (15.11), for which $\varepsilon(\varphi_0) = -1$ and $\sigma(\varphi_0) = +1$, originate from the Lagrangian (10.9), we can assert that the *Lagrangian* (10.9) *implies the following commutation relations*:

$$\begin{aligned}
&[\varphi_0^{\pm}(\boldsymbol{k}), \varphi_0^{\pm}(\boldsymbol{q})]_{_} = 0 && [\varphi_0^{\dagger\pm}(\boldsymbol{k}), \varphi_0^{\dagger\pm}(\boldsymbol{q})]_{_} = 0\\
&[\varphi_0^{\mp}(\boldsymbol{k}), \varphi_0^{\pm}(\boldsymbol{q})]_{_} = \pm\tau(\varphi_0)\delta^3(\boldsymbol{k}-\boldsymbol{q})\,\mathsf{id}_{\mathcal{F}} && [\varphi_0^{\dagger\mp}(\boldsymbol{k}), \varphi_0^{\dagger\pm}(\boldsymbol{q})]_{_} = \pm\tau(\varphi_0)\delta^3(\boldsymbol{k}-\boldsymbol{q})\,\mathsf{id}_{\mathcal{F}}\\
&[\varphi_0^{\pm}(\boldsymbol{k}), \varphi_0^{\dagger\pm}(\boldsymbol{q})]_{_} = 0 && [\varphi_0^{\dagger\pm}(\boldsymbol{k}), \varphi_0^{\pm}(\boldsymbol{q})]_{_} = 0\\
&[\varphi_0^{\mp}(\boldsymbol{k}), \varphi_0^{\dagger\pm}(\boldsymbol{q})]_{_} = \pm\delta^3(\boldsymbol{k}-\boldsymbol{q})\,\mathsf{id}_{\mathcal{F}} && [\varphi_0^{\dagger\mp}(\boldsymbol{k}), \varphi_0^{\pm}(\boldsymbol{q})]_{_} = \pm\delta^3(\boldsymbol{k}-\boldsymbol{q})\,\mathsf{id}_{\mathcal{F}}
\end{aligned} \tag{15.21}$$

where 0 denotes the zero operator on $\mathcal{F}$ and $\tau(\varphi_0)$ takes care of is the field neutral ($\varphi_0^\dagger = \varphi_0$, $\tau(\varphi_0) = 1$) or charged ($\varphi_0^\dagger \neq \varphi_0$, $\tau(\varphi_0) = 0$) and ensures a correct commutation relations in the Hermitian case (see (7.28)).

Since the equations (15.9) are consequences of the Lagrangian (10.7), we can assert that the next *(anti)commutation relations follow from the Lagrangian* (10.7):

$$\begin{aligned}
&[\varphi_0^{\pm}(\boldsymbol{k}), \varphi_0^{\pm}(\boldsymbol{q})]_{\varepsilon} = 0 && [\varphi_0^{\dagger\pm}(\boldsymbol{k}), \varphi_0^{\dagger\pm}(\boldsymbol{q})]_{\varepsilon} = 0\\
&[\varphi_0^{\mp}(\boldsymbol{k}), \varphi_0^{\pm}(\boldsymbol{q})]_{\varepsilon} = \pm\tau(\varphi_0)\delta^3(\boldsymbol{k}-\boldsymbol{q})\,\mathsf{id}_{\mathcal{F}} && [\varphi_0^{\dagger\mp}(\boldsymbol{k}), \varphi_0^{\dagger\pm}(\boldsymbol{q})]_{\varepsilon} = \pm\tau(\varphi_0)\delta^3(\boldsymbol{k}-\boldsymbol{q})\,\mathsf{id}_{\mathcal{F}}\\
&[\varphi_0^{\pm}(\boldsymbol{k}), \varphi_0^{\dagger\pm}(\boldsymbol{q})]_{\varepsilon} = 0 && [\varphi_0^{\dagger\pm}(\boldsymbol{k}), \varphi_0^{\pm}(\boldsymbol{q})]_{\varepsilon} = 0\\
&[\varphi_0^{\mp}(\boldsymbol{k}), \varphi_0^{\dagger\pm}(\boldsymbol{q})]_{\varepsilon} = \pm\delta^3(\boldsymbol{k}-\boldsymbol{q})\,\mathsf{id}_{\mathcal{F}} && [\varphi_0^{\dagger\mp}(\boldsymbol{k}), \varphi_0^{\pm}(\boldsymbol{q})]_{\varepsilon} = \pm\delta^3(\boldsymbol{k}-\boldsymbol{q})\,\mathsf{id}_{\mathcal{F}}
\end{aligned} \tag{15.22}$$

where $\varepsilon = -1$ (commutation relations) for a Hermitian filed, $\varphi_0^\dagger = \varphi_0$, and $\varepsilon = \pm 1$ (commutation or anticommutation relations) for a non-Hermitian filed, $\varphi_0^\dagger \neq \varphi_0$.

At last, since the Lagrangian (10.8) entails (15.10), the *Lagrangian* (10.8) *implies the following (anti)commutation relations* :

$$\begin{aligned}
&[\varphi_0^{\pm}(\boldsymbol{k}), \varphi_0^{\pm}(\boldsymbol{q})]_{\varepsilon} = 0 && [\varphi_0^{\dagger\pm}(\boldsymbol{k}), \varphi_0^{\dagger\pm}(\boldsymbol{q})]_{\varepsilon} = 0\\
&[\varphi_0^{\mp}(\boldsymbol{k}), \varphi_0^{\pm}(\boldsymbol{q})]_{\varepsilon} = \pm\tau(\varphi_0)\delta^3(\boldsymbol{k}-\boldsymbol{q})\,\mathsf{id}_{\mathcal{F}} && [\varphi_0^{\dagger\mp}(\boldsymbol{k}), \varphi_0^{\dagger\pm}(\boldsymbol{q})]_{\varepsilon} = \pm\tau(\varphi_0)\delta^3(\boldsymbol{k}-\boldsymbol{q})\,\mathsf{id}_{\mathcal{F}}\\
&[\varphi_0^{\pm}(\boldsymbol{k}), \varphi_0^{\dagger\pm}(\boldsymbol{q})]_{\varepsilon} = 0 && [\varphi_0^{\dagger\pm}(\boldsymbol{k}), \varphi_0^{\pm}(\boldsymbol{q})]_{\varepsilon} = 0\\
&[\varphi_0^{\mp}(\boldsymbol{k}), \varphi_0^{\dagger\pm}(\boldsymbol{q})]_{\varepsilon} = \mp\varepsilon\delta^3(\boldsymbol{k}-\boldsymbol{q})\,\mathsf{id}_{\mathcal{F}} && [\varphi_0^{\dagger\mp}(\boldsymbol{k}), \varphi_0^{\pm}(\boldsymbol{q})]_{\varepsilon} = \mp\varepsilon\delta^3(\boldsymbol{k}-\boldsymbol{q})\,\mathsf{id}_{\mathcal{F}}
\end{aligned} \tag{15.23}$$

where $\varepsilon = -1$ (commutation relations) for a Hermitian filed, $\varphi_0^\dagger = \varphi_0$, and $\varepsilon = \pm 1$ (commutation or anticommutation relations) for a non-Hermitian filed, $\varphi_0^\dagger \neq \varphi_0$.

It should be emphasized, for a Hermitian (neutral, real) field, when $\varepsilon = -1$ in (15.22) and (15.23), the *commutation* relations (15.21), (15.22), and (15.23) coincide and, due to $\tau(\varphi_0) = 1$ in this case, are identical with (7.28); thus, they correctly reproduce the already established results in Sect. 7. However, for a *non-Hermitian* (charged) field, for which $\tau(\varphi_0) = 0$, we have *three* independent sets of (anti)commutation relations:

(i) the commutation relations (15.21) correspond to the Lagrangians (10.7) and (10.8), with the *choice* $\varepsilon = -1$ for the both ones, and the Lagrangian (10.9);

(ii) the *anticommutation* relations (15.22) with $\varepsilon = +1$ correspond to the Lagrangian (10.7) with the *choice* $\varepsilon = +1$;

(iii) the *anticommutation* relations (15.23) with $\varepsilon = +1$ correspond to the Lagrangian (10.8) with the *choice* $\varepsilon = +1$.

The relations (15.23) with $\varepsilon = +1$ differ from (15.22) with $\varepsilon = +1$ only in the sign before the δ-function in the last row. This is quite understandable as the Lagrangian (10.8) can be obtained from (10.7) by replacing $\tilde{\varphi}$ with $\tilde{\varphi}^\dagger$ and $\tilde{\varphi}^\dagger$ with $\tilde{\varphi}$. If we make the same change in (15.22), i.e. $\varphi_0^\pm \leftrightarrow \varphi_0^{\dagger\pm}$, we see that (15.22) transforms into (15.23). Since (15.22) and (15.23) are identical (resp. different) for $\varepsilon = -1$ (resp. $\varepsilon = +1$), we conclude that the theory is invariant (resp. non-invariant) under the change $\varphi_0 \leftrightarrow \varphi_0^\dagger$ or, equivalently, $\varphi_0^\pm \leftrightarrow \varphi_0^{\dagger\pm}$, called *charge conjugation* [3, 5, 11], if and only if it is quantized via commutators (resp. anticommutators) if one starts from any one of the Lagrangians (10.7) and (10.8). The theory is always charge symmetric, i.e. invariant under charge conjugation, if one starts from the Lagrangian (10.9).

Thus, for a free non-Hermitian scalar field, we see a principal difference between the Lagrangian (10.9), on one hand, and the Lagrangians (10.7) and (10.8), on the other hand: the first Lagrangian entails quantization with commutators, while the other two imply quantization either with commutators (identical with the one of the previous case) or with anticommutators and one needs a *new additional condition/hypothesis* to make a distinction between these two cases. As it is well known, the correct quantization of a free scalar field is via commutators, not by anticommutators [3, 5, 11]. Usually (see *loc. cit.*) this result is derived, for a charged field, from the Lagrangian (10.2) by invoking a *new additional condition*, like charge symmetry, or positivity of the Hilbert space metric, or spin-statistics theorem.[43] The above considerations show that these additional conditions are not required if one starts from the Lagrangian (10.9); in fact, these conditions are corollaries from it, as we saw with the charge symmetry and spin-statistics theorem (saying that a scalar field, which is a spin zero field, must be quantized via commutators). This is not a surprising result, if we recall that the Lagrangian (10.9) is a sum of the Lagrangians of two (independent)

[43] The particular additional conditions mentioned above are, in fact, equivalent to *postulating* quantization via commutators in the case of free scalar field if one starts from someone of the Lagrangians (10.2), (10.7), and (10.8).

Hermitian scalar fields (see Sect. 10) for which a similar result was established in Sect. 7. In conclusion, the Lagrangian (10.9) is richer in consequences than the Lagrangians (10.7) and (10.8);[44] the cause for this is that $\tilde{\varphi}$ and $\tilde{\varphi}^\dagger$ enter in (10.9) on equal footing, i.e. (10.9) is invariant under the change $\tilde{\varphi} \leftrightarrow \tilde{\varphi}^\dagger$, which cannot be said relative to (10.7) and (10.8).

Relying on the above discussion, the commutation relations (15.21) will be accepted from now on in this paper. As we proved, under the hypotheses made, they are equivalent to the initial system (10.16) of Klein-Gordon equations. If, by some reason one rejects these hypotheses, the system (10.16) of Klein-Gordon equations will be equivalent to the trilinear relations (13.11)–(13.13) corresponding to the Lagrangians (10.7)–(10.9). But, at present, it seems that correct description of the real physical world is given by (15.21), not by the more general trilinear equations mentioned, i.e. there are indications that the so-called parafields, satisfying trilinear equations similar to (13.13), do not exist in the Nature [23].

Similarly to the said at the end of Sect. 7, the considerations in the present section naturally lead to the operator-valued distribution character of the field variables and hence of the creation/annihilation operators. However, such a rigorous treatment is out of the range of this paper, in which it will be incorporated in the appearance of Dirac's delta function in some formulae.

Ending this section, we want to say that, due to the above considerations, the Lagrangian (10.9) is the 'best' one for the correct description of arbitrary, neutral or charged, free scalar field.

16 The vacuum and normal ordering

The arguments, leading to a correct definition of a vacuum and the need of normal ordering of compositions (products) of creation and/or annihilation operators, are practically the same as in the Hermitian case, studied in Sect. 8. Without repeating them *mutatis mutandis*, we shall point only to the difference when the field φ_0 is non-Hermitian (charged). There are two of them: (i) since in this case we have two types of annihilation operators, viz. $\varphi_0^-(\boldsymbol{k})$ and $\varphi_0^{\dagger\,-}(\boldsymbol{k})$, the condition (8.3) should be doubled, i.e. to it one must add the equality $\varphi_0^{\dagger\,-}(\boldsymbol{k})(\mathcal{X}_0) = 0$, $\mathcal{X}_0$ being the vacuum (state vector); (ii) as now the field possesses a non-vanishing charge operator, the combinations of (14.2) with the commutation relations (15.21) leads to infinities, like (8.4) for the momentum operator of a Hermitian field.[45]

Thus, arguments, similar to the ones in Sect. 8, lead to the following definition of a vacuum for a free arbitrary scalar field.

Definition 16.1. The vacuum of a free arbitrary scalar field φ_0 is its physical state that contains no particles and possesses vanishing 4-momentum and (total) charge. It is described

[44] And also the Lagrangian (10.2) which is two times (10.7) and is, usually, used in the literature.

[45] Applying (13.3) and (15.21), the reader can easily obtain the versions of (8.4) for a non-Hermitian field. The results will be senseless infinities, like the ones in (8.4), which are removed via normal ordering (*vide infra*).

by a state vector, denoted by $\mathcal{X}_0$ (in momentum picture) and called also the vacuum (of the field), such that:

$$\mathcal{X}_0 \neq 0 \tag{16.1a}$$
$$\mathcal{X}_0 = \tilde{\mathcal{X}_0} \tag{16.1b}$$
$$\varphi_0^-(\boldsymbol{k})(\mathcal{X}_0) = \varphi_0^{\dagger\,-}(\boldsymbol{k})(\mathcal{X}_0) = 0 \tag{16.1c}$$
$$\langle \mathcal{X}_0 | \mathcal{X}_0 \rangle = 1. \tag{16.1d}$$

As we said above, the formulae (13.3) and (14.2), together with the commutation relations (15.21), imply senseless (infinity) values for the 4-momentum and charge of the vacuum. They are removed by redefining the dynamical variables, like the Lagrangian, momentum operator and charge operator, by writing the compositions (products) of the field, and/or creation and/or annihilation operators in normal order, exactly in the same way as described in Sect. 8. Besides, the definition of the normal ordering operator (mapping) $\mathcal{N}$ is also retained the same as in Sect. 8, with the only remark that now it concerns all creation/annihilation operators, i.e. $\varphi_0^{\pm}(\boldsymbol{k})$ and $\varphi_0^{\dagger\,\pm}(\boldsymbol{k})$.

Since the evident equalities $\mathcal{N}(\varphi_0^{+}(\boldsymbol{k}) \circ \varphi_0^{\dagger\,-}(\boldsymbol{k})) = \mathcal{N}(\varphi_0^{\dagger\,-}(\boldsymbol{k}) \circ \varphi_0^{+}(\boldsymbol{k})) = \varphi_0^{+}(\boldsymbol{k}) \circ \varphi_0^{\dagger\,-}(\boldsymbol{k})$ and $\mathcal{N}(\varphi_0^{-}(\boldsymbol{k}) \circ \varphi_0^{\dagger\,+}(\boldsymbol{k})) = \mathcal{N}(\varphi_0^{\dagger\,+}(\boldsymbol{k}) \circ \varphi_0^{-}(\boldsymbol{k})) = \varphi_0^{\dagger\,+}(\boldsymbol{k}) \circ \varphi_0^{-}(\boldsymbol{k})$ hold, the *three* momentum operators (13.3) transform, after normal ordering, into a *single momentum operator*, viz. into the operator

$$\mathcal{P}_\mu = \frac{1}{1+\tau(\varphi_0)} \int k_\mu|_{k_0=\sqrt{m^2c^2+\boldsymbol{k}^2}} \{\varphi_0^{\dagger\,+}(\boldsymbol{k}) \circ \varphi_0^{-}(\boldsymbol{k}) + \varphi_0^{+}(\boldsymbol{k}) \circ \varphi_0^{\dagger\,-}(\boldsymbol{k})\}\, \mathrm{d}^3\boldsymbol{k}\,. \tag{16.2}$$

Similarly, the *three* charge operators (14.2) transform, after normal ordering, into a *single charge operator*, viz. the operator

$$\mathcal{Q} = q \int \{\varphi_0^{\dagger\,+}(\boldsymbol{k}) \circ \varphi_0^{-}(\boldsymbol{k}) - \varphi_0^{+}(\boldsymbol{k}) \circ \varphi_0^{\dagger\,-}(\boldsymbol{k})\}\, \mathrm{d}^3\boldsymbol{k}\,. \tag{16.3}$$

One can verify the equations

$$\mathcal{N}(\varphi_0^{-}(\boldsymbol{k}) \overset{\leftrightarrow}{A} \circ \varphi_0^{\dagger\,+}(\boldsymbol{k})) = -\mathcal{N}(\varphi_0^{\dagger\,+}(\boldsymbol{k}) \overset{\leftrightarrow}{A} \circ \varphi_0^{-}(\boldsymbol{k})) = -\varphi_0^{\dagger\,+}(\boldsymbol{k}) \overset{\leftrightarrow}{A} \circ a_s^{-}(\boldsymbol{k})$$
$$\mathcal{N}(\varphi_0^{\dagger\,-}(\boldsymbol{k}) \overset{\leftrightarrow}{A} \circ \varphi_0^{+}(\boldsymbol{k})) = -\mathcal{N}(\varphi_0^{+}(\boldsymbol{k}) \overset{\leftrightarrow}{A} \circ \varphi_0^{\dagger\,-}(\boldsymbol{k})) = -a_s^{+}(\boldsymbol{k}) \overset{\leftrightarrow}{A} \circ a_s^{\dagger\,-}(\boldsymbol{k}),$$

with $A = k_\mu \frac{\partial}{\partial k^\mu}$, as a result of which the *three* angular momentum operators (14.15) transform, after normal ordering, into a *single* orbital angular momentum operator given by

$$\mathcal{L}_{\mu\nu} = x_\mu \mathcal{P}_\nu - x_\nu \mathcal{P}_\mu + \frac{\mathrm{i}\hbar}{2(1+\tau(\varphi_0))} \int \mathrm{d}^3\boldsymbol{k} \Big\{ \varphi_0^{\dagger +}(\boldsymbol{k}) \Big(k_\mu \frac{\overleftrightarrow{\partial}}{\partial k^\nu} - k_\nu \frac{\overleftrightarrow{\partial}}{\partial k^\mu} \Big) \circ \varphi_0^{-}(\boldsymbol{k})$$
$$+ \varphi_0^{+}(\boldsymbol{k}) \Big(k_\mu \frac{\overleftrightarrow{\partial}}{\partial k^\nu} - k_\nu \frac{\overleftrightarrow{\partial}}{\partial k^\mu} \Big) \circ \varphi_0^{\dagger -}(\boldsymbol{k}) \Big\} \Big|_{k_0=\sqrt{m^2c^2+\boldsymbol{k}^2}} \quad (16.4)$$

where $\mathcal{P}_\mu$ is given by (16.2). This equation, in Heisenberg picture and expressed via the Heisenberg creation and annihilation operators (13.5), reads

$$\tilde{\mathcal{L}}_{\mu\nu} = \frac{\mathrm{i}\hbar}{2(1+\tau(\tilde{\varphi}_0))} \int \mathrm{d}^3\boldsymbol{k} \Big\{ \tilde{\varphi}_0^{\dagger +}(\boldsymbol{k}) \Big(k_\mu \frac{\overleftrightarrow{\partial}}{\partial k^\nu} - k_\nu \frac{\overleftrightarrow{\partial}}{\partial k^\mu} \Big) \circ \tilde{\varphi}_0^{-}(\boldsymbol{k})$$
$$+ \tilde{\varphi}_0^{+}(\boldsymbol{k}) \Big(k_\mu \frac{\overleftrightarrow{\partial}}{\partial k^\nu} - k_\nu \frac{\overleftrightarrow{\partial}}{\partial k^\mu} \Big) \circ \tilde{\varphi}_0^{\dagger -}(\boldsymbol{k}) \Big\} \Big|_{k_0=\sqrt{m^2c^2+\boldsymbol{k}^2}} . \quad (16.5)$$

In a case of neutral (Hermitian) scalar field, when $\varphi_0^\dagger = \varphi_0$ and $\tau(\varphi_0) = 1$, the last expression for the orbital angular momentum operator reproduces the one presented in [12, eq. (3.54)], due to the first equality in (14.7).

Applying (16.4), (14.7), (13.6) and (15.21), one can verify the equations

$$[\varphi_0, \mathcal{L}_{\mu\nu}]_{\_} = x_\mu[\varphi_0, \mathcal{P}_\nu]_{\_} - x_\nu[\varphi_0, \mathcal{P}_\mu]_{\_} \quad [\varphi_0^\dagger, \mathcal{L}_{\mu\nu}]_{\_} = x_\mu[\varphi_0^\dagger, \mathcal{P}_\nu]_{\_} - x_\nu[\varphi_0^\dagger, \mathcal{P}_\mu]_{\_}, \quad (16.6)$$

which in Heisenberg picture respectively read

$$[\tilde{\varphi}(x), \tilde{\mathcal{L}}_{\mu\nu}]_{\_} = \mathrm{i}\hbar(x_\mu\partial_\nu - x_\nu\partial_\mu)\tilde{\varphi}(x) \quad [\tilde{\varphi}^\dagger(x), \tilde{\mathcal{L}}_{\mu\nu}]_{\_} = \mathrm{i}\hbar(x_\mu\partial_\nu - x_\nu\partial_\mu)\tilde{\varphi}^\dagger(x). \quad (16.7)$$

These equations, together with (2.7), express the relativistic covariance of the theory considered [11].

Similarly, applying (16.3), (13.6) and (15.21), we obtain the equations

$$[\varphi_0, \mathcal{Q}]_{\_} = q\varphi_0 \quad [\varphi_0^\dagger, \mathcal{Q}]_{\_} = -q\varphi_0^\dagger, \quad (16.8)$$

which in Heisenberg picture take the form (10.27). Analogously, we have

$$[\varphi_0^\pm(\boldsymbol{k}), \mathcal{Q}]_{\_} = q\varphi_0^\pm(\boldsymbol{k}) \quad [\varphi_0^{\dagger\pm}(\boldsymbol{k}), \mathcal{Q}]_{\_} = -q\varphi_0^{\dagger\pm}(\boldsymbol{k}), \quad (16.9)$$

which, evidently, entail

$$[\mathcal{P}_\mu, \mathcal{Q}]_{\_} = 0 \quad [\mathcal{Q}, \mathcal{Q}]_{\_} = 0 \quad [\mathcal{L}_{\mu\nu}, \mathcal{Q}]_{\_} = 0. \quad (16.10)$$

At last, we shall derive the commutation relations between the components of the orbital angular momentum operator (16.4), which coincides with the total angular momentum operator. To simplify the proof and to safe some space, we shall work in Heisenberg picture and employ the Heisenberg creation and annihilation operators (13.5), which satisfy the same commutation relations as their momentum picture counterparts. At first, we notice that (16.5) and (15.21) imply the equations ($p_0 := \sqrt{m^2c^2 + \boldsymbol{p}^2}$)

$$\begin{aligned} [\tilde{\varphi}_0^{\pm}(\boldsymbol{p}),\, \tilde{\mathcal{L}}_{\mu\nu}]_{\_} &= \mathrm{i}\hbar \Big\{ p_\mu \frac{\partial}{\partial p^\nu} - p_\nu \frac{\partial}{\partial p^\mu} \Big\} \tilde{\varphi}_0^{\pm}(\boldsymbol{p}) \\ [\tilde{\varphi}_0^{\dagger\pm}(\boldsymbol{p}),\, \tilde{\mathcal{L}}_{\mu\nu}]_{\_} &= \mathrm{i}\hbar \Big\{ p_\mu \frac{\partial}{\partial p^\nu} - p_\nu \frac{\partial}{\partial p^\mu} \Big\} \tilde{\varphi}_0^{\dagger\pm}(\boldsymbol{p}). \end{aligned} \tag{16.11}$$

If $-(\mu \leftrightarrow \nu)$ denotes antisymmetrization with respect to the indices μ and ν, i.e. a subtraction of the previous terms combined with the change $\mu \leftrightarrow \nu$ and $+(\tilde{\varphi}_0^{\pm}(\boldsymbol{p}) \leftrightarrow \tilde{\varphi}_0^{\dagger\pm}(\boldsymbol{p}))$ means that one has to add the previous terms by making the change $\tilde{\varphi}_0^{\pm}(\boldsymbol{p}) \leftrightarrow \tilde{\varphi}_0^{\dagger\pm}(\boldsymbol{p})$, then we get by applying (16.5), (16.11) and (16.4):

$$\begin{aligned} &[\tilde{\mathcal{L}}_{\varkappa\lambda},\, \tilde{\mathcal{L}}_{\mu\nu}]_{\_} \\ &= \frac{\mathrm{i}\hbar}{2(1+\tau(\tilde{\varphi})} 2\mathrm{i}\hbar \int \mathrm{d}^3\boldsymbol{k} \Big\{ k_\mu \frac{\partial\, \tilde{\varphi}_0^{\dagger +}(\boldsymbol{k})}{\partial k^\nu} k_\varkappa \frac{\partial\, \tilde{\varphi}_0^{-}(\boldsymbol{k})}{\partial k^\lambda} - k_\varkappa \frac{\partial\, \tilde{\varphi}_0^{\dagger +}(\boldsymbol{k})}{\partial k^\lambda} k_\mu \frac{\partial\, \tilde{\varphi}_0^{-}(\boldsymbol{k})}{\partial k^\nu} \\ &\qquad + (\tilde{\varphi}_0^{\pm}(\boldsymbol{k}) \leftrightarrow \tilde{\varphi}_0^{\dagger\pm}(\boldsymbol{k})) - (\varkappa \leftrightarrow \lambda) - (\mu \leftrightarrow \nu) \Big\} \\ &= \mathrm{i}\hbar \frac{\mathrm{i}\hbar}{(1+\tau(\tilde{\varphi})} \int \mathrm{d}^3\boldsymbol{k} \Big\{ \eta_{\mu\lambda}\, \tilde{\varphi}_0^{\dagger +}(\boldsymbol{k}) k_\varkappa \frac{\partial\, \tilde{\varphi}_0^{-}(\boldsymbol{k})}{\partial k^\nu} - \eta_{\varkappa\nu}\, \tilde{\varphi}_0^{\dagger +}(\boldsymbol{k}) k_\mu \frac{\partial\, \tilde{\varphi}_0^{-}(\boldsymbol{k})}{\partial k^\lambda} \\ &\qquad + (\tilde{\varphi}_0^{\pm}(\boldsymbol{k}) \leftrightarrow \tilde{\varphi}_0^{\dagger\pm}(\boldsymbol{k})) - (\varkappa \leftrightarrow \lambda) - (\mu \leftrightarrow \nu) \Big\} \\ &= \mathrm{i}\hbar \big\{ \eta_{\varkappa\nu}\, \tilde{\mathcal{L}}_{\lambda\mu} - (\varkappa \leftrightarrow \lambda) - (\mu \leftrightarrow \nu) \big\} = -\mathrm{i}\hbar \big\{ \eta_{\varkappa\mu}\, \tilde{\mathcal{L}}_{\lambda\nu} - (\varkappa \leftrightarrow \lambda) - (\mu \leftrightarrow \nu) \big\}, \end{aligned}$$

where $k_0 := \sqrt{m^2c^2 + \boldsymbol{k}^2}$ in the integrands, the terms containing derivatives with respect to k^ν were integrated by parts and the antisymmetries relative to $\varkappa$ and λ and μ and ν were taken into account. The explicit form of the result obtained is:

$$[\tilde{\mathcal{L}}_{\varkappa\lambda},\, \tilde{\mathcal{L}}_{\mu\nu}]_{\_} = -\mathrm{i}\hbar \big\{ \eta_{\varkappa\mu}\, \tilde{\mathcal{L}}_{\lambda\nu} - \eta_{\lambda\mu}\, \tilde{\mathcal{L}}_{\varkappa\nu} - \eta_{\varkappa\nu}\, \tilde{\mathcal{L}}_{\lambda\mu} + \eta_{\lambda\nu}\, \tilde{\mathcal{L}}_{\varkappa\mu} \big\}, \tag{16.12}$$

which in momentum picture reads

$$[\mathcal{L}_{\varkappa\lambda},\, \mathcal{L}_{\mu\nu}]_{\_} = -\mathrm{i}\hbar \big\{ \eta_{\varkappa\mu}\, \mathcal{L}_{\lambda\nu} - \eta_{\lambda\mu}\, \mathcal{L}_{\varkappa\nu} - \eta_{\varkappa\nu}\, \mathcal{L}_{\lambda\mu} + \eta_{\lambda\nu}\, \mathcal{L}_{\varkappa\mu} \big\}. \tag{16.13}$$

It should be noted the minus sign in the multiplier $-\mathrm{i}\hbar$ in the r.h.s. of (16.12) relative to a similar one in the last equation in [12, eqs. (3.51)] for a neutral scalar field.

The equations (16.6)–(16.13) are valid also before the normal ordering is performed, i.e. if the orbital angular momentum, momentum and charge operators are replaced with any one of the corresponding operators in (14.15), (13.3) and (14.2), respectively.

We would like to emphasize, equation (16.12) (or (16.13)) is a consequence of (16.5) and (16.11), which is equivalent to (16.7), and this conclusion is independent of the validity of the commutation relations (15.21) and/or the normal ordering (before normal ordering equation (16.12) follows from (16.11) and (14.5)). Similar result concerns equations (16.8) and (16.10).

So, we see that, at the very end of building of the theory of free scalar fields, all of the three Lagrangians (10.7)–(10.9) lead to one and the same final theory.[46] This is a remarkable fact which is far from evident at the beginning and all intermediate stages of the theory.

Acting with the operators (16.2) and (16.3) on the vacuum $\mathcal{X}_0$, we get

$$\mathcal{P}_\mu(\mathcal{X}_0) = 0 \quad \mathcal{Q}(\mathcal{X}_0) = 0 \quad \mathcal{L}_{\mu\nu}(\mathcal{X}_0) = 0 \tag{16.14}$$

which agrees with definition 16.1 and takes off the problem with the senseless expressions for the 4-momentum, charge and orbital angular momentum of the vacuum before redefining the dynamical variables via normal ordering.

As a result of the above uniqueness of the momentum operator after normal ordering, the *three* systems of field equations (13.11)–(13.13), together with the conditions (13.14), transform after normal ordering into the next *unique* system of equations:[47]

$$\begin{aligned}[][\varphi_0^{\pm}(\boldsymbol{k}), \varphi_0^{\dagger +}(\boldsymbol{q}) \circ \varphi_0^{-}(\boldsymbol{q}) + \varphi_0^{+}(\boldsymbol{q}) \circ \varphi_0^{\dagger -}(\boldsymbol{q})]_{\_} \\ \pm (1 + \tau(\varphi_0))\varphi_0^{\pm}(\boldsymbol{k})\delta^3(\boldsymbol{q} - \boldsymbol{k}) = f^{\pm}(\boldsymbol{k}, \boldsymbol{q})\end{aligned} \tag{16.15a}$$

$$\begin{aligned}[][\varphi_0^{\dagger\pm}(\boldsymbol{k}), \varphi_0^{\dagger +}(\boldsymbol{q}) \circ \varphi_0^{-}(\boldsymbol{q}) + \varphi_0^{+}(\boldsymbol{q}) \circ \varphi_0^{\dagger -}(\boldsymbol{q})]_{\_} \\ \pm (1 + \tau(\varphi_0))\varphi_0^{\dagger\pm}(\boldsymbol{k})\delta^3(\boldsymbol{q} - \boldsymbol{k}) = f^{\dagger\pm}(\boldsymbol{k}, \boldsymbol{q})\end{aligned} \tag{16.15b}$$

$$\int q_\mu|_{q_0=\sqrt{m^2c^2+\boldsymbol{q}^2}} f^{\pm}(\boldsymbol{k}, \boldsymbol{q})\,\mathrm{d}^3\boldsymbol{q} = \int q_\mu|_{q_0=\sqrt{m^2c^2+\boldsymbol{q}^2}} f^{\dagger\pm}(\boldsymbol{k}, \boldsymbol{q})\,\mathrm{d}^3\boldsymbol{q} = 0. \tag{16.15c}$$

Applying (7.4) with $\varepsilon = -1$, one can verify that (16.15) are identically valid due to the commutation relations (15.21). In this sense, we can say that the commutation relations (15.21) play a role of field equations with respect to the creation and annihilation operators (under the hypotheses made in their derivation).

17 State vectors

A state vector of a free arbitrary scalar field is, of course, given via the general formula (9.1) in which, now, the momentum operator $\mathcal{P}_\mu$ is given by (16.2). This means that the evolution

[46] Recall (see Sect. 15), the Lagrangians (10.7) and (10.8) require an additional hypothesis for the establishment of the commutation relations (15.21) and, in this sense the arising from them theory is not equivalent to the one build from the Lagrangian (10.9).

[47] The normal ordering must be applied only to the anticommutators in (13.11)–(13.13) as these terms originate from the corresponding momentum operators (13.3) before normal ordering.

operator $\mathcal{U}(x, x_0)$ is

$$\mathcal{U}(x, x_0) = \exp\Big\{ \frac{1}{\mathrm{i}\hbar} \frac{x^\mu - x_0^\mu}{1 + \tau(\varphi_0)} \int k_\mu|_{k_0 = \sqrt{m^2c^2 + \boldsymbol{k}^2}} \{ \varphi_0^{\dagger\,+}(\boldsymbol{k}) \circ \varphi_0^-(\boldsymbol{k}) + \varphi_0^+(\boldsymbol{k}) \circ \varphi_0^{\dagger\,-}(\boldsymbol{k}) \} \,\mathrm{d}^3\boldsymbol{k} \Big\} . \tag{17.1}$$

A state vector of a state with fixed 4-momentum is, of course, described by (9.4).

Similarly to the neutral field case, the amplitude, describing a transition from an initial state $\mathcal{X}_i(x_i)$ to final state $\mathcal{X}_f(x_f)$, is (9.7) and admits the representation (9.8) through the 'S-matrix' $\mathcal{U}(x_i, x_f)$. The expansion of the exponent in (17.1) into a power series results in the following series for $\mathcal{U}(x_i, x_f)$ (cf. (9.9) and (9.10))

$$\mathcal{U}(x_i, x_f) = \mathsf{id}_{\mathcal{F}} + \sum_{n=1}^{\infty} \mathcal{U}^{(n)}(x_i, x_f) \tag{17.2}$$

$$\begin{aligned} \mathcal{U}^{(n)}(x_i, x_f) := {} & \frac{1}{n!} \frac{1}{\big(\mathrm{i}\hbar(1 + \tau(\varphi_0))\big)^n} (x_i^{\mu_1} - x_f^{\mu_1}) \dots (x_i^{\mu_n} - x_f^{\mu_n}) \\ \times \int & \mathrm{d}^3\boldsymbol{k}^{(1)} \dots \mathrm{d}^3\boldsymbol{k}^{(n)} k_{\mu_1}^{(1)} \cdots k_{\mu_n}^{(n)} \{ \varphi_0^{\dagger\,+}(\boldsymbol{k}^{(1)}) \circ \varphi_0^-(\boldsymbol{k}^{(1)}) + \varphi_0^+(\boldsymbol{k}^{(1)}) \circ \varphi_0^{\dagger\,-}(\boldsymbol{k}^{(1)}) \} \\ & \circ \dots \circ \{ \varphi_0^{\dagger\,+}(\boldsymbol{k}^{(n)}) \circ \varphi_0^-(\boldsymbol{k}^{(n)}) + \varphi_0^+(\boldsymbol{k}^{(n)}) \circ \varphi_0^{\dagger\,-}(\boldsymbol{k}^{(n)}) \} \end{aligned} \tag{17.3}$$

where $k_0^{(a)} = \sqrt{m^2c^2 + (\boldsymbol{k}^{(a)})^2}$, $a = 1, \dots, n$.

According to (9.4) and the considerations in Sect. 12, a state vector of a state containing n' particles and n'' antiparticles, $n', n'' \ge 0$, such that the i'^{th} particle has 4-momentum $p'_{i'}$ and the i''^{th} antiparticle has 4-momentum $p''_{i''}$, where $i' = 0, 1, \dots, n'$ and $i'' = 0, 1, \dots, n''$, is given by the equality

$$\begin{aligned} \mathcal{X}(x; p'_1; \dots; p'_{n'}; p''_1; \dots; p''_{n''}) & \\ = \frac{1}{\sqrt{n'!n''!}} \exp\Big\{ & \frac{1}{\mathrm{i}\hbar}(x^\mu - x_0^\mu) \sum_{i'=1}^{n'} (p'_{i'})_\mu + \frac{1}{\mathrm{i}\hbar}(x^\mu - x_0^\mu) \sum_{i''=1}^{n''} (p''_{i''})_\mu \Big\} \\ & \times \big(\varphi_0^+(\boldsymbol{p}'_1) \circ \dots \circ \varphi_0^+(\boldsymbol{p}'_{n'}) \circ \varphi_0^{\dagger\,+}(\boldsymbol{p}''_1) \circ \dots \circ \varphi_0^{\dagger\,+}(\boldsymbol{p}''_{n''}) \big)(\mathcal{X}_0), \end{aligned} \tag{17.4}$$

where, in view of the commutation relations (15.21), the order of the creation operators is inessential. If $n' = 0$ (resp. $n'' = 0$), the particle (resp. antiparticle) creation operators and the first (resp. second) sum in the exponent should be absent. In particular, the vacuum corresponds to (17.4) with $n' = n'' = 0$. The state vector (17.4) is an eigenvector of the momentum operator (16.2) with eigenvalue (4-momentum) $\sum_{i'=1}^{n'} p'_{i'} + \sum_{i''=1}^{n''} p''_{i''}$ and is also an eigenvector of the charge operator (16.3) with eigenvalue $(-q)(n' - n'')$.[48]

[48] Recall (see Sect. 12), the operator $\varphi_0^+(\boldsymbol{k})$ creates a particle with 4-momentum k_μ and charge $-q$, while $\varphi_0^{\dagger\,+}(\boldsymbol{k})$ creates a particle with 4-momentum k_μ and charge $+q$, where, in the both cases, $k_0 = \sqrt{m^2c^2 + \boldsymbol{k}^2}$.

The reader may verify, using (15.21) and (12.2), that the transition amplitude between two states of a charged field, like (17.4), is:

$$\begin{aligned}
&\langle\, \mathcal{X}(y; q'_1;\dots;q'_{n'};q''_1;\dots;q''_{n''})|\, \mathcal{X}(x; p'_1;\dots;p'_{m'};p''_1;\dots;p''_{m''})\rangle \\
&= \frac{1}{n'!n''!}\delta_{m'n'}\delta_{m''n''}\exp\Big\{\frac{1}{\mathrm{i}\hbar}(x^\mu-y^\mu)\sum_{i'=1}^{n'}(p'_{i'})_\mu+\frac{1}{\mathrm{i}\hbar}(x^\mu-y^\mu)\sum_{i''=1}^{n''}(p''_{i''})_\mu\Big\} \\
&\quad\times\sum_{(i'_1,\dots,i'_{n'})}\delta^3(\boldsymbol{p}'_{n'}-\boldsymbol{q}'_{i'_1})\delta^3(\boldsymbol{p}'_{n'-1}-\boldsymbol{q}'_{i'_2})\dots\delta^3(\boldsymbol{p}'_1-\boldsymbol{q}'_{i'_{n'}}) \\
&\quad\times\sum_{(i''_1,\dots,i''_{n''})}\delta^3(\boldsymbol{p}''_{n''}-\boldsymbol{q}''_{i''_1})\delta^3(\boldsymbol{p}''_{n''-1}-\boldsymbol{q}''_{i''_2})\dots\delta^3(\boldsymbol{p}''_1-\boldsymbol{q}''_{i''_{n''}}) \qquad (17.5)
\end{aligned}$$

where the summations are over all permutations $(i'_1,\dots,i'_{n'})$ of $(1,\dots,n')$ and $(i''_1,\dots,i''_{n''})$ of $(1,\dots,n'')$. The conclusions from this formula are similar to the ones from (9.16) in Sect. 9. For instance, the only non-forbidden transition from an n'-particle + n''-antiparticle state is into n'-particle + n''-antiparticle state; the both states may differ only in the spacetime positions of the (anti)particles in them. This result is quite natural as we are dealing with free particles/fields.

In particular, if $\mathcal{X}_n$ denotes any state containing n particles and/or antiparticles, $n = 0,1,\dots$, then (17.5) says that

$$\langle\, \mathcal{X}_n|\, \mathcal{X}_0\rangle = \delta_{n0}, \tag{17.6}$$

which expresses the stability of the vacuum.

We shall end the present section with a simple example. Consider the one (anti)particle states $\varphi_0^+(\boldsymbol{p})(\mathcal{X}_0)$ and $\varphi_0^{\dagger+}(\boldsymbol{p})(\mathcal{X}_0)$. Applying (16.2), (16.3), (16.4) and (15.21), we find ($p_0 := \sqrt{m^2c^2+\boldsymbol{p}^2}$):[49]

$$\begin{aligned}
&\mathcal{P}_\mu(\varphi_0^+(\boldsymbol{p})(\mathcal{X}_0)) = p_\mu\varphi_0^+(\boldsymbol{p})(\mathcal{X}_0) \qquad \mathcal{Q}(\varphi_0^+(\boldsymbol{p})(\mathcal{X}_0)) = -q\varphi_0^+(\boldsymbol{p})(\mathcal{X}_0) \\
&\mathcal{P}_\mu(\varphi_0^{\dagger+}(\boldsymbol{p})(\mathcal{X}_0)) = p_\mu\varphi_0^{\dagger+}(\boldsymbol{p})(\mathcal{X}_0) \quad \mathcal{Q}(\varphi_0^{\dagger+}(\boldsymbol{p})(\mathcal{X}_0)) = +q\varphi_0^{\dagger+}(\boldsymbol{p})(\mathcal{X}_0)
\end{aligned} \tag{17.7}$$

$$\begin{aligned}
\mathcal{L}_{\mu\nu}(x)(\varphi_0^+(\boldsymbol{p})(\mathcal{X}_0)) &= \Big\{(x_\mu p_\nu - x_\nu p_\mu) - \mathrm{i}\hbar\Big(p_\mu\frac{\partial}{\partial p_\nu} - p_\nu\frac{\partial}{\partial p_\mu}\Big)\Big\}(\varphi_0^+(\boldsymbol{p})(\mathcal{X}_0)) \\
\mathcal{L}_{\mu\nu}(x)(\varphi_0^{\dagger+}(\boldsymbol{p})(\mathcal{X}_0)) &= \Big\{(x_\mu p_\nu - x_\nu p_\mu) - \mathrm{i}\hbar\Big(p_\mu\frac{\partial}{\partial p_\nu} - p_\nu\frac{\partial}{\partial p_\mu}\Big)\Big\}(\varphi_0^{\dagger+}(\boldsymbol{p})(\mathcal{X}_0)).
\end{aligned} \tag{17.8}$$

These results agree completely with the interpretation of $\varphi_0^+(\boldsymbol{k})$ and $\varphi_0^{\dagger+}(\boldsymbol{k})$ as operators creating one (anti)particle states.

[49] In Heisenberg picture and in terms of the Heisenberg creation/annihilation operators, in equations (17.8) the terms proportional to $(x_\mu p_\nu - x_\nu p_\mu)$ are absent and tildes over all operators should be added. Equations (17.7) remain unchanged in Heisenberg picture (in terms of the corresponding Heisenberg operators).

18 Conclusion

The main results of this paper, dealing with a study of free Hermitian or non-Hermitian scalar fields, may be formulated as follows:

The creation and annihilation operators in momentum representation in momentum picture are introduced without an explicit appeal to the Fourier transform of the field operator(s). However, they are (up to constant phase factor and, possibly, normalization) identical with the known ones introduced in momentum representation in Heisenberg picture.

The quantization with commutators, not by anticommutators, is derived from the field equations (in momentum picture) without involving the spin-statistics theorem (or other additional condition), if one stars from a suitable Lagrangian.

The (system of) field equation(s) in terms of creation and annihilation operators is derived. It happens to be similar to a kind of paracommutation relations.[50]

An analysis of the derivation of the standard commutation relations is given. It is shown that, under some explicitly presented conditions, they are equivalent to the (system of) field equation(s) and are not additional to it conditions in the theory.

In forthcoming paper(s), we intend to investigate other free fields, like vector and spinor ones, in momentum picture.

References

[1] Bozhidar Z. Iliev. Pictures and equations of motion in Lagrangian quantum field theory. In Frank Columbus, editor, *Progress in Mathematical Physics*, pages ??–?? Nova Science Publishers, Inc., Suite, 2004. To appear. http://www.arXiv.org e-Print archive, E-print No. hep-th/0302002, February 2003.

[2] Bozhidar Z. Iliev. Momentum picture of motion in Lagrangian quantum field theory. http://www.arXiv.org e-Print archive, E-print No. hep-th/0311003, November 2003.

[3] N. N. Bogolyubov and D. V. Shirkov. *Introduction to the theory of quantized fields*. Nauka, Moscow, third edition, 1976. In Russian. English translation: Wiley, New York, 1980.

[4] J. D. Bjorken and S. D. Drell. *Relativistic quantum mechanics*, volume 1 and 2. McGraw-Hill Book Company, New York, 1964, 1965. Russian translation: Nauka, Moscow, 1978.

---

[50] More precisely, elsewhere we shall show how the parabose-commutation relations for free arbitrary scalar field can be derived from the Klein-Gordon equations in terms of creation and annihilation operators.

[5] Paul Roman. *Introduction to quantum field theory*. John Wiley&Sons, Inc., New York-London-Sydney-Toronto, 1969.

[6] Lewis H. Ryder. *Quantum field theory*. Cambridge Univ. Press, Cambridge, 1985. Russian translation: Mir, Moscow, 1987.

[7] A. I. Akhiezer and V. B. Berestetskii. *Quantum electrodynamics*. Nauka, Moscow, 1969. In Russian. English translation: Authorized English ed., rev. and enl. by the author, Translated from the 2d Russian ed. by G.M. Volkoff, New York, Interscience Publishers, 1965. Other English translations: New York, Consultants Bureau, 1957; London, Oldbourne Press, 1964, 1962.

[8] Pierre Ramond. *Field theory: a modern primer*, volume 51 of *Frontiers in physics*. Reading, MA Benjamin-Cummings, London-Amsterdam-Don Mills, Ontario-Sidney-Tokio, 1 edition, 1981. 2nd rev. print, Frontiers in physics vol. 74, Adison Wesley Publ. Co., Redwood city, CA, 1989; Russian translation from the first ed.: Moscow, Mir 1984.

[9] N. N. Bogolubov, A. A. Logunov, and I. T. Todorov. *Introduction to axiomatic quantum field theory*. W. A. Benjamin, Inc., London, 1975. Translation from Russian: Nauka, Moscow, 1969.

[10] N. N. Bogolubov, A. A. Logunov, A. I. Oksak, and I. T. Todorov. *General principles of quantum field theory*. Nauka, Moscow, 1987. In Russian. English translation: Kluwer Academic Publishers, Dordrecht, 1989.

[11] J. D. Bjorken and S. D. Drell. *Relativistic quantum fields*, volume 2. McGraw-Hill Book Company, New York, 1965. Russian translation: Nauka, Moscow, 1978.

[12] C. Itzykson and J.-B. Zuber. *Quantum field theory*. McGraw-Hill Book Company, New York, 1980. Russian translation (in two volumes): Mir, Moscow, 1984.

[13] Silvan S. Schweber. *An introduction to relativistic quantum field theory*. Row, Peterson and Co., Evanston, Ill., Elmsford, N.Y., 1961. Russian translation: IL (Foreign Literature Pub.), Moscow, 1963.

[14] Bozhidar Z. Iliev. On operator differentiation in the action principle in quantum field theory. In Stancho Dimiev and Kouei Sekigava, editors, *Proceedings of the 6th International Workshop on Complex Structures and Vector Fields, 3–6 September 2002, St. Knstantin resort (near Varna), Bulgaria*, "Trends in Complex Analysis, Differential Geometry and Mathematical Physics", pages 76–107. World Scientific, New Jersey-London-Singapore-Hong Kong, 2003.
http://www.arXiv.org e-Print archive, E-print No. hep-th/0204003, April 2002.

[15] A. M. L. Messiah. *Quantum mechanics*, volume I and II. Interscience, New York, 1958. Russian translation: Nauka, Moscow, 1978 (vol. I) and 1979 (vol. II).

[16] P. A. M. Dirac. *The principles of quantum mechanics*. Oxford at the Clarendon Press, Oxford, fourth edition, 1958. Russian translation in: P. Dirac, Principles of quantum mechanics, Moscow, Nauka, 1979.

[17] E. Prugovečki. *Quantum mechanics in Hilbert space*, volume 92 of *Pure and applied mathematics*. Academic Press, New York-London, second edition, 1981.

[18] Bozhidar Z. Iliev. On momentum operator in quantum field theory. http://www.arXiv.org e-Print archive, E-print No. hep-th/0206008, June 2002, June 2002.

[19] H. S. Green. A generalized method of field quantization. *Phys. Rev.*, 90(2):270–273, 1953.

[20] D. V. Volkov. On quantization of half-integer spin fields. *Zh. Eksperim. i Teor. Fiz. (Journal of experimental and theoretical physics)*, 36(5):1560–1566, 1959. In Russian. English translation: Soviet Phys.–JETP, vol. 9, p. 1107, 1959.

[21] D. V. Volkov. S-matrix in the generalized quantization method. *Zh. Eksperim. i Teor. Fiz. (Journal of experimental and theoretical physics)*, 38(2):518–523, 1960. In Russian. English translation: Soviet Phys.–JETP, vol. 11, p. 375, 1960.

[22] O. W. Greenberg and A. M. I. Messiah. Symmetrization postulate and its experimental foundation. *Phys. Rev.*, 136B(1B):248–267, 1964.

[23] O. W. Greenberg and A. M. I. Messiah. Selection rules for parafields and the absence of para particles in nature. *Phys. Rev.*, 138B(5B):1155–1167, 1965.

[24] R. F. Streater and A. S. Wightman. *PCT, spin and statistics and all that*. W. A. Benjamin, Inc., New York-Amsterdam, 1964. Russian translation: Nauka, Moscow, 1966.

[25] Res Jost. *The general theory of quantized fields*. American Mathematical Society, Rhode Island, 1965. Russian translation: Mir, Moscow, 1967.

[26] A. B. Govorkov. Parastatistics and internal symmetries. In N. N. Bogolyubov, editor, *Physics of elementary particles and atomic nuclei*, volume 14, No. 5, of *Particles and nuclei*, pages 1229–1272. Energoatomizdat, Moscow, 1983. In Russian.

[27] G. C. Wick. Calculation of scattering matrix. *Physical Review*, 80(2):268, 1950. Russian translation in [30, pp. 245–253].

[28] W. Pauli and V. Weisskopf. Über die Quantizierung der skalaren relativistischen Wellengleichung (On the quantization of the scalar relativistic wave equation). *Helv. Phys. Acta*, 7:709–731, 1934. In German. Russian translation in [31, pp. 194–214].

[29] J. Schwinger. The theory of quantized fields. I. *Physical Review*, 82(6):914, 1951. Russian translation in [30, pp. 115–137].

[30] *Novejshee razvitie kvantovoj electrodinamiki. Sbornik statej (The newest development of quantum electrodynamics. Collection of papers),* editor Ivanenko D. D., Moscow, 1954. IL (Foreign Literature Pub.). In Russian.

[31] Wolfgang Pauli. *Works on quantum theory. Articles 1928–1958*. Nauka Publ., Moscow, 1977. In Russian.

In: Quantum Field Theory: New Research
Editor: O. Kovras, pp. 67-101
ISBN 1-59454-509-X

Chapter 2

FIELD THEORY LAGRANGIAN APPROACH TO NUCLEAR STRUCTURE

***Tapas Sil*[1]*, S. K. Patra*[2]*, B. K. Sharma*[2]*, M. Centelles*[1]*, and X. Viñas*[1]**
[1] Departament d'Estructura i Constituents de la Mat eria,
Facultat de F´sica, Universitat de Barcelona,
Diagonal *647*, *08028* Barcelona, Spain
[2] Institute of Physics, Sachivalaya Marg,
Bhubaneswar *751 005*, India.

Abstract

We show that in the search of a unified mean field description of finite nuclei and of nuclear and neutron matter even at high densities, the relativistic nuclear model derived from effective field theory and density functional theory methods constitutes a competitive framework. The model predicts a soft equation of state, owing to the additional meson interaction terms, consistently with the results of the microscopic Dirac-Brueckner-Hartree-Fock theory and recent experimental observations from heavy ion collisions. In finite systems, after inclusion of the pairing correlations, the model is able to describe both stable and exotic nuclei. We address two examples at the limits of the nuclear landscape. On the one hand, we analyze the giant halo effect and the isoscalar giant monopole resonance in very neutron-rich Zr isotopes. On the other hand, we discuss the structure of superheavy nuclei with double shell closures.

Keywords: Superheavy elements, binding energies, shell structure, relativistic mean field, effective field theory

PACS number(s): 21.60.-n, 21.10.Dr, 21.30.Fe, 27.90.+b

1 Introduction

The mean field treatment of the relativistic field theory of hadrons known as quantum hadrodynamics (QHD) has been found to be a very successful framework for describing diverse bulk and single-particle properties of nuclear matter and finite nuclei [1, 2, 3]. The QHD theory is based on a Lagrangian density which uses the nucleon (as Dirac particle) and the isoscalar-scalar σ, the isoscalar-vector ω, isovector-vector ρ and the pseudo-scalar π mesons as the relevant degrees of freedom in order to understand many aspects of the nuclear many-body problem. In the relativistic mean field (RMF) approach the nucleus is described in terms of Dirac quasiparticles moving in classical meson fields. Due to the definite ground-state spin and parity of the nuclear system, the contribution of the π meson vanishes at the mean field level. The mean field approximation of QHD automatically generates important ingredients of the nuclear problem like the spin-orbit force, or the finite range and density dependence of the nuclear interaction.

The original linear $\sigma - \omega$ version of QHD [1, 4] gives a very stiff equation of state (EOS) with a nuclear matter incompressibility modulus $K_\infty \sim 600$ MeV. Also, the model does not yield the average properties of the ground-state of finite nuclei in good enough agreement with the experimental values. To remove these deficiencies, the linear $\sigma - \omega$ model was complemented with cubic and quartic non-linearities of the σ meson [5]. Adjusting some coupling constants and meson masses from the properties of a small number of finite nuclei, the non-linear $\sigma - \omega$ model (called hereafter standard RMF model) produces an excellent description of binding energies, radii, spectra, and excitation properties of spherical and deformed nuclei along the whole periodic table [2]. The RMF theory was proposed to be renormalizable, and thus the scalar self-interactions were limited to a quartic polynomial and scalar-vector or vector-vector self-interactions were not allowed. However, the renormalizability of the Lagrangian gets compromised by the use of coupling constants that are not assigned with their bare experimental values but with effective values to have proper results for finite nuclei.

More recently, inspired by the modern concepts of effective field theory (EFT) and of density functional theory (DFT) for hadrons, Furnstahl, Serot and Tang [6, 7] abandoned renormalizability and proposed a chiral effective Lagrangian to derive an energy functional for the nuclear many-body problem. The mean field treatment of the new formulation, now onwards known as E-RMF theory, extends the standard RMF theory by allowing more general couplings [3, 7]. An EFT assumes that there exist natural scales to a given problem and that the only degree of freedom relevant for its description are those which can resolve the dynamics at such scale. The unknown dynamics, which corresponds to heavier degrees of freedom is integrated and appears as coupling constants of the theory, which are fitted to the known experimental data. The Lagrangian of Furnstahl, Serot and Tang has to be understood as an EFT of low-energy QCD. Hence, it contains the lowest-lying hadronic degree of freedom and incorporates all the infinite couplings in general non-renormalizable, consistent with the underlying symmetry of QCD. Therefore, it is mandatory to develop a suitable scheme of expansion and truncation. To do that, one assign first an index ν to each term of the Lagrangian. This index is provided by some organizing principle, as for instance, the naive dimensional analysis [8]. Next the Lagrangian is organized in powers of ν and truncated. For the truncation to be consistent, the coupling constants have to exhibit naturalness (i.e. they are of the order of unity when written in an appropriate dimensionless form) and none of them can be arbitrarily dropped out to given order without any additional symmetry arguments. In the nuclear structure problem, the basic expansion parameters are the ratios of the scalar and vector fields and of the Fermi momentum k_F to the nucleon mass M, as these ratios are small in normal situations (typically $k_F/M = 1/3$ at saturation density).

From the truncated EFT Lagrangian, the energy functional can be constructed in terms of the nuclear densities and auxiliary meson fields. Thus RMF theory can be regarded as a covariant formulation of DFT in the sense of Kohn and Sham [9]. From this energy functional one can define a set of Kohn-Sham equations which minimize the energy with respect to densities and fields. In this way all the source terms in the Kohn-Sham equations are local. As far as the free parameters of the RMF have been fitted to experimental data, the corresponding mean field energy functional is a good approximation to the exact one, unknown energy functional of the ground state densities of the nucleonic system which includes all higher order correlations, through the powers of the auxiliary classical mean fields. This combination of EFT and DFT provides an approach for dealing with the nuclear problem through Kohn-Sham (Hartree) equations with the advantage that further contributions, at the mean field level or beyond, can be incorporated in a systematic and controlled manner.

References [7, 10, 11] have shown that it suffices to go to fourth order in the expansion parameter ν. At this level one recovers the standard non-linear $\sigma - \omega$ plus some additional non-linear scalar-vector and vector-vector meson interactions besides tensor couplings. The free parameters of the energy functional have been optimized by fitting to the ground-state observables of a few doubly-magic nuclei, as is typical in the RMF strategy. The corresponding fits, that were named G1 and G2 in Ref. [7], display naturalness and the results are not dominated by the last terms retained. This confirms the usefulness of the EFT concepts and validates the truncation of the effective Lagrangian at the first lower orders. The ideas of EFT have allowed [10] to elucidate the empirical success of the previous RMF models, like the original $\sigma - \omega$ model of Walecka [4] and its extensions including cubic and quartic scalar self-interactions [5]. However, these conventional RMF models truncate the Lagrangian at the same level without further physical rationale or symmetry arguments.

The impact of each one of the new couplings introduced in the E-RMF model on the properties of nuclear matter and of the nuclear surface has been analyzed in Ref. [12]. That the model derived from EFT can provide a unified framework to accommodate the successful phenomenology of the traditional RMF models for finite nuclei and to extend them reliably for applications in regions of higher densities than around saturation was shown in Refs. [13, 14]. In fact, nowadays heavy ion collisions can compress nuclear matter in the laboratory to several times the saturation density value. These large densities are envisaged to be present within core-collapse supernovae and their remnant neutron stars. A common practice in nuclear phenomenology is to extrapolate the models adjusted to the experimental properties of nuclei at normal densities for predictions of such very dense systems. While all the models agree similarly for the normal stable nuclei, their extrapolations can differ significantly. It is therefore meaningful to compare the scenarios for dense matter predicted by the RMF and E-RMF models. Microscopic Dirac-Brueckner-Hartree-Fock calculations [15, 16] and recent experimental data [17, 18] suggest that the nuclear equation of state (EOS) at high densities is rather soft. We will see that the E-RMF energy functional allows one to explain the situation.

During the last decades much effort has been devoted to measure masses of nuclei far from stability. The planned radioactive ion beam facilities bring renewed and well-founded expectations to the field. The available new experimental data turn out to be a demanding benchmark for the predictions of currently existing relativistic and non-relativistic nuclear force parameters. In Ref. [19] we verified the ability of the E-RMF model for describing the ground-state properties of different isotopic and isotonic chains from the valley of β stability up to the drip lines. The residual pairing interaction was treated in a modified BCS approach which takes into account quasibound levels owing to their centrifugal barrier. Also, the convergence of the E-RMF approach was studied for some specific doubly-magic nuclei far from stability in Ref. [20] and remarkable agreement with experiment was found. In the mass region of superheavy nuclei the E-RMF parametrizations have been applied for investigating the next possible shell closures beyond $Z = 82$ and $N = 126$, through the analysis of several indicators such as two-nucleon separation energies, two-nucleon shell gaps, average pairing gaps, and the shell correction energy [21]. Other applications of the model based on EFT include the description of asymmetric nuclear matter at finite temperature [22], calculations of the Landau parameters [23], investigations of the nuclear spin-orbit force [24], or studies of pion-nucleus scattering [25].

The rest of the paper is organized as follows. In the second section we summarize the E-RMF model based on EFT. The third section is devoted to the study of the infinite nuclear and neutron matter in the E-RMF model, paying special attention to the possible extrapolations to dense systems by comparing with microscopic Dirac-Brueckner-Hartree-Fock calculations [15, 16]. The fourth section exemplifies the ability of the E-RMF model for describing exotic nuclei far from the $\beta-$stability line in the case of very neutron-rich Zr isotopes. In the fifth section we analyze the application of the E-RMF model to superheavy elements. Often, we will compare the predictions obtained from the parametrizations based on EFT with the results from the standard non-linear $\sigma - \omega$ NL3 parameter set [26], taken as a reference. NL3 is regarded as one of the best representatives of the RMF model with only scalar self-interactions because of its proven performance in describing many nuclear phenomena. A summary and the conclusions are given in the last section.

2 Formalism

The E-RMF model used here has been developed in Ref. [7], where the reader can find the details of the construction of the effective Lagrangian with a non-linear realization of chiral symmetry. Further insight into the model and the underlying concepts can be gained from Refs. [3, 6, 10, 11]. To solve the equations of motion of the theory one applies the relativistic mean field or Hartree approximation. The meson fields are replaced with their ground-state expectation values, and thus they are treated as classical fields. In such an approach the pseudoscalar field of the pions does not contribute explicitly because it has a vanishing expectation value. The quantum structure is introduced by expanding the nucleon field on a single-particle basis. For systems with time reversal symmetry, as there can be no currents, only the time-like component of the vector meson and photon fields contributes. Charge conservation implies that only the third component in isospin space of the isovector rho-meson field does not vanish. As a final product, one obtains the following energy density functional of the EFT relativistic model for applications to finite nuclei in mean field approach [3, 7]:

$$
\begin{aligned}
\mathcal{E}(\mathbf{r}) \;=\; & \sum_{\alpha} \varphi_{\alpha}^{\dagger} \Bigg\{ -i\boldsymbol{\alpha}\cdot\boldsymbol{\nabla} + \beta(M-\Phi) + W + \frac{1}{2}\tau_3 R + \frac{1+\tau_3}{2} A \\
& - \frac{i}{2M}\beta\boldsymbol{\alpha}\cdot\left(f_v \boldsymbol{\nabla} W + \frac{1}{2} f_\rho \tau_3 \boldsymbol{\nabla} R + \lambda \boldsymbol{\nabla} A \right) + \frac{1}{2M^2}\left(\beta_s + \beta_v \tau_3\right)\Delta A \Bigg\} \varphi_{\alpha} \\
& + \left(\frac{1}{2} + \frac{\kappa_3}{3!}\frac{\Phi}{M} + \frac{\kappa_4}{4!}\frac{\Phi^2}{M^2} \right) \frac{m_s^2}{g_s^2}\Phi^2 - \frac{\zeta_0}{4!}\frac{1}{g_v^2} W^4 \\
& + \frac{1}{2g_s^2}\left(1 + \alpha_1 \frac{\Phi}{M}\right)(\boldsymbol{\nabla}\Phi)^2 - \frac{1}{2g_v^2}\left(1 + \alpha_2 \frac{\Phi}{M}\right)(\boldsymbol{\nabla} W)^2 \\
& - \frac{1}{2}\left(1 + \eta_1 \frac{\Phi}{M} + \frac{\eta_2}{2}\frac{\Phi^2}{M^2}\right)\frac{{m_v}^2}{{g_v}^2} W^2 - \frac{1}{2g_\rho^2}(\boldsymbol{\nabla} R)^2 - \frac{1}{2}\left(1 + \eta_\rho \frac{\Phi}{M}\right)\frac{m_\rho^2}{g_\rho^2} R^2
\end{aligned}
$$

$$-\frac{1}{2e^2}(\nabla A)^2 + \frac{1}{3g_\gamma g_v} A\Delta W + \frac{1}{g_\gamma g_\rho} A\Delta R. \tag{1}$$

In the present form the coupling constants should be of order unity according to the naturalness assumption. In Eq. (1) τ_3 is the third component of the isospin operator. The index α runs over all occupied nucleon states $\varphi_\alpha(\mathbf{r})$ of the positive energy spectrum. The meson fields are $\Phi \equiv g_s\phi_0(\mathbf{r})$ (isoscalar scalar σ meson), $W \equiv g_v V_0(\mathbf{r})$ (isoscalar vector ω meson), and $R \equiv g_\rho b_0(\mathbf{r})$ (isovector vector ρ meson), and the photon field is $A \equiv eA_0(\mathbf{r})$.

From the functional (1) one derives the field equations obeyed by the nucleonic and the mesonic fields. The variation of Eq. (1) with respect to $\varphi_\alpha^\dagger$ gives the Dirac equation fulfilled by the nucleons, and the variations with respect to the various meson fields result in the Klein-Gordon equations obeyed by the mesons. The expressions for the densities and the field equations of the E-RMF model can be found in previous works [3, 7, 13, 14, 20] and we shall not repeat them here. In practice we solve the Dirac equation in coordinate space by transforming it into a Schrödinger-like equation and iterate numerically the final set of coupled equations till consistency is reached.

Let us now describe the more relevant implications of the new terms of the energy density (1). With the inclusion of the quartic vector self-interaction ζ_0 and the terms η_1 and η_2 one is able to obtain a desirable positive value of the coupling constant κ_4 of the quartic scalar self-interaction. This is so for realistic nuclear matter properties and at the same time keeping all the parameters within the bounds of naturalness. Furthermore, these bulk couplings ζ_0, η_1, and η_2 confer an extra density dependence to the scalar and vector self-energies [13, 14] which is consistent with the output of microscopic Dirac-Brueckner-Hartree-Fock calculations that start from the bare nucleon-nucleon interaction in free space. In the E-RMF model the bulk symmetry energy coefficient J depends on the coupling η_ρ in addition to the usual coupling g_ρ. The new coefficient η_ρ is useful to fit J and in turn to tune, relative to J, the stiffness of the nucleus against pulling neutrons apart from protons as the neutron excess is increased [12].

In the standard RMF model the only parameter not related with the saturation conditions is the mass of the scalar meson m_s. The additional couplings α_1 and α_2 in the E-RMF energy density are helpful to improve on the description of the nuclear surface properties (e.g., surface energy and surface thickness) without spoiling the bulk properties [12]. The quantities β_s, β_v, g_γ and $\lambda = \frac{1}{2}\lambda_p(1+\tau_3) + \frac{1}{2}\lambda_n(1-\tau_3)$ take care of effects related with the electromagnetic structure of the pion and the nucleon (the constants $g_\gamma^2/4\pi = 2.0$, $\lambda_p = 1.793$ and $\lambda_n = -1.913$ are given their experimental values) [7]. The tensor coupling f_v between the ω meson and the nucleon adds momentum and spin dependence to the interaction. It introduces a corrective term in the spin-orbit potential as compared with the expression in the standard RMF model [19, 24]. Due to the existence of a trade-off between the size of the ω tensor coupling and the size of the scalar field, it is possible to obtain parameter sets that provide excellent fits to nuclear masses, radii and spin-orbit splittings with a larger value of the equilibrium effective mass than in models that ignore such coupling.

In the applications to be presented below we shall employ the E-RMF parameter sets G1 and G2 of Ref. [7]. The masses of the nucleon and of the ω and ρ mesons are $M = 939$ MeV, $m_v = 782$ MeV, and $m_\rho = 770$ MeV, respectively. The parameters m_s, g_s, g_v, g_ρ, η_1, η_2, η_ρ, κ_3, κ_4, ζ_0, f_v, α_1, and α_2 of G1 and G2 were fitted by a least-squares optimization procedure to 29 observables (binding energies, charge form factors and spin-orbit splittings near the Fermi surface) of the nuclei ^{16}O, ^{40}Ca, ^{48}Ca, ^{88}Sr and ^{208}Pb, as described in Ref. [7]. The constants β_s, β_v and f_ρ were then chosen to reproduce the experimental charge radii of the nucleon. We report in Table 1 the values of the parameters and the saturation properties of the sets G1 and G2 as well as those of the NL3 parameters [26]. An interesting feature is that the set G2 has a positive κ_4 coupling, as opposed to G1 and to most of the successful RMF parametrizations such as NL3. Formally, a negative value of κ_4 is not acceptable because the energy spectrum then has no lower bound [27]. We note that the value of the effective mass at saturation M^*_∞/M in the EFT sets (~ 0.65) is larger than the usual value in the RMF parameter sets (~ 0.60), which is due to the presence of the tensor coupling f_v of the ω meson to the nucleon. Also, the nuclear matter incompressibility of the G1 and G2 sets ($K = 215$ MeV) is visibly smaller than that of the NL3 set ($K = 271$ MeV).

3 Nuclear and Neutron Matter

In an infinite medium of uniform nuclear matter all of the terms with gradients in the energy density $\mathcal{E}$ and in the field equations vanish. In this limit the nucleon density is given by

$$\rho = \frac{\gamma}{(2\pi)^3} \int_0^{k_F} d^3k = \frac{\gamma}{6\pi^2} k_F^3, \tag{2}$$

where k_F is the Fermi momentum, and the degeneracy factor γ is 4 for symmetric nuclear matter and 2 for pure neutron matter. The reader can find the E-RMF expression of $\mathcal{E}$ for asymmetric nuclear matter at finite temperature in Ref. [22].

The relevance of relativistic effects in the nuclear EOS was soon realized when the relativistic Dirac-Brueckner-Hartree-Fock (DBHF) calculations provided a clue for solving the Coester band problem [15]. The microscopic DBHF theory suggests a soft EOS at high densities [15, 28]. The recent experimental data [17, 18] also rule out the possibility of a strongly repulsive nuclear EOS. Typical representatives of the standard RMF theory like the NL3 parameter set cannot follow the trend of the DBHF results even at slightly high densities [13]. In contrast to the conventional RMF model, the E-RMF calculations at high density regimes yield results in accordance with the DBHF theory. It has to be noted that

Table 1: Parameters of the relativistic interactions used in this work, in dimensionless form, and their saturation properties in nuclear matter (energy per particle, density, incompressibility, effective mass, and symmetry energy coefficient).

	G1	G2	NL3
m_s/M	0.540	0.554	0.541
$g_s/4\pi$	0.785	0.835	0.813
$g_v/4\pi$	0.965	1.016	1.024
$g_\rho/4\pi$	0.698	0.755	0.712
κ_3	2.207	3.247	1.465
κ_4	−10.090	0.632	−5.668
ζ_0	3.525	2.642	0.0
η_1	0.071	0.650	0.0
η_2	−0.962	0.110	0.0
η_ρ	−0.272	0.390	0.0
α_1	1.855	1.723	0.0
α_2	1.788	−1.580	0.0
$f_v/4$	0.108	0.173	0.0
$f_\rho/4$	1.039	0.962	0.0
β_s	0.028	−0.093	0.0
β_v	−0.250	−0.460	0.0
a_v (MeV)	−16.14	−16.07	−16.24
ρ_∞ (fm^{-3})	0.153	0.153	0.148
K (MeV)	215.0	215.0	271.5
M^*_∞/M	0.634	0.664	0.595
J (MeV)	38.5	36.4	37.40

relativistic models which resort to density-dependent couplings are also consistent with the DBHF calculations [29].

In Figure 1 we present the density dependence of the nuclear matter scalar and vector self-energies calculated with G1, G2, NL1 [30] and NL3 versus the DBHF result. While G2 follows the nature of the DBHF self-energies quite remarkably, at densities only slightly above saturation the NL3 results soon depart from the DBHF behaviour. Thus, the success of the usual RMF model with only scalar self-interactions for describing the saturation point and the data for finite nuclei is not followed by a proper description of the microscopic DBHF calculations. This is caused importantly by a too restrictive treatment of the ω-meson term [13, 14, 28]. While in the standard RMF model the vector potential increases linearly with density and gets stronger, in DBHF it bends down with density. Moreover,

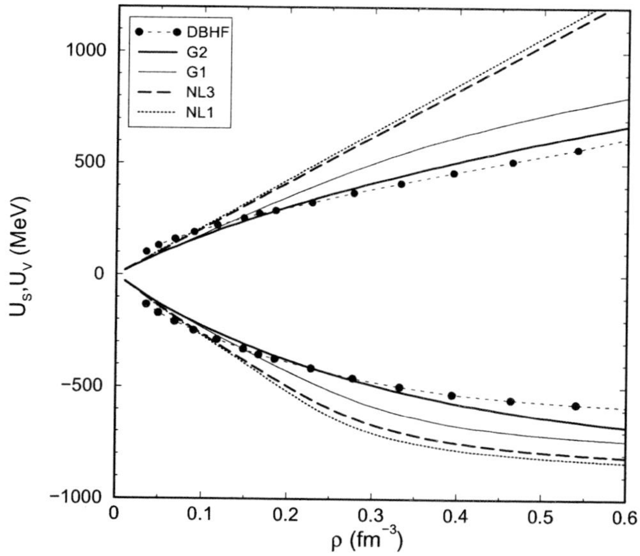

Figure 1: The density dependence of the scalar (U_s) and vector (U_v) self-energies using the relativistic parameter sets NL1, NL3, G1, and G2 is compared with the result of the DBHF theory [15].

the scalar potential overestimates the DBHF result at high density in order to compensate for the strong repulsion in the vector channel. The additional self- and cross-interactions ζ_0, η_1, and η_2 included in the E-RMF sets result in a richer density dependence of the mesonic mean fields which brings about the improvement in comparison with the DBHF calculations [13].

Figure 1 demonstrates the importance of meson self-interactions at higher densities and exposes the inadequacy of restricted models which neglect them for applications to such conditions. This argument is further supported by Figure 2 in which the variation of the binding energy per particle is plotted as a function of the density. We can see that the calculations of dense matter based on the RMF sets NL1 and NL3 deviate largely from DBHF, while the E-RMF calculations with G1 and, specially, G2 agree better with the density dependence of the EOS of the DBHF theory. One can realize that in spite of the fact that the incompressibility of NL1 is within the empirical boundaries ($K_\infty = 212$ MeV for NL1), the EOS of this set soon becomes stiff with increasing density and does not follow the DBHF trend. The E-RMF parameter sets give a soft EOS both around saturation and at high densities. A similar situation prevails in the EOS of neutron matter (Figure 3), though the agreement of G1 and G2 with the DBHF calculation is not as remarkable as in the case of symmetric matter. From the point of view of the comparison with DBHF, this would indicate that the present E-RMF model still needs an improvement in the treatment of the isovector sector, like consideration of additional cross couplings involving the rho-meson field or the introduction of an isovector scalar meson.

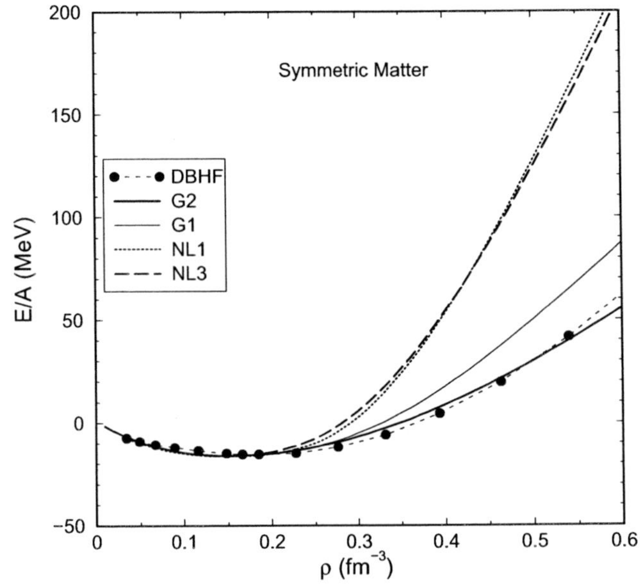

Figure 2: Energy per particle of symmetric nuclear matter for the same cases as in Figure 1.

The average densities of terrestrial nuclei are not very far from the values around the saturation point of the nuclear EOS, where the E-RMF sets produce similar results to NL3. Hence, one can expect that in finite nuclei the G1 and G2 interactions also will yield results on a par with the celebrated NL3 parametrization. That this is indeed the case is illustrated in the next section for the bulk properties of finite nuclei near and away from the β-stability valley.

4 Structure of Exotic Nuclei

Exotic nuclei far from the stability line have attracted much attention in the nuclear physics community from both the theoretical and the experimental sides. One expects to find very different properties from the normal nuclei as soon as one leaves the β-stability region and approaches the drip lines. Neutron-rich nuclei near the drip line and the occurrence of closed shells are very important in nuclear astrophysics because their properties strongly influence how stable neutron-rich nuclei are formed through the r-process. It is expected that in very neutron-rich nuclei the shell structure be strongly modified, with some of the traditional shell gaps disappearing and with new ones appearing.

Another interesting feature of some exotic nuclei is the appearance of a halo structure

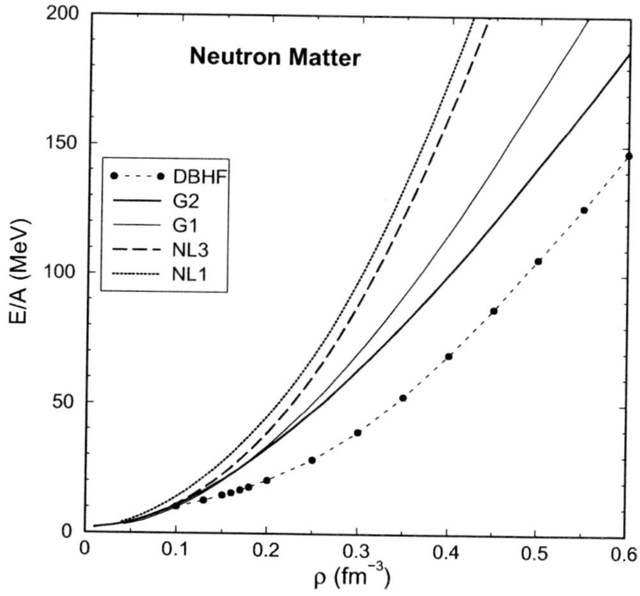

Figure 3: Energy per particle of neutron matter for the same cases as in Figure 1.

which was experimentally discovered in ^{11}Li [31] and which has also been observed in ^{11,14}Be and ^{17}B [32]. In some heavier neutron rich nuclei a sudden increase of the neutron radii close to the neutron drip line, the so-called giant halo, has been predicted by theoretical relativistic Hartree-Bogoliubov (RHB) calculations for Zr [33] and Ca [34] isotopes.

Neutron-rich nuclei near the drip line usually have a very small Fermi level and thus valence nucleons can easily scatter to the continuum states through the pairing correlations. Consequently, it is mandatory to properly take into account the coupling between the bound and the continuum for dealing with nuclei near the drip lines. In the relativistic domain, the microscopic HFB theory should, in principle, be used. Although the simple BCS theory fails in describing nuclei near the drip lines [35], it can still be used if some refinements to the standard BCS method are added, such as the resonant continuum coupling [36, 37] or if one takes into account quasibound levels owing to their centrifugal barrier [13]. These variations of the BCS method in general allow one to describe nuclei in the vicinity of the drip lines with very reasonable accuracy and avoiding the difficulties of a full RHB calculation.

In this section, we analyze the giant halo effect in Zr isotopes using the E-RMF approximation together with the pairing prescription of Ref. [13] which allows one to describe isotopic (isotonic) chains with magic Z (N) numbers from the proton to the neutron drip lines. As far as many properties of the exotic nuclei are modified when one approaches the drip line, we will discuss afterwards a different problem related with excited states, namely, the excitation energy of the isoscalar giant monopole resonance. From nonrelativistic RPA calculations [38] it is known that in nuclei near the drip line the monopole strength distribution is much affected by the presence of the low-energy threshold stemming from tiny bound nucleons. We study here whether the E-RMF parametrizations in constrained calculations are able to identify the main trends exhibited by the monopole RPA strength near the drip lines.

4.1 Treatment of Pairing

To deal with the pairing correlations we shall use here a simplified prescription which has proven to be in good agreement with RHB calculations [19]. For each kind of nucleon we assume a constant pairing matrix element G_q, which simulates the zero range of the pairing force, and include quasibound levels in the BCS calculation as done in Ref. [39]. These quasibound states mock up the influence of the continuum in the pairing calculation. We restrict the available space of α_q states to one harmonic oscillator shell above and below of the Fermi level, to avoid the unrealistic pairing of highly excited states and to confine the region of influence of the pairing potential to the vicinity of the Fermi level. As explained in Ref. [13], the solution of the pairing equations provides the chemical potential μ_q and the average pairing gap Δ_q for each kind of nucleon.

The quasibound levels of positive single-particle energy are retained by the centrifugal barrier (neutrons) or the centrifugal-plus-Coulomb barrier (protons). The wave functions of the considered quasibound levels are mainly localized in the classically allowed region and decrease exponentially outside it. As a consequence, the unphysical nucleon gas which surrounds the nucleus if continuum levels are included in the normal BCS approach is eliminated. We have shown in Ref. [19], by comparison with available RHB results, that the procedure is able to predict well the position of the proton and neutron drip lines or, e.g., the behavior of the neutron and charge radii far from stability. Also, the calculated pairing gaps turn out to be scattered around the empirical average $12/\sqrt{A}$ MeV.

4.2 Giant Halo in Zr Isotopes

As we have mentioned, giant halo nuclei are predicted by the RMF calculations near the neutron drip line for Zr [33] and Ca [34] isotopes. With the new radioactive isotope beam facilities it is expected to reach experimentally the lighter giant halo nuclei of Zr. Our calculation is performed with the E-RMF set G2 in spherical symmetry due to the fact that non-relativistic and relativistic calculations above ^{122}Zr predict the nuclei to be spherical [33]. The neutron and proton constant matrix elements are parametrized as $G_q = C_q/A$ $(q = p, n)$. In the calculations presented in this section we choose $C_n = 16$ MeV and $C_p = 14$ MeV because with these pairing constants we obtain pairing correlation energies (i.e., binding energies referred to the E-RMF values without pairing) from ^{122}Zr to ^{138}Zr similar to those displayed in Figure 5 of Ref. [37]. The latter calculation was performed in the BCS-plus-resonant (r-BCS) continuum approximation with the RMF parameter set NL-SH employing a zero-range pairing force, which simulated well the RHB calculations of Ref. [33] with NL-SH.

One of the signatures of the giant halo consists in a sudden increase of the neutron root mean square (rms) radius in the isotopic chain due to the scattering of Cooper pairs to the continuum containing low-lying resonances of small angular momentum, which in our approach are represented by the quasibound levels. Figure 4 displays the neutron and proton rms radii for the Zr isotopic chain from $A = 80$ to $A = 120$ obtained using our pairing approach with the G2 parameter set. One can clearly appreciate the kink at $A = 122$. The neutron radii obtained with G2 reproduce the overall trends of the results of Ref. [37] that were computed with the NL-SH set in the r-BCS approximation. It is to be noted that we use a pairing force with a constant matrix element instead of a zero-range pairing force as in Ref. [37]. Another difference with Ref. [37] is that our calculation does not take into account the resonance width, which may contribute to reduce the pairing gap near the drip line.

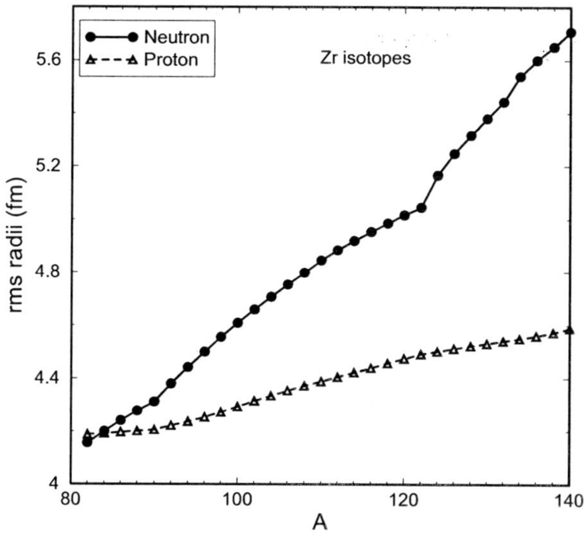

Figure 4: Neutron and proton rms radii calculated with the G2 set for the Zr isotopic chain as a function of the mass number.

The Zr isotopes with a neutron number beyond $N = 82$ develop a large shell gap and start progressively to fill up the weakly bound and quasibound (continuum) $2f_{7/2}$, $3p_{3/2}$, $3p_{1/2}$, $2f_{5/2}$, $1h_{9/2}$ and $1i_{13/2}$ single-particle neutron energy levels. This can be seen in Figure 5 where the neutron spectra of two representative nuclei, ^{128}Zr and ^{140}Zr, are displayed. In our model the $1i_{13/2}$ and $1h_{9/2}$ are quasibound levels and correspond to low-lying resonant levels [37]. The $3p_{1/2}$ and $2f_{5/2}$ levels lie in the continuum up to $A = 134$ and $A = 140$, respectively, while the $2f_{7/2}$ and $3p_{3/2}$ states are always bound levels from $A = 124$ on. It should be pointed out that the considered levels lying in the continuum are always quasibound levels for $N = 82$ owing to their relatively high centrifugal barrier ($l > 2$). In our calculation only the $3p_{1/2}$ orbit does not appear as a quasibound level because of its small centrifugal barrier.

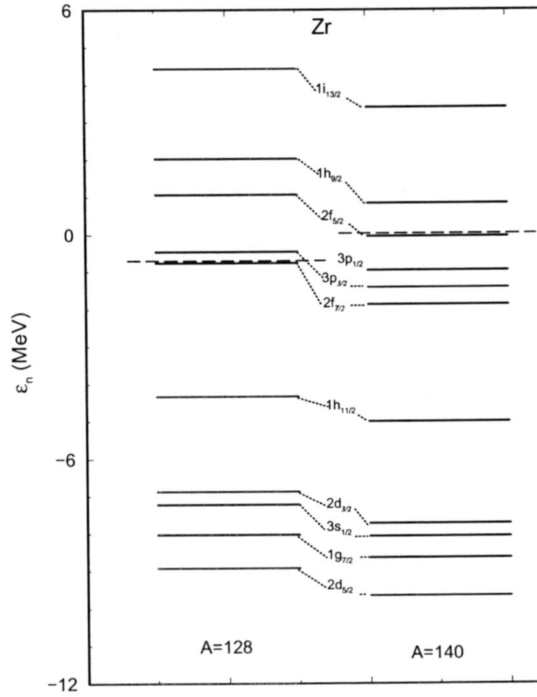

Figure 5: Neutron spectra of the ^{128}Zr and ^{140}Zr isotopes as predicted by the G2 set.

It is just the occupancies of $2f_{7/2}$, $3p_{3/2}$, $3p_{1/2}$, and $2f_{5/2}$ levels which mainly contribute to the enhancement of the neutron rms beyond $N = 82$, as discussed in earlier literature [33, 37]. In the lighter Zr isotopes one observes the progressive filling of the $1h_{11/2}$ state and the almost negligible occupancy of the states beyond the $N = 82$ core. After $N = 82$, the occupancy of the weakly bound and quasibound $3p_{3/2}$, $3p_{1/2}$, $2f_{5/2}$, $1h_{9/2}$ and $1i_{13/2}$ states starts to be progressively important when the number of neutrons beyond the core increases. In our model, the $3p_{1/2}$ state appears when $A = 134$ as a tiny bound state which causes the small kink between $A = 132$ and $A = 134$ that can be seen in Figure 4.

The rms radii of the neutron orbits above the $N = 82$ core and of the $2d_{3/2}$ and $1h_{11/2}$ states of the core, as well as the radii of the quasibound $1h_{9/2}$ and $1i_{13/2}$ levels, are displayed in Figure 6. The large rms radii of the $2f_{5/2}$, $3p_{3/2}$ and $3p_{1/2}$ orbits can clearly be seen in this figure. These large rms radii are basically due to two different reasons. First, the principal quantum number n is large (2 or 3) which makes the wave functions corresponding to these orbitals extend quite far. The second reason lies in the fact that the $2f_{5/2}$, $3p_{3/2}$ and $3p_{1/2}$ levels are extremely weakly bound, or even unbound, for $N > 82$. For instance, the single particle energy of the $3p_{3/2}$ level runs from -0.16 MeV in ^{124}Zr to -0.77 MeV in ^{140}Zr. Due to the last reason, these levels show up a relatively strong dependence with the mass number A. However, the rms radii of the $1h_{11/2}$ and $2f_{7/2}$ orbitals are roughly constant with A due to the larger binding energy of these states. The quasi-bound $1h_{9/2}$ and $1i_{13/2}$ states also exhibit a nearly constant rms radii as a function of A. In this case the reason is rather that the small principal quantum number ($n = 1$) pushes the significant part of the wave function inside enough for not being affected by the increasing number of nucleons outside the ^{122}Zr core. We note that for obtaining the contribution of the states displayed in Figure 6 to the total neutron rms radius, the degeneracy $2j + 1$ and the occupancy v^2 of these levels has to be taken into account, which gives an increasing contribution with A. For instance, the contribution to the total $\langle r_n^2 \rangle$ radius from the $2f_{7/2}$, $3p_{3/2}$ and $2f_{5/2}$ states is 0.59, 0.50 and 0.06 fm^2 in ^{124}Zr, whereas it is 2.63, 1.80 and 1.53 fm^2 in the drip line nucleus ^{140}Zr. This explains the increasing tendency of the rms radii in Figure 4 beyond the $N = 82$ core.

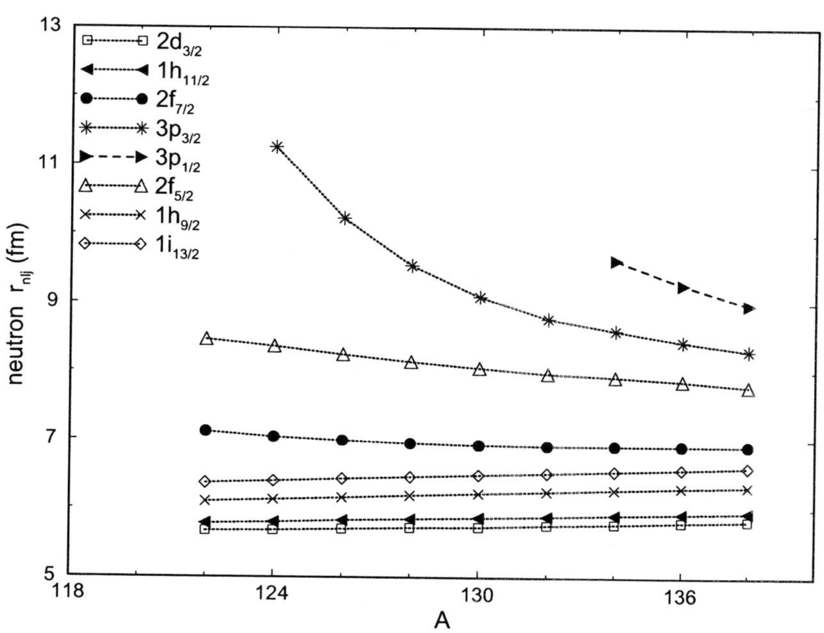

Figure 6: Change with mass number of the rms radii of various neutron orbits for Zr isotopes calculated with the G2 force parameters.

Another indicator of a giant halo is a very small neutron chemical potential μ_n. This is just the situation we find using the E-RMF set G2, with the discussed pairing prescription, in the neutron rich Zr isotopes beyond $N = 82$. In our calculation, μ_n ranges from -0.89 MeV for ^{124}Zr to practically zero in ^{140}Zr. As a consequence of this almost vanishing value of μ_n beyond the $N = 82$ core, the binding energies are roughly constant, ranging from 943.7 MeV in ^{124}Zr to 951.9 MeV in ^{140}Zr, and the two-neutron separation energies S_{2n} are close to zero. We have calculated the two-neutron separation energies along the Zr isotopic chain for the G2 and NL-SH parameter sets. In both parameter sets shell effects appear at $N = 50$ and 82, as expected. Beyond $N = 82$, S_{2n} decreases faster for NL-SH than for G2 indicating that although the general features of giant halo nuclei are unchanged, fine details can be force dependent. In Figure 7 we display the calculated neutron densities of some selected Zr isotopes. When the neutron number is significantly above the $N = 82$ core the central density starts to progressively decrease, while a halo develops in the outer region. Some neutrons of the core are scattered by the pairing correlations to the states beyond the Fermi level, with larger rms radii with the increasing number of the neutrons in the outer part of the density distribution of the nuclei beyond ^{122}Zr.

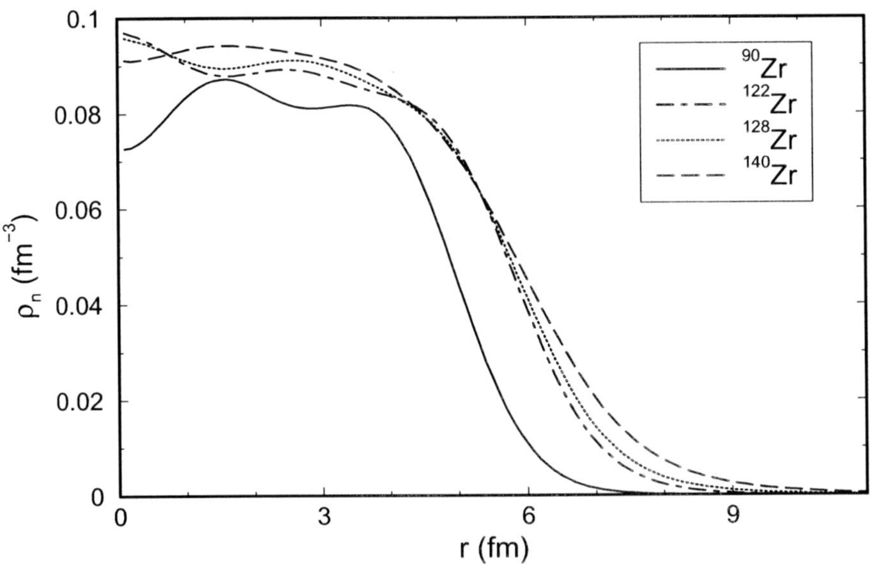

Figure 7: Radial dependence of the neutron densities of Zr isotopes.

The simplified treatment of the pairing correlations used here, which is discussed in more detail in Ref. [19], is thus seen to be able to describe the bulk properties of nuclei near the drip lines [13, 19] and also to reproduce correctly the main features of the giant halo nuclei. Only some finer details such as the behavior of the $3p$ levels in the giant halo problem discussed here, would require of an improved treatment of the pairing correlations using more sophisticated methods such as the r-BCS or RHB approaches. On the other hand, the study presented here, together with the examples discussed in Refs. [13, 19], proves the ability of the RMF approach based on EFT for describing exotic isospin-rich nuclei far from the β-stability valley when a pairing residual interaction is included. Notice that only information about a few stable magic nuclei was used in the fit of the coupling constants of the E-RMF sets, and thus the results near the drip lines are predictions of the model.

4.3 Breathing Mode Energy Near the Neutron Drip Line

It is to be expected that in neutron rich nuclei, and in particular in giant halo nuclei, the excitation energy of collective modes be strongly modified as compared with stable nuclei. For further prospect, we next address with the example of the Zr isotopes the trends predicted by the G2 set for the behavior of the excitation energy of the isoscalar giant monopole resonance (GMR) in approaching the limits of neutron stability. As we have seen in the previous subsection, in Zr isotopes beyond $A = 122$ the last filled levels are weakly bound. Thus, particle-hole excitations from the occupied $2f_{7/2}$, $3p_{3/2}$, $3p_{1/2}$ and $2f_{5/2}$ states to the continuum will give important contributions to the low-energy part of the RPA strength. The situation for these Zr isotopes is similar to that found in the ^{110}Ni nucleus for which the RPA strength has been analyzed in Ref. [38] by means of non-relativistic Skyrme force calculations. Although in such kind of very neutron-rich nuclei the monopole RPA strength is broad and it is not concentrated in a single peak [38], the mean energy of the monopole response should exhibit a downwards behavior when one moves from stable nuclei towards the neutron drip line due to the increase of the amount of strength in the low energy region of the resonance.

Constrained calculations are one of the means to estimate the average energy of the breathing mode. For example, RMF constrained calculations have been performed with different parameter sets to obtain the excitation energies of the GMR of some selected nuclei in Refs. [40, 41, 42, 43]. A reasonable good agreement has been found between the results of these calculations with the results from more sophisticated approaches such as the time-dependent RMF formalism [44] or the relativistic RPA [45].

Here we follow the method of Refs. [40, 41, 42, 43] to perform the constrained calculations with the E-RMF model. One has to solve the self-consistent equations for the nucleonic and mesonic fields derived from the constrained energy

$$E_c(\eta) = \int d\mathbf{r} \left[\mathcal{E} - \eta \sum_\alpha \varphi_\alpha^\dagger (r^2 - R_0^2) \varphi_\alpha \right] , \qquad (3)$$

where $\mathcal{E}$ is the energy density given by Eq. (1) and R_0 the rms radius of the ground state. The solution of the corresponding equations of motion gives spinors $\varphi_\alpha(\eta)$ and mesonic fields which depend on the Lagrange multiplier η.

The binding energy $E(\eta)$, obtained by integrating Eq. (1) with the nuclear and meson fields solution to the constrained problem, has a minimum at $\eta = 0$ which corresponds to the ground-state energy with rms radius R_0. Expanding $E(\eta)$ in a harmonic approximation about R_0 one obtains the constrained incompressibility of the finite nucleus as

$$K_A^c = \frac{1}{A} R_0^2 \frac{\partial^2 E(\eta)}{\partial R_\eta^2}\bigg|_{\eta=0}, \tag{4}$$

with R_η being the rms radius computed with the constrained spinors $\varphi_\alpha(\eta)$. The constrained incompressibility of Eq. (4) is just the constant entering the harmonic restoring force.

The mass parameter of the monopole oscillation is given by

$$B = \frac{1}{A} \int d\mathbf{r}\, u(\mathbf{r})^2 \mathcal{E}(\mathbf{r}), \tag{5}$$

where $u(\mathbf{r})$ is the displacement field which is determined by the solution of the continuity equation for the monopole oscillation [40, 41, 42, 43]. In the non-relativistic limit and with a Tassie transition density, which assumes that there exists a single-collective state, the displacement field is $u(r) = r$ and the expression of the mass parameter becomes

$$B_{nr} = M \int d\mathbf{r}\, r^2 \rho(\mathbf{r}) = M \langle r^2 \rangle. \tag{6}$$

The frequency of the constrained monopole vibration using the non-relativistic mass parameter is

$$E_c = \sqrt{\frac{A K_A^c}{B_{nr}}}. \tag{7}$$

We have performed the constrained calculation switching off the pairing correlations, as in the non-relativistic studies of giant resonances in nuclei near the drip lines [38]. Our estimate of the excitation energy of the GMR of the nucleus ^{90}Zr from the constrained calculation with the E-RMF set G2 is 17.2 MeV. It agrees fairly well with the experimental centroid energy 17.9 ± 0.2 MeV [46].

Figure 8 displays the finite nucleus incompressibility K_A^c calculated using the G2 set for even Zr isotopes ranging from $A = 90$ to $A = 138$. The finite nucleus incompressibilities are roughly constant from $A = 90$ up to $A = 122$, when the $1h_{11/2}$ level is completely filled. From $A = 122$ on, the finite nucleus incompressibility decreases quite fast till the neutron drip line is reached. One can try to understand qualitatively this downward tendency as follows. Inspired by the liquid drop formula, the finite nucleus incompressibility can be expanded [47] into a bulk contribution K_∞ (the nuclear matter incompressibility modulus), plus surface $K_{\rm surf}$, Coulomb $K_{\rm Coul}$ and volume-symmetry $K_{\rm sym}$ terms, apart from corrections of higher order. Within a scaling model approach the quantities $K_{\rm surf}$, $K_{\rm Coul}$, and $K_{\rm sym}$ are negative [43, 49]. When the mass number A increases approaching the drip lines, the surface and Coulomb terms become comparatively less important. However, the symmetry contribution, which is large in the RMF parametrizations, multiplied by a large average asymmetry factor $(N-Z)^2/A^2$ makes finally the nuclei near the neutron drip line softer than the stable nuclei. Though the numerical coefficients of the expansion of the nucleus incompressibility K_A into its various contributions are different between the scaling and the constrained models [47, 48], one can still expect that the volume-symmetry term is at the origin of the reduction of K_A^c as the nuclei come close to the neutron drip point.

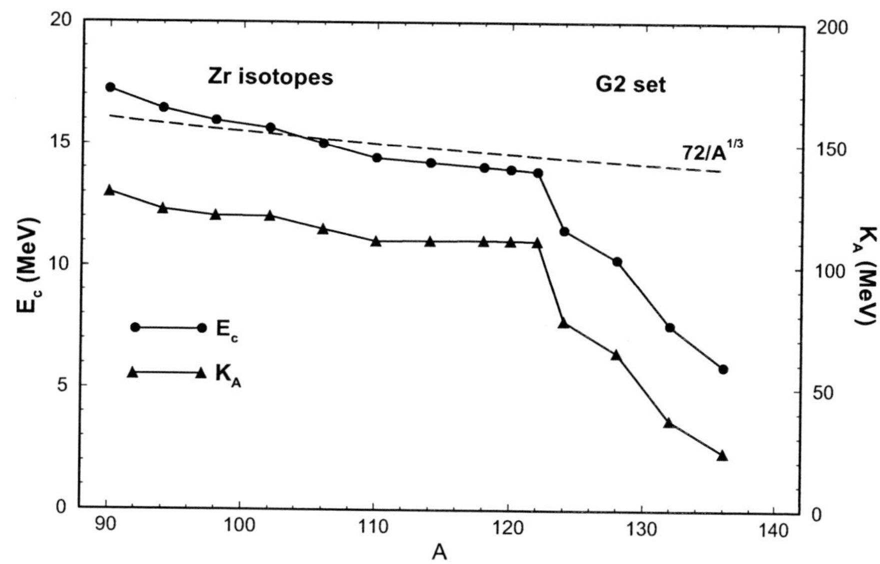

Figure 8: Average energy E_c of the isoscalar giant monopole resonance and finite nucleus incompressibility K_A obtained from constrained calculations with the G2 set for Zr isotopes.

From a more microscopic point of view, when $A > 122$ the weakly bound neutron levels $2f_{7/2}$, $3p_{3/2}$, $3p_{1/2}$ and $2f_{5/2}$, which have a large rms radius (see Figure 6), start to be occupied. Neutrons in these levels behave almost as extremely asymmetric nuclear matter, which is strongly softened as compared with the symmetric one [50]. According to this, when the number of neutrons outside the $A = 122$ core increases, their contribution to K_A^c is smaller and thus, on average, the finite nucleus incompressibility of the Zr isotopes that develop a giant halo is smaller than the one of the stable Zr nuclei.

Due to the fact that the Zr nuclei beyond $A = 122$ have a large rms radius, the mass denominator (6) also increases when one moves from $A = 122$ towards the neutron drip line. This fact together with the decreasing of the finite nucleus incompressibility reduces strongly the excitation energy of the GMR beyond $A = 122$, as evidenced by Figure 8. It is known that the experimental GMR excitation energies roughly follow the empirical law $E_{\text{GMR}} \sim 80A^{1/3}$ MeV [47]. The excitation energy of the GMR of the Zr isotopes from $A = 90$ to $A = 122$ can be nicely fitted by an $A^{1/3}$ law, as indicated by the dashed line in Figure 8. This behaviour breaks down for the isotopes with $A > 122$ pointing out again that for these nuclei the neutrons which occupy the weakly bound levels above the $1h_{11/2}$ orbit are softer than the neutrons belonging to the $A = 122$ core.

As shown in Ref. [43], the energy of the constrained monopole oscillation (7) can be nominally written in the nonrelativistic language of RPA sum rules as $E_c = \sqrt{m_1/m_{-1}}$ [51]. The sum rules, or moments of the strength function $S(E)$ of the giant resonance, are defined as

$$m_k = \int_0^\infty E^k S(E) dE \tag{8}$$

for integer k. The m_1 sum rule turns out to be proportional to the mass denominator B_{nr}, while the inverse energy weighted sum rule m_{-1} can be computed as [51]

$$m_{-1} = -\frac{1}{2} A \frac{\partial R_\eta^2}{\partial \eta}\bigg|_{\eta=0} = \frac{1}{2} \frac{\partial^2 E(\eta)}{\partial \eta^2}\bigg|_{\eta=0}. \tag{9}$$

From this point of view, the strong reduction of E_c when $A > 122$ is basically due to an increasingly large inverse energy weighted moment of the RPA strength. The latter, due to the power E^{-1} in (8), reflects the important contribution to the low-energy part of the RPA strength distribution which arises from the particle-hole transitions to the continuum from the weakly bound energy levels $2f_{7/2}$, $3p_{3/2}$, $3p_{1/2}$ and $2f_{5/2}$.

5 Predictions in the Land of Superheavy Elements

In continuance of our study of the nuclear structure predictions of the E-RMF model in the regions of the nuclear landscape away from the stable nuclei where the parameters were fitted, in this section we address spherical calculations of superheavy elements (SHE). We shall concentrate on finding out where the next doubly-magic shell closures beyond $N = 126$ and $Z = 82$ are located according to the E-RMF model.

Experimental efforts at the leading laboratories for synthesizing new elements in the superheavy mass region have already produced some light isotopes of $Z = 110$–112 at GSI and Dubna [52] and even heavier isotopes of $Z = 112$–116 at Dubna [53]. Most of the detected nuclei with $Z \sim 110$ are deformed, consistently with the predicted occurrence of a deformed shell closure at $Z = 108$ and $N = 162$ [54, 55, 56]. Therefore, quadrupole deformations [54, 55, 56, 57, 58], and even in some cases triaxial calculations [59], have to be taken into account for describing the new nuclei around $Z = 110$. However, when one is concerned with identifying the location of the N and Z values of the next spherical *double* shell closure beyond ^{208}Pb, most of the calculations with relativistic and non-relativistic mean field models have been performed in spherical symmetry [60, 61, 62, 63]. Of course, one has to keep in mind that the study of the spherical shell structure is valid only for the doubly-magic nuclei. The addition of deformation degrees of freedom in the calculations would certainly change the picture in the details and add deformed shell closures, e.g., like those predicted around $Z = 108$ and $N = 162$ [54, 55, 56]. But it should not change drastically the predictions for the values of N and Z where the strongest shell effects show up already in the spherical calculation. Certainly, for a quantitative discussion, one needs to account for deformation effects which would serve to extend the island of shell stabilized superheavy nuclei and to decide on the specific form of the ground-state shapes of those nuclei.

In the nonrelativistic framework, the macroscopic-microscopic models predict spherical shell closures at $Z = 114$ and $N = 184$ [55]. The Hartree-Fock calculations with Skyrme forces show, in general, the most pronounced shell effects at $Z = 124$, $Z = 126$ and $N = 184$ [60, 61, 62, 63]. However, the conventional RMF theory typically prefers $Z = 120$ and $N = 172$ as the best candidates for spherical shell closures [60, 61, 62, 63]. In view of these discrepancies in the predicted shell closures for SHE, it is interesting to reinvestigate them using the more general E-RMF model.

5.1 Shell Closures

In normal nuclei a large gap in the single-particle spectrum is interpreted as the indication of a shell closure. We start by inspecting the neutron single-particle spectra of the ^{292}120, ^{304}120 and ^{378}120 nuclei, displayed in Figure 9, calculated using the G1, G2 and NL3 parameter sets. As mentioned, $Z = 120$ is found to be a magic number in many RMF calculations [60, 61, 62, 63]. The three parameter sets show a large gap at $N = 172$ and $N = 258$. However, for $N = 184$ a moderate gap is found mainly for the E-RMF sets, G1 and G2, which is smaller for NL3. In the level spectrum of the system with $N = 258$ and $Z = 120$, one can again find appreciable energy gaps across the neutron numbers $N = 198$ ($1j_{13/2}$ level) and $N = 228$ ($1k_{17/2}$ level) in all the considered parameter sets. By comparing the spectra for the three systems with $N = 172$, 184 and 258, it can be noticed that the gap between two particular levels is strongly modified along the isotopic chain. However, the level gaps are not as distinct as in lighter nuclei. In calculations of SHE the level spectra become very involved due to the presence of levels with a high degree of degeneracy. Therefore, it is imperative to look for other quantities to be able to reliably identify the shell closures and magic numbers of SHE, apart from the analysis of the single-particle level structure.

We next shall consider three energy indicators for locating the nucleon shell closures. First, a sudden jump in the two-neutron (two-proton) separation energies of even-even nu-

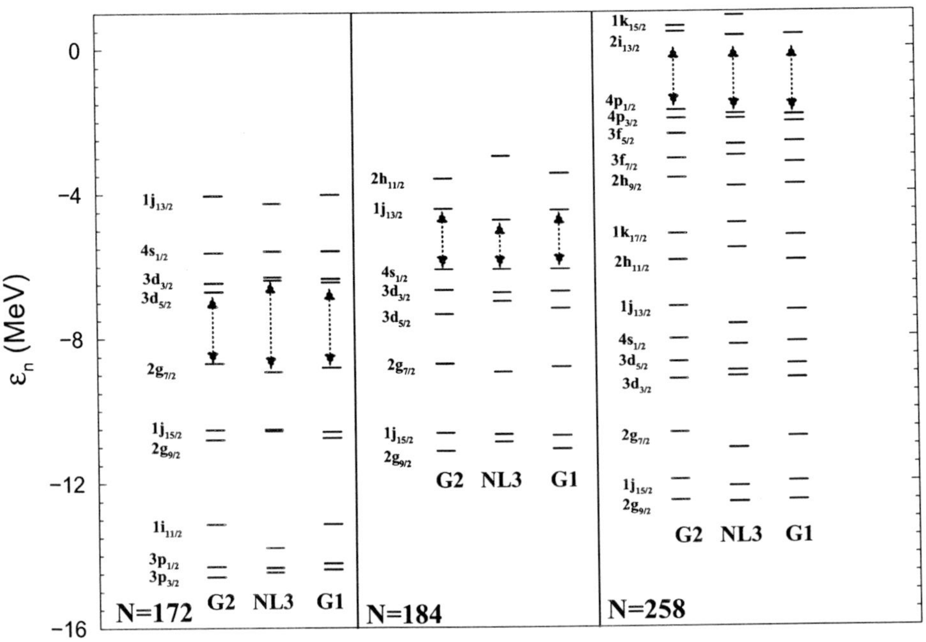

Figure 9: Single-particle neutron spectra in the vicinity of the Fermi level for the superheavy isotopes $^{292}120$, $^{304}120$, and $^{378}120$ computed with the G1, G2 and NL3 parameter sets.

clei, defined as $S_{2q} = E(N_q - 2) - E(N_q)$, where N_q is the number of neutrons (protons) in the nucleus for $q = n$ ($q = p$). Second, the two-neutron (two-proton) shell gap defined as the second difference of the binding energy [60]: $\delta_{2q}(N_q) = E(N_q + 2) - 2E(N_q) + E(N_q - 2)$. This quantity measures the size of the step found in the two-nucleon separation energy and, therefore, it is strongly peaked at magic shell closures. Third, for closed shell nuclei the average pairing gaps Δ_q obtained in the calculations should vanish.

In Figure 10, we display these energy indicators calculated with the E-RMF set G2 and with NL3 along the isotopic chain of $Z = 120$. The two-neutron separation energies S_{2n}, displayed in the top panel of the figure, show sudden jumps after the neutron numbers $N = 172$, 184 and 258 indicating possible neutron shell closures. The two-neutron shell gap δ_{2n} along the same isotopic chain is displayed in the middle panel of Figure 10. Sharp peaks in δ_{2n} are found at the same neutron numbers 172, 184 and 258, though the peak at $N = 184$ is less pronounced than the peaks for $N = 172$ and $N = 258$. Also, the peak in δ_{2n} at $N = 258$ is more marked in NL3 than in G2. The curve for the neutron pairing gaps displayed in the bottom panel of Figure 10 shows a structure of arches which vanish only at $N = 172$, 184 and 258 with G2, and at $N = 172$ and 258 with NL3. Therefore, all the three analyzed observables point out to the same neutron numbers as the best candidates for shell closures for $Z = 120$ with the G2 parametrization. The neutron pairing gap calculated with NL3 does not vanish at $N = 184$. The proton pairing gap is zero along the whole isotopic chain, for both G2 and NL3, and thus we have not plotted it. The results obtained with the set G1 show the same global nature as with G2 and NL3. The peak in δ_{2n} occurring at $N = 172$ is lower in G1 than in G2, and the peak at $N = 184$ is very much quenched in the G1 set. As in the case of NL3, the neutron gap Δ_n at $N = 184$ does not vanish for G1 ($\Delta_n \approx 0.7$ MeV).

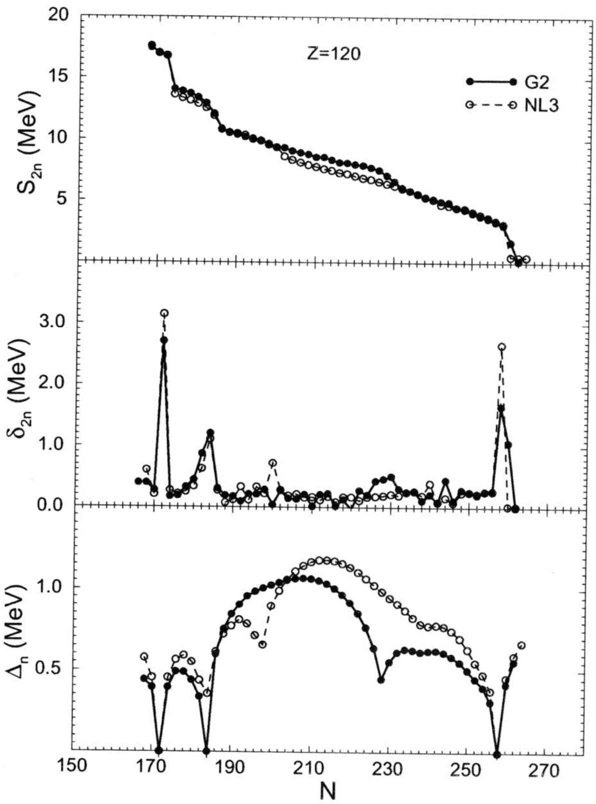

Figure 10: Two-neutron separation energy S_{2n}, two-neutron shell gap δ_{2n}, and neutron average pairing gap Δ_n for $Z = 120$ isotopes obtained from spherical calculations with the relativistic parameter sets G2 and NL3. The proton average pairing gap Δ_p vanishes in the whole isotopic chain.

Now we proceed to the discussion of the isotonic chains of $N = 172$ and $N = 184$ obtained with E-RMF set G2 and which are displayed in Figure 11. For $N = 172$ all the indicators show a very robust closure at $Z = 120$ and a much weaker shell closure at $Z = 114$. This is appreciated, e.g., from the strength of the corresponding two-proton shell gap δ_{2p}. For $N = 184$ proton shell closures are found at $Z = 114$ and $Z = 120$. In this case the strength of δ_{2p} for both atomic numbers is similar (though smaller than the two-proton shell gap found with the combination $N = 172$ and $Z = 120$). Moreover, from the left bottom panel of the Figure 11, it can be seen that below $Z = 110$, the neutron pairing gap does not vanish, meaning that the shell closure for $N = 172$, which is very strong combined with $Z = 120$, is washed out. Thus, in SHE the magicity of a particular neutron (proton) number very much depends on the number of protons (neutrons) present in the nucleus.

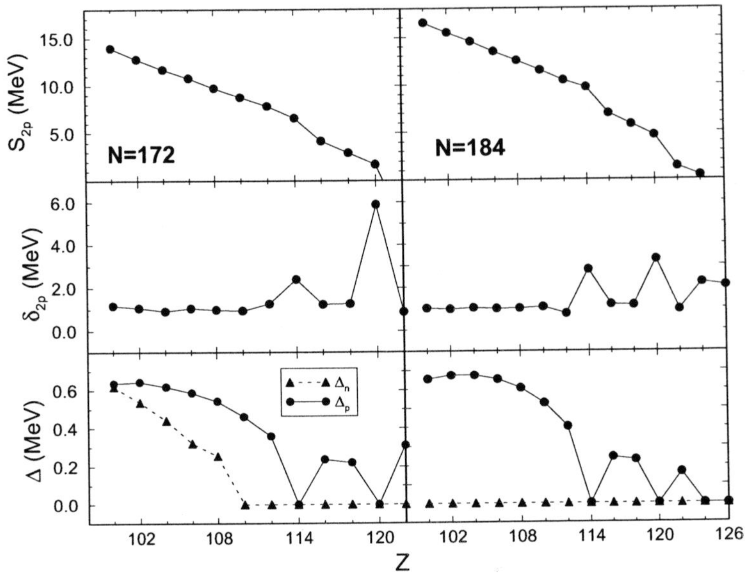

Figure 11: Two-proton separation energy S_{2p}, two-proton shell gap δ_{2p}, and proton Δ_p and neutron Δ_n average pairing gaps for $N = 172$ and $N = 184$ isotones obtained from spherical calculations with the parameter set G2.

From the above discussions we conclude that the E-RMF parameter set G2 clearly points out towards the robust double magic character of the combinations ($N = 172, Z = 120$) and ($N = 258, Z = 120$). Similar conclusions are obtained with the G1 and NL3 parameter sets [21]. Also, for the particular case of the new set G2 the combinations $Z = 114$ and $Z = 120$ with $N = 184$ show evidences of a shell closure, although less strong than in the previous cases. A double shell closure in the ($Z = 114, N = 184$) nucleus has been traditionally predicted by the macroscopic-microscopic models [55].

5.2 Shell Corrections

The indicators discussed in the previous section, which allow one to identify the doubly magic nuclei, correspond to energy differences between neighbouring nuclei. However, they do not have a direct connection with the shell corrections which stabilize a given SHE against fission. In a liquid droplet model picture SHE are unstable against spontaneous fission due to the fact that the large Coulomb repulsion cannot be compensated by the nuclear surface tension. However, SHE may still exist because the quantal shell corrections generate local minima in the nuclear potential energy surface which provide additional stabilization. For experimentally known shell closures (up to $N = 126$ and $Z = 82$), the shell corrections are strongly peaked around the magic numbers [64]. Thus, the shell correction energy also represents a test for checking the robustness of the shell closures.

In Figure 12 we display the total (neutron-plus-proton) shell correction energies calculated employing the Strutinsky smoothing procedure [21, 65] for the $Z = 114$ and $Z = 120$ isotopic chains, using the parameter sets G2 and NL3. The calculations have been performed in spherical symmetry and thus the computed shell corrections represent in general an upper bound to the actual ones. Deformation could bring additional shell stabilization. From the figure one can see that the isotopic chain of $Z = 120$ shows a large negative shell correction for $N = 172$. Another local minimum, less pronounced, is also found around $N = 182 - 184$. One observes that in superheavy nuclei the shell correction energy at the shell closures does not display the very sharp jumps typical of normal mass nuclei. Rather, the shell corrections depict a landscape of broad areas of shell stabilized nuclei [61, 62, 63]. Still, in these areas the closed shell superheavy nuclei show more negative shell corrections than their neighbours. Looking at the results for $Z = 114$ presented in Figure 12 it can be realized that the shell corrections in the $Z = 114$ isotopes are weaker than for the $Z = 120$ chain, which means less stability. Again, two dips are found at $N = 172$ and $N = 184$, although in this case the minimum at $N = 184$ is deeper than the one at $N = 172$. The study of the shell correction energy reveals that the shell stabilized regions of SHE are in good agreement with the previous predictions for shell closures derived from the analysis of the energy indicators.

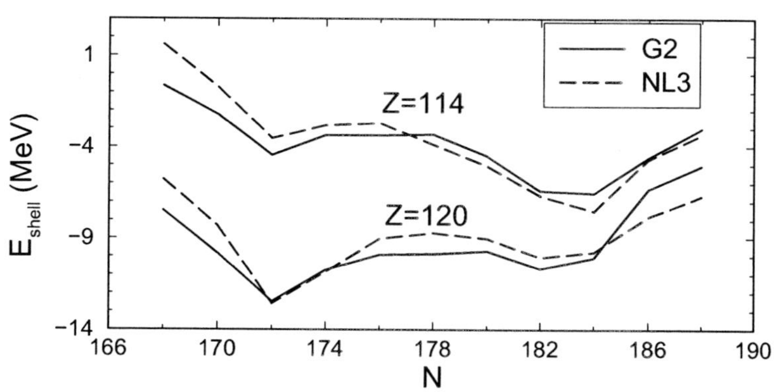

Figure 12: Total shell correction energy for $Z = 114$ and $Z = 120$ isotopes in spherical calculations with the G2 and NL3 sets.

5.3 Density Profiles and Spin-Orbit Potentials

From a naive point of view one expects that for a large nucleus the neutron density profile will show a relatively flat region at the interior, modulated by some wiggles due to shell effects. In the case of protons one also expects that the Coulomb repulsion will push them towards the surface so that the proton density will develop a depression in the center. However, some deviations from this pattern can arise in superheavy nuclei. To exemplify the situation, we display in Figure 13 the density profiles of neutrons and protons for the superheavy nuclides $^{292}120$ (close to the proton drip point), $^{304}120$, and $^{378}120$ (close to the neutron drip point). For the purpose of comparison with the situation in smaller nuclei, we have drawn in the same figure the neutron and proton density profiles of the isotopes ^{100}Sn (proton drip line nucleus), ^{132}Sn, and ^{176}Sn (neutron drip line nucleus).

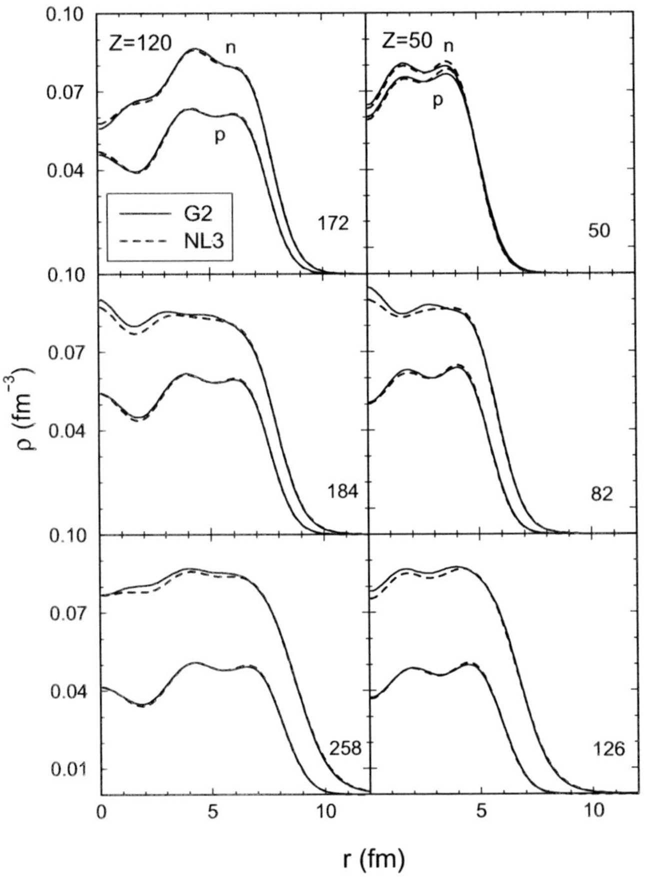

Figure 13: The radial neutron and proton density distributions predicted by the sets G2 and NL3 for the $Z = 120$ superheavy isotopes with $N = 172$, 184, and 258 (left panels), in comparison with the results for the tin isotopes with $N = 50$, 82, and 126 (right panels).

Inspecting the behavior of the tin isotopes with increasing neutron number N, one observes that the neutron density extends progressively toward the outside, while it shows only a small increase in the interior. Driven by the proton-neutron interaction, the proton density also extends more and more to the outside. As a result, since $Z = 50$ is fixed, there is a notable reduction of the average proton density in the nuclear interior. (See Ref. [66] for a detailed RHB study of the tin chain.) These general trends are also observed in the evolution with N of the nucleon densities of the $Z = 120$ isotopes displayed on the left side of Figure 13.

It is immediately noted that the neutron density profile of the $^{292}120$ superheavy nucleus shows an accentuated dip from $r \sim 4$ fm to the origin. As also pointed out in Ref. [60], the reason lies in the fact that for $N = 172$ the last filled neutron levels correspond to a large orbital angular momentum (2g and 1j levels, see Figure 9). Such orbits are mainly located at the surface and thus generate the central dip. This is not the case for the system with $N = 184$, where the last occupied neutron levels (4s and 3d) give an important contribution to the central density. For $N = 258$ neutrons the situation lies somehow in between of the two previous cases due to the contribution of the 4p and 3f orbitals near the Fermi level. For the tin isotopes shown in Figure 13, the neutron orbits in the vicinity of the Fermi energy consist of a bunch of low angular momentum levels together with the intruder level of higher angular momentum. The neutron density profiles of the three tin isotopes show the normal pattern, though for $N = 50$ one can recognize a dip around the center which has the same nature discussed for the superheavy nucleus $N = 172$, now because of the 1g neutron level.

The proton density profiles of the three superheavy isotopes of $Z = 120$ depicted in Figure 13 show a similar pattern. Again, there is an effect due to the orbitals around the Fermi level. The 2f and 1i proton orbits of the $Z = 120$ nuclides push their protons away from the center and as a consequence the proton density develops a pocket around $r \sim 2$ fm. On the other hand, the increase of the proton density which is observed close to the origin is reminiscent of the fingerprint of the 3s protons. The proton densities of the tin isotopes also exhibit a depression near the center. This time it is occasioned by the 1g proton level, which is the last filled level for $Z = 50$. However, due to the smaller Coulomb repulsion and to the 2p orbits close in energy to the 1g level, the effect is not as remarkable as for the proton density of $Z = 120$.

We now come to the discussion of the spin-orbit potential in the superheavy mass region, because it is responsible for the strong reduction of the spin-orbit splitting of low angular momentum energy levels found in the self-consistent calculations of SHE. In the relativistic models the spin-orbit force is automatically included in the interaction from the outset. It appears explicitly when the lower spinor of the relativistic wave function is eliminated in favor of the upper spinor. One then obtains a Schrödinger-like equation that contains a spin-orbit term which reads [24, 67]:

$$H_{so} = \frac{1}{2M^2} V_{so}(r)\, \mathbf{L}\cdot\mathbf{S}, \tag{10}$$

$$V_{so}(r) = \frac{M^2}{\bar{M}^2}\frac{1}{r}\left(\frac{d\Phi}{dr} + \frac{dW}{dr}\right) + 2f_v \frac{M}{\bar{M}}\frac{1}{r}\frac{dW}{dr}, \tag{11}$$

where we have made $\bar{M} = M - \frac{1}{2}(\Phi + W)$. This spin-orbit potential includes the contribution of the tensor coupling of the ω meson to the nucleon, which has an important bearing on the spin-orbit force [7, 24, 12]. For simplicity, we have neglected in (11) the small contributions of the ρ meson and of the Coulomb field which make $V_{so}(r)$ slightly different for neutrons and protons.

Figure 14 displays the radial dependence of V_{so} given by Eq. (11) for the isotopes of $Z = 120$ and $Z = 50$, whose density distributions we have just discussed. A common feature of both the tin and the superheavy isotopes is that, as expected, the spin-orbit potential develops a well at the surface region of the nuclear density distributions. As the system becomes more and more neutron rich, the depth of this well experiments a gradual reduction and the position of the bottom of the potential is shifted outwards, which brings about a weaker spin-orbit force.

There are two distinctive trends of the spin-orbit potential of superheavy nuclei with respect to normal nuclei. One is that the spin-orbit well at the surface is less deep in the case of the SHE. The other one is the strong upward bump that V_{so} develops around $2-4$ fm from the origin. This bump can be explained in connection with the spatial distribution of the densities. Consider the case of $N = 172$. The nucleon densities are sharply reduced in the center (Figure 13). To the extent that the meson fields follow the change of the densities, this causes V_{so} to develop a sharp bump in the interior of the nucleus [60, 63]. As seen from Figure 14, the ensuing bump is largest for $N = 172$ and decreases with increasing neutron number as the central region of the neutron densities flattens out.

The strong increase of V_{so} near the origin has an outstanding effect on the energy splitting of spin-orbit partner levels in SHE. Large angular momentum states whose wave function is mostly localized around the nuclear surface basically feel the attractive part of V_{so}, and thus present normal spin-orbit splittings. However, for low angular momentum states there is a strong overlap of the wave function with the positive region of V_{so} which dramatically reduces the spin-orbit splittings (they may even have the opposite sign for some parameter sets [60]). This effect is corroborated by looking at the splittings of spin-orbit partners in the SHE spectra represented in Figure 9.

Little differences are seen in Figure 14 between the predictions of the G2 and NL3 sets for the spin-orbit potential. The higher effective mass at saturation of G2 ($M^*_\infty = 0.66$) with respect to NL3 ($M^*_\infty = 0.6$) is compensated by the contribution of the tensor coupling f_v in the G2 set, since there exists a trade-off between the size of the ω tensor coupling and

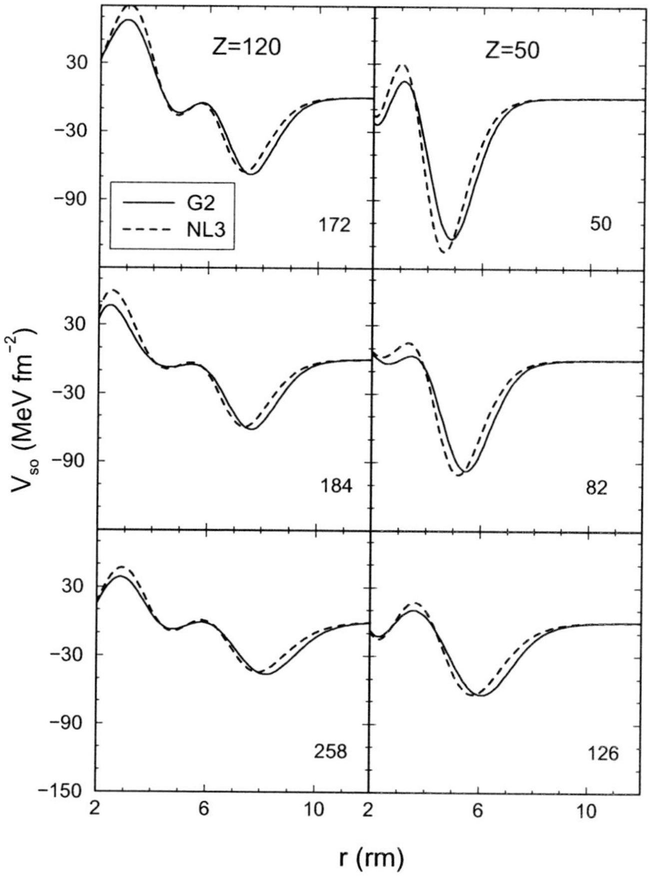

Figure 14: Same as Figure 13 but for the radial dependence of the spin-orbit potential V_{so} defined in Eq. (11).

the size of the scalar field [12, 24]. As noticed in Ref. [19] the contribution of f_v to Eq. (11) accounts for roughly one-third of the spin-orbit strength in the case of the G2 parameter set.

Still, inspecting Figure 14, one may observe that the bottom of V_{so} is located at slightly larger values of r in the G2 set than in the NL3 set. Also, the spin-orbit well at the surface tends to be slightly deeper in G2 than in NL3 for the $Z = 120$ isotopes (the opposite happens for tin between $N = 50$ and $N = 82$). Finally, the upward bumps appearing in the spin-orbit potential of the SHE at $r \sim 3$ fm are larger if V_{so} is calculated with NL3. Thus, it may be expected that the spin-orbit splitting of low angular momentum energy levels of SHE will be smaller with NL3 than with G2. Since for the SHE the strength of V_{so} at the surface is a little stronger and shifted towards slightly larger distances, the spin-orbit splitting for high angular momentum energy levels should be larger with G2 than with NL3. These predictions for the splittings of the energy levels of SHE coming from the small differences in V_{so} obtained with the two considered parameter sets, can be seen in the neutron single-particle spectra previously displayed.

6 Concluding Remarks

The effective field theory model derived from the chiral effective Lagrangian proposed by Furnstahl, Serot and Tang [6] contains, in addition to the standard nonlinear RMF theory, other nonlinear scalar-vector, vector-vector and tensor couplings consistent with the underlying symmetries of QCD. The Lagrangian is expanded in powers of the fields and their derivatives and is organized in such a way that the results are not dominated by the highest-order terms retained. None of the couplings present in the expansion at a given order can be eliminated without a symmetry argument. The coupling constants and some meson masses of the truncated effective Lagrangian, or equivalently of the energy density functional, are taken as the effective parameters of the theory and are fitted to measured observables of a few doubly-magic nuclei (sets G1 and G2). Thus, the model can be interpreted as a covariant formulation of density functional theory where the effective functional approximates the exact (unknown) energy functional of the many-body nuclear system by expanding it in powers of auxiliary meson fields.

We have checked the extrapolations of the model to the infinite medium by comparing its results with the Dirac-Brueckner-Hartree-Fock calculations of nuclear and neutron matter above the normal saturation density. The sets G1 and G2 derived from the effective field theory predict a rather soft equation of state both around saturation and at high densities. These trends are in agreement with the output of the DBHF theory and recent experimental observations from energetic heavy ion collisions [17, 18]. At variance with this, the standard nonlinear RMF parameter sets produce an EOS which is much too stiff with increasing density because of the restricted density dependence of the meson fields in the model.

We have analyzed the predictive power of the E-RMF model for describing finite nuclei in extreme conditions, like those found at the border of the nuclear chart. The study of exotic nuclei requires to include the pairing correlations. Our approach consisted of a modified BCS approximation with constant pairing matrix elements where the continuum is represented through the quasi-bound levels retained by their centrifugal barrier. It simulates the effects of the coupling to the continuum which are incorporated in more sophisticated treatments of the pairing correlation, like the relativistic Hartree-Bogoliubov approach or the resonant continuum-coupling BCS calculations that take into account the width of the resonant states [35, 37].

We studied very neutron-rich Zr isotopes up to the neutron drip line. Previous RHB calculations with the NL-SH set predict that these nuclei exhibit a giant halo [33]. This effect consists of a noticeable enhancement of the rms radius of the neutron density distribution due to the progressive occupancy of tiny bound levels above the $1h_{11/2}$ level which closes the shell with $N = 82$ neutrons. Our E-RMF calculations with the G2 parameter set produce comparable results to those obtained with RHB calculations with the NL-SH set. It is known that for stable medium and heavy nuclei the excitation energy of the isoscalar giant monopole resonance follows an $A^{-1/3}$ law. Non-relativistic calculations of the breathing mode in some neutron-rich nuclei showed that the RPA strength becomes broader as compared with normal isotopes and that a large amount of strength concentrates in the low-energy region, because of the transitions from weakly bound levels to the continuum. We have performed constrained Hartree calculations with G2 for the Zr chain. The results predict that the finite nuclei incompressibilities and the average excitation energy of the breathing mode should fall down steeply for the isotopes with the largest isospin content. This fact would reflect an enhancement of the low-energy part of the RPA strength when the nuclei approach the neutron drip line.

Moving to another edge of the nuclear landscape, we paid attention to the predictions of the E-RMF sets for the next spherical magic numbers beyond $Z = 82$ and $N = 126$. The determination of the shell closures in superheavy elements is more involved than in normal nuclei where a large gap in the level spectra usually signals the possible magic numbers, and one has to study other indicators like two-nucleon separation energies, two-nucleon shell gaps, and the pairing gap. We also analyzed the shell correction energy, which provides a stabilizing effect to superheavy nuclei against fission. Our spherical prospect must be understood in connection with the occurrence of double shell closures. Additional deformed shell closures may appear in the analyzed region of superheavy elements. We contrasted the density distributions and spin-orbit potentials of superheavy nuclei against those of normal mass nuclei, with some selected examples from near the proton drip line to near the neutron drip line. The G2 parameter set predicts strong shell closures for $Z = 120$ in combination with $N = 172$ and $N = 258$. Again, the E-RMF predictions for finite systems are in agreement with the results obtained with the fine tuned standard RMF parameter sets. Interestingly enough, the G2 set presents some indications of a shell closure for $Z = 114$ and $N = 184$, which the macroscopic-microscopic models have traditionally predicted to be a doubly magic nucleus.

In concluding we remark that we tried to show that in the quest for a unified mean field description of finite nuclei, even in exotic regions of the nuclear landscape, as well as of nuclear and neutron matter up to densities several times above the saturation density, the relativistic mean field model motivated by effective field theory is one reliable candidate. Surely, this is not the only way of obtaining such a unified description. Other implementations of effective field theory for the nuclear many-body problem, formulations of the relativistic model with inclusion of other mesons, or with density-dependent coupling vertices, may probably deliver also a consistent description similarly to the E-RMF model. Nevertheless, with the present findings we hope to have illustrated the plausibility and promising potential of the application of effective field theory methods to the nuclear structure problem.

Acknowledgments

T. S, M. C., and X. V. acknowledge financial support from the DGI (Ministerio de Ciencia y Tecnolog´a, Spain) and FEDER under grant BFM2002-01868 and from DGR (Catalonia) under grant 2001SGR-00064. T. S. also thanks the Spanish Education Ministry grant SB2000-0411.

References

[1] B. D. Serot and J. D. Walecka, *Adv. Nucl. Phys.* **16**, 1 (1986).

[2] P. Ring, *Prog. Part. Nucl. Phys.* **37**, 193 (1996).

[3] B. D. Serot and J. D. Walecka, *Int. J. Mod. Phys.* **E6**, 515 (1997).

[4] J. D. Walecka, *Ann. Phys. (N.Y.)* **83**, 491 (1974).

[5] J. Boguta and A. R. Bodmer, *Nucl. Phys.* **A292**, 413 (1977).

[6] R. J. Furnstahl, B. D. Serot, and H. B. Tang, *Nucl. Phys.* **A598**, 539 (1996).

[7] R. J. Furnstahl, B. D. Serot, and H. B. Tang, *Nucl. Phys.* **A615**, 441 (1997); *ibid* **A640**, 505 (1998).

[8] H. Georgi, *Phys. Lett.* **B298**, 187 (1993).

[9] W. Kohn and L. J. Sham, *Phys. Rev.* A **140**, 1133 (1965).

[10] R. J. Furnstahl and B. D. Serot, *Nucl. Phys.* **A671**, 447 (2000).

[11] J. J. Rusnak and R. J. Furnstahl, *Nucl. Phys.* **A627**, 495 (1997).

[12] M. Del Estal, M. Centelles, and X. Viñas, *Nucl. Phys.* **A650**, 443 (1999).

[13] M. Del Estal, M. Centelles, X. Viñas, and S. K. Patra, *Phys. Rev.* C **63**, 024314 (2001).

[14] M. Centelles, M. Del Estal, X. Viñas, and S. K. Patra, *The Nuclear Many-Body Problem 2001*, NATO Science Series II Vol. 53 (Kluwer, Dordrecht, 2002), p. 97.

[15] R. Brockmann and R. Machleidt, *Phys. Rev. C* **42**, 1965 (1990).

[16] G. Q. Li, R. Machleidt, and R. Brockmann, *Phys. Rev. C* **45**, 2782 (1992).

[17] C. Sturm *et al.*, *Phys. Rev. Lett.* **86**, 39 (2001); C. Fuchs, A. Faessler, E. Zabrodin, and Yu-Ming Zheng, *Phys. Rev. Lett.* **86**, 1974 (2001).

[18] P. Danielewicz, R. Lacey, and W. G. Lynch, *Science* **298**, 1592 (2002).

[19] M. Del Estal, M. Centelles, X. Viñas, and S. K. Patra, *Phys. Rev. C* **63**, 044321 (2001).

[20] M. A. Huertas, *Phys. Rev. C* **66**, 024318 (2002).

[21] Tapas Sil, S. K. Patra, B. K. Sharma, M. Centelles, and X. Viñas, nucl-th/0310010, *Phys. Rev. C* (2004) in print.

[22] P. Wang, *Phys. Rev. C* **61**, 054904 (2000).

[23] J. C. Caillon, P. Gabinski, and J. Labarsouque, *Nucl. Phys.* **A696**, 623 (2001).

[24] R. J. Furnstahl, J. J. Rusnak and B. D. Serot, *Nucl. Phys.* **A632**, 607 (1998).

[25] B. C. Clark, R. J. Furnstahl, L. K. Kerr, J. J. Rusnak and S. Hama, *Phys. Lett.* **B427**, 231 (1998).

[26] G. A. Lalazissis, J. König, and P. Ring, *Phys. Rev.* C **55**, 540 (1997).

[27] G. Baym, *Phys. Rev.* **117**, 886 (1960).

[28] Y. Sugahara and H. Toki, *Nucl. Phys.* **A579**, 557 (1994).

[29] S. Typel and H. H. Wolter, *Nucl. Phys.* **A656**, 331 (1999); S. Typel, T. v. Chossy, and H. H. Wolter, *Phys. Rev. C* **67**, 034002 (2003).

[30] P. -G. Reinhard, M. Rufa, J. Maruhn, W. Greiner, and J. Friedrich, *Z. Phys.* **A323**, 13 (1986).

[31] I. Tanihata et al, *Phys. Rev. Lett.* **55**, 2676 (1985).

[32] I. Tanihata, *J. Phys.* **G22**, 157 (1996).

[33] J. Meng and P. Ring, *Phys. Rev. Lett.* **80**, 460 (1998).

[34] J. Meng, H. Toki, J. Y. Zeng, S. Q. Zhang and S.-G. Zhou, *Phys. Rev.* C **65**, 041302 (1990).

[35] J. Dobaczewski, H. Flocard, and J. Treiner, *Nucl. Phys.* **A422**, 103 (1984); J. Dobaczewski, W. Nazarewicz, T. R. Werner, J.-F. Berger, R. C. Chin, and J. Dechargé, *Phys. Rev. C* **53**, 2809 (1996).

[36] N. Sandulescu, Nguyen Van Giai, and R. J. Liotta, *Phys. Rev. C* **61**, 061301 (2000).

[37] N. Sandulescu, L. S. Geng, H. Toki, and G. C. Hillhouse, *Phys. Rev. C* **68**, 054323 (2003).

[38] H. Hamamoto, H. Sagawa, and X. Z. Zhang, *Phys. Rev. C* **53**, 765 (1996); *Phys. Rev. C* **55**, 2361 (1997); *Phys. Rev. C* **56**, 3121 (1997).

[39] E. Chabanat, P. Bonche, P. Haensel, J. Meyer, and R. Schaeffer, *Nucl. Phys.* **A635**, 231 (1998).

[40] T. Maruyama, and T. Suzuki, *Phys. Lett.* **B219**, 43 (1989).

[41] M. V. Stoitsov, P. Ring, and M. M. Sharma, *Phys. Rev.* **C50**, 1445 (1994).

[42] M. V. Stoitsov, M. L. Cescato, P. Ring, and M. M. Sharma, *J. Phys.***G20**, L149 (1994).

[43] S. K. Patra, X. Viñas, M. Centelles and M. Del Estal, *Nucl. Phys.***A703**, 240 (2002).

[44] D. Vretenar, G. A. Lalazissis, R. Behnsch, W Pöschl, and P. Ring, *Nucl. Phys.* **A621**, 853 (1997).

[45] J. Piekarewicz, *Phys. Rev.* **C64**, 024307 (2001).

[46] D. H. Youngblood, H.C. Clark, Y.-W. Lui, *Phys. Rev. Lett.***82**, 691 (1999).

[47] J. P. Blaizot, *Phys. Rep.* **64**, 171 (1980).

[48] B. K. Jennings and A. D. Jackson, *Phys. Rep.* **66**, 141 (1980).

[49] S. K. Patra, X. Viñas, M. Centelles and M. Del Estal, *Phys. Rev.* **C65**, 044304 (2002).

[50] I. Bombaci and U. Lombardo, *Phys. Rev.* **C44**, 1892 (1991).

[51] O. Bohigas, A. M. Lane and J. Martorell, *Phys. Rev.* **51**, 267 (1979).

[52] S. Hofmann, *Rep. Prog. Phys.* **61**, 639 (1998); *Eur. Phys. J.* **A15**, 195 (2002); S. Hofmann, and G. Münzenberg, *Rev. Mod. Phys.* **72**, 733 (2000).

[53] Yu. Ts. Oganessian *et al*, *Eur. Phys. J.* **A5**, 63 (1999); *Nature* **400**, 242 (1999); *Eur. Phys. J.* **A15**, 201 (2002).

[54] T. Bürvenich, K. Rutz, M. Bender, P.-G. Reinhard, J. A. Maruhn, and W. Greiner, *Eur. Phys. J.* **A3**, 139 (1998).

[55] P. Möller, and J. R. Nix, *Nucl. Phys.* **A549**, 84 (1992); *J. Phys.* **G20**, 1681 (1994).

[56] R. Smolańczuk, *Phys. Rev.* **C56**, 812 (1997).

[57] Zhongzhou Ren, Fei Tai, and Ding-Han Chen, *Phys. Rev. C* **66**, 064306 (2002).

[58] S. Goriely, M. Samyn, P. -H. Heenen, J. M. Pearson, and F. Tondeur, *Phys. Rev. C* **66**, 024326 (2002).

[59] T. Bürvenich, M. Bender, J. A. Maruhn, and P. -G. Reinhard, *Phys. Rev. C* **69**, 014307 (2004).

[60] M. Bender, K. Rutz, P. -G. Reinhard, J. A. Maruhn, and W. Greiner, *Phys. Rev. C* **60**, 034304 (1999).

[61] A. T. Kruppa, M. Bender, W. Nazarewicz, P. -G. Reinhard, T. Vertse, and S. Ćwiok, *Phys. Rev. C* **61**, 034313 (2000).

[62] M. Bender, W. Nazarewicz, P. -G. Reinhard, *Phys. Lett.* **B515**, 42 (2001).

[63] P. -G. Reinhard, M. Bender, and J. A. Maruhn, *Comm. Mod. Phys.* **2**, A177 (2002).

[64] B. Nerlo-Pomorska, K. Pomorski, J. Bartel, and K. Dietrich, *Phys. Rev.* **C66**, 051302 (2002).

[65] P. Ring and P. Schuck, *The Nuclear Many-Body Problem* (Springer-Verlag, Berlin, 1980).

[66] J. Meng and I. Tanihata, *Nucl. Phys.* **A650**, 176 (1999).

[67] G.A. Lalazissis, D. Vretenar and P. Ring, *Phys. Rev.* **C57**, 2294 (1998).

In: Quantum Field Theory: New Research
Editor: O. Kovras, pp. 103-122
ISBN 1-59454-509-X

Chapter 3

QUANTUM FIELD THEORY WITHOUT DIVERGENCE: QUANTIZATION OF FREE FIELDS

Shi-Hao Chen*
Department of Physics,
Harbin Institute of Technology, Harbin 150006;
Institute of Theoretical Physics,
Northeast Normal University, Changchun 130024, P. R. China

Abstract

We present a new Lagrangian density $\mathcal{L} = \mathcal{L}_f + \mathcal{L}_w$, $\mathcal{L}_f$ describes F-particles which form the given left-handed world, $\mathcal{L}_w$ describes W-particles which form the unknown right-handed world, $\mathcal{L}_f$ and $\mathcal{L}_w$ are symmetric, independent of each other before quantization and dependent on each other after quantization. $\langle 0 \,|H|\, 0\rangle$is naturally obtained. From this it is possible to determine the cosmological constant and to correct non-perturbational methods which depend on the energy of the vacuum state.

Keywords: Energy of vacuum state; Quantization of free fields; Transformation operators
PACS numbers: 11.10.Ef, 11.30.Ly, 11.20, 11.90.+t

1 Introduction

There are the following six problems which haven't been solved contently in the conventional quantum field theory (QFT).

1. The issue of the cosmological constant.

*E-mail: shchen@nenu.edu.cn

2. The problem of the divergence of Feynman integrals with loop diagrams.
3. The problem of the origin of asymmetry in the electroweak unified theory.
4. The problem of triviality of φ^4–theory.
5. The problems of dark matter and the origin of some cosmic phenomena.
6. The problem of the origin of asymmetry of matter and antimatter in quantity.

In brief, we construct a new Lagrangian and a new quantization method on the basis of a new conjecture, thereby give possible solutions to the four problems above.

There is an inconsistency between the conventional QFT and the general theory of relativity.

As is well known, before re-defining a Hamilton H as a normal-ordered product, the energy E_0 of the vacuum state is divergent. Because we may arbitrarily choose the zero point of energy in QFT, we can re-define E_0 to be zero, i.e., re-defining H as a normal-ordered product . This is, in fact, equivalent to demand in the conventional QFT.

$$\{a_{\mathbf{p}s}, a^+_{\mathbf{p}s}\} = \{b_{\mathbf{p}s}, b^+_{\mathbf{p}s}\} = [c_{\mathbf{k}\lambda}, c^+_{\mathbf{k}\lambda}] = 0,$$

But in fact these commutation relations are equal to 1, and in other cases, e.g. when propagators are derived, they must also be 1 and E_0 must be divergent. In the other hand, according to general theory of relativity, E_0 will cause a gravitational effect. Thus the conventional QFT is inconsistent with the general theory of relativity and the issue of cosmological constant arises.

According to the conventional viewpoint, divergence of Feynman integrals with loop diagrams is a necessary result of 'point-particle model', and it has been solved by introducing the bare mass and the bare charge or some concepts equivalent to them. This paper will show that this is not right and we can obtain a self-consistent theory which satisfies the following conditions: there is only one sort of physical parameters which are measurable and finite, and all Feynman integrals with loop diagrams are convergent.

In order to eliminate divergence of Feynman integrals with loop diagrams, many methods have been tried . For example, G. Scharf attempted to solve the divergent problem with the causal approach[1]. There is no divergence in some super-symmetric theories. But the super-symmetry theory lacks experiment foundations.

In order to explain the origin of left-right asymmetry, people generalize the standard electroweak unified model. According to the given generalized electroweak unified models which are left-right symmetric before symmetry spontaneously breaking, asymmetry is caused by symmetry spontaneously breaking[2]. In such models there must be many unknown particles with massive mass. Such models are troublesome. Hence the origin of asymmetry should be explored continuously.

More than 23% of matter in cosmos is dark matter (4% is bright matter). What is dark matter? Many hypothesis have been proposed. But this problem is still not solved contently. We think that asymmetry of left-right and existence of dark matter imply that there is possibly an unknown world. It is seen from the above mentioned that the conventional QFT is not perfect and should be corrected.

The train of thought of the present theory is as follows.

1. A new symmetry and a new Lagrangian density.

It is difficult to solve the problems above on the basis of the conventional QFT. In order to solve the problems, we present the following conjecture [3].

Conjecture There are two sorts of particles ——$F-particles$ described by $\mathcal{L}_f$ and $W-particles$ described by $\mathcal{L}_w$. $\mathcal{L}=\mathcal{L}_f+\mathcal{L}_w$, $\mathcal{L}_f$ and $\mathcal{L}_w$ are independent of each other before quantization and dependent on each other after quantization. The properties of a F-particle are the same as those of the W-particle corresponding to it.

We explain the conjecture as follows.

According to the conjecture, there is one sort of W-particles which is the correspondent of a sort of F-particles, e.g., there are $W-$electrons and $W-$photons corresponding to $F-$electrons and $F-$photons. There is no coupling between F-fields and W-fields, hence the energy determined by $\mathcal{L}_f$ and the energy determined by $\mathcal{L}_w$ are respectively conservational, and a real F-particle and a real W-particle cannot transform from one to another. But after quantization, $\mathcal{L}_f$ and $\mathcal{L}_w$ will be dependent on each other and the two sorts of virtual particles can transform from one to another.

Because there is no coupling between the $F-fields$ in $\mathcal{L}_f$ and the $W-fields$ in $\mathcal{L}_w$ by a quantizable field, there is no affection of the W-fields for the F-fields except gravitation, and vice versa. W-matter is entirely dark for the F-world and cannot be detected by the F-world via any method except gravitation, and vice versa. On the other hand, because the Lagrangian density $\mathcal{L}_f$ is the same as that of the conventional QED, the results obtained from the conventional QED can also be obtained from the present theory. Thus, the present theory does not contradict experimental confirmations and the standard electroweak unified model.

The physics basis of the conjecture is to re-explain the physics meanings of negative energies. The relativistic theory is very perfect, and existence of negative energies is its essential character. We think that positive energies and negative energies depend on each other, not only are negative energies not a difficulty, but have profound physical meanings. Existence of antiparticles is only, in fact, a result of particle-inversion symmetry, and do not reveal the essence of negative energies. For example, we can also suppose that there are particles and antiparticles with negative energy. From this, we think that existence of positive energies and negative energies imply that there are two sorts of particles and the two sorts of particles are symmetric. The present paper supposes that the two sorts of particles possess all positive energies. In fact, this is not necessary. Because $\mathcal{L}_F$ and $\mathcal{L}_W$ are independent of each other, there is no interaction and mutual transformation of the two sorts of matter. Thus no contradiction will appear if there is matter with negative energy. In the other paper[3] we suppose that there are both matter with negative energy (W-particles) and matter with positive energy (F-particles) and try to solve the problems above.

We call the conjecture the F-W (fire-water) symmetry conjecture. We may also call conjecture the L-R (left-right) symmetry conjecture since $\mathcal{L}_f$ and $\mathcal{L}_w$ describe respectively the left-hand world (matter world) and right-hand world (dark-matter world) and $\mathcal{L}_f + \mathcal{L}_w$ is left-right symmetry.

2. Transformation operators and a new method to quantize fields.

Because there are the two sorts of particles, we can define transformation operators which transform a F-particle into a W-particle or a W-particle into a F-particle (see (3.23)), and can quantize fields by them replacing creation and annihilation operators in the conventional QFT. Consequently it is necessary that the coupling coefficient g_f and the mass m_{ef} respectively become operators G_F and M_F determined by S_w , g_w and m_{ew} respectively become operators G_W and M_W determined by S_f. Here S_w and S_f are the scattering operators respectively determined by $\mathcal{L}_w$ and $\mathcal{L}_f$. Thus after quantization, $\mathcal{L}_f$ and $\mathcal{L}_w$ will be dependent on each other.

3. Two sorts of corrections.

In the conventional QED, there are two sorts of parameters, e.g., the physical charge and the bare charge, and one of corrections originating S equivalent to S_f. In contrast with the conventional QED, in the present theory there is only one sort of parameters defined at so-called subtraction point $g_f(q_2, q_1) = g_w(q_2, q_1) = g_0$ and $m_{ef}(q) = m_{ew}(q) = m_{e0}$, but there are two sorts of corrections originating from S_w and S_f to scattering amplitudes, g_0 and m_{e0}. Consequently both S_w and S_f determine the loop-diagram corrections. When all n-loop corrections originating from S_f and S_w are simultaneously considered, the integrands causing divergence in $\langle F_f \mid S_f \mid F_i \rangle$ or $\langle W_f \mid S_w \mid W_i \rangle$ will cancel each other out, hence all Feynman integrals are convergent. For example, the one-loop correction to the mass of a free F-electron is

$$\begin{aligned}\delta m &= m_{ef}^{(1)}(q) = m_{eff}^{(1)}(q) + m_{efw}^{(1)}(q) \\ &= \frac{3m\alpha}{4i\pi^3}\int d^4k\left\{\frac{1}{(k^2+m^2)^2} - \frac{1}{(k^2+m^2)^2}\right\} = 0,\end{aligned} \tag{1.1}$$

where $m_{eff}^{(1)}$ originates from S_f , $m_{efw}^{(1)}$ originates from S_w. Thus it is unnecessary to introduce counter-terms and regularization. We give a set of complete Feynman rules to evaluate Feynman integrals by the new concepts.

4. There is only corrections to vertexes.

A correction to a propagator can be regarded as the sum of partial corrections to the two vertexes joining the propagator. Similarly, correction to an external line can be regarded as the partial correction to the vertex joining the external line. Both ideas are equivalent. But the new idea has not practical significance in the conventional QFT. In contrast with the conventional QFT, the new idea has practical significance in the new QFT. A correction with n-loops to a vertex is determined by a whole Feynman diagram group with n-loops (WFDGnL) originating from S_w and S_f in the present theory. The WFDGnL contains the corrections to a propagator or an external line. Such Feynman integral corresponding to the WFDGnL must be convergent. The correction determined by a WFDGnL to the mass of a free particle must be zero. Consequently, there is only corrections to vertexes in the present theory. This is comprehensible since the corrections to a mass and a external line are determined by coupling constant and all corrections are zero if coupling constant is zero.

5. $\langle 0 \mid H \mid 0\rangle \equiv E_0 = E_{f0} + E_{w0} = 0$ is naturally derived. Thus sum of the cosmological constant and contribution of Higgs fields can be determined according to data of astronomical observation, and it is possible to correct non-perturbational methods which depend on the energy of the ground state in QFT.

6. Generalizing the present theory to the electroweak unified theory, we will see a possible origin of asymmetry. According to this model, $\mathcal{L} = \mathcal{L}_w + \mathcal{L}_f$ is symmetric, hence the world is symmetric in essence. But the world observed by us is asymmetric since $\mathcal{L}_w$ or $\mathcal{L}_f$ is asymmetric. In this model there is no unknown particle with a massive mass.

7. Because there is no interaction between the F-particles and the W-particles by a quantizable field, the only possibility is that there is repulsion or gravitation between the two sorts of matter. If the new interaction is gravitation, W-matter is the candidate for dark matter[4]

8. If we can determine a coupling coefficient $g(p_1, p_2)$ for any momenta meeting at a vertex, we can get a accurate Lagragian density $\mathcal{L}(g(p_1, p_2))$and the corresponding scattering operator $S(g(p_1, p_2))$, and get accurate scattering amplitudes by only tree figures coming the scattering operator $S(g(p_1, p_2))$. But this is impossible. We can only determine $g(p_1, p_2)$ for some momenta meeting at a vertex, e.g., $g(q_1, q_2)$, here $g(q_1$ and $q_2)$ are the momenta at the subtraction point, hence $\mathcal{L}(g(p_1, p_2))$ and $S(g(p_1, p_2))$ not practical. In fact, we can only determine approximate $\mathcal{L}(g(q_1, q_2))$ and $S(g(q_1, q_2))$, and get scattering amplitudes by only $S(g(q_1, q_2))$ and perturbation. Thus loop-diagram correction is necessary. From $S(g(q_1, q_2))$ we can get $S(g^{(1-loop)}(p_1, p_2))$ and $S(g^{(2-loop)}(p_1, p_2))$, etc..

The present theory contains four parts. The first part takes QED as an example to illuminate the method to reconstruct QFT, and give the solutions to the issue of the cosmological constant and the problem of divergent Feynman integrals in QED. The first part is the present paper and following two papers. The second part discuss the problems on dark matter[4]. The third part discusses the problem of the origin of asymmetry in the electroweak unified theory in detail. The fourth part discusses the problem of the origin of asymmetry of matter and antimatter in quantity. The fifth part discusses the problem of triviality of φ^4−theory.

2 Lagrangian density

We suppose the Lagrangian density for the free Dirac fields and the Maxwell fields to be

$$\mathcal{L}_0 = \mathcal{L}_{f0} + \mathcal{L}_{w0}, \tag{2.1}$$

$$\mathcal{L}_{f0} = -\overline{\psi}(x)(\gamma_\mu \partial_\mu + m)\psi(x) - \frac{1}{2}\partial_\mu A_\nu \partial_\mu A_\nu, \tag{2.2}$$

$$\mathcal{L}_{w0} = \overline{\underline{\psi}}(x)(\gamma_\mu \partial_\mu + m)\underline{\psi}(x) - \frac{1}{2}\partial_\mu \underline{A}_\nu \partial_\mu \underline{A}_\nu, \tag{2.3}$$

(2.2) and (2.3) imply the Lorentz gauge to be already fixed. $\mathcal{L}_{f0}$ is the same as that of conventional QED. The difference between (2.1) and the corresponding Lagrangian density in the conventional QED is $\mathcal{L}_{w0}$ which describes W-particles. We call ψ, A_μ, $\underline{\psi}$ and $\underline{A}_\mu$ the F-electron field, the F-photon field, the W-electron field and the W-photon field, respectively. The signs of the fermion parts in $\mathcal{L}_{f0}$ and $\mathcal{L}_{w0}$ are opposite, the signs of the boson parts are the same. The difference comes from the difference of properties of fermions and bosons. This difference is not essential. The key of matter is that F-particles and W-particles are symmetric. In fact, redefining field operators by transformation operators, we can also have $\mathcal{L}_{f0}$ and $\mathcal{L}_{w0}$ to be symmetric.

The conjugate fields corresponding to the fields are respectively

$$\pi_\psi = \frac{\partial \mathcal{L}}{\partial \dot{\psi}} = i\psi^+, \qquad \pi_\mu = \frac{\partial \mathcal{L}}{\partial \dot{A}_\mu} = \dot{A}_\mu, \tag{2.4}$$

$$\pi_{\underline{\psi}} = \frac{\partial \mathcal{L}}{\partial \dot{\underline{\psi}}} = -i\underline{\psi}^+, \qquad \underline{\pi}_\mu = \frac{\partial \mathcal{L}}{\partial \dot{\underline{A}}_\mu} = \dot{\underline{A}}_\mu. \tag{2.5}$$

From the Noether's theorem, we obtain the conservational quantities

$$H_0 = H_{F0} + H_{W0}, \tag{2.6}$$

$$H_{F0} = \int d^3x [\psi^+ \gamma_4 (\gamma_j \partial_j + m) \cdot \psi + \frac{1}{2}\left(\dot{A}_\mu \cdot \dot{A}_\mu + \partial_j A_\nu \cdot \partial_j A_\nu\right)], \tag{2.7}$$

$$H_{W0} = -\int d^3x[(\underline{\psi}^+\gamma_4(\gamma_j\partial_j + m)\cdot\underline{\psi} - \frac{1}{2}(\dot{\underline{A}}_\mu \cdot \dot{\underline{A}}_\mu + \partial_j\underline{A}_\nu \cdot \partial_j\underline{A}_\nu)], \tag{2.8}$$

$$Q = Q_F + Q_W, \quad Q_F = \int d^3x\psi^+\cdot\psi, \quad Q_W = \int d^3x\underline{\psi}^+\cdot\underline{\psi}. \tag{2.9}$$

The global gauge transformations corresponding to (2.9) are

$$\psi \to \psi' = e^{i\alpha}\psi, \ \ \underline{\psi} \to \underline{\psi}' = e^{-i\alpha}\underline{\psi}\,, A_\mu \to A'_\mu = A_\mu, \ \underline{A}_\mu \to \underline{A}'_\mu = \underline{A}_\mu. \tag{2.10}$$

The Euler-Lagrange equations of motion being derived from the Hamilton's variational principle are

$$i\frac{\partial}{\partial t}\psi = \hat{H}_0\psi, \quad \Box A_\mu = 0, \tag{2.11}$$

$$i\frac{\partial}{\partial t}\underline{\psi} = \hat{H}_0\underline{\psi}, \quad \Box\underline{A}_\mu = 0. \tag{2.12}$$

It is seen from (2.2)-(2.3) and (2.11)-(2.12) that although $\mathcal{L}_{f0} \neq \mathcal{L}_{w0}$, the equations satisfied by $\underline{\psi}$ and $\underline{A}_\mu$ are the same as those satisfied by ψ and A_μ, respectively. This implies that for a relativistic physical system, only equations of motion are insufficient for complete description of all properties of the system. A complete Lagrangian density is very necessary.

When ψ, etc., are regarded as the classical fields and

$$\partial_\mu A_\mu = \partial_\mu \underline{A}_\mu = 0, \tag{2.13}$$

ψ and $\underline{\psi}$ can be expanded in terms of the complete set of plane-wave solutions

$$\frac{1}{\sqrt{V}}u_{\mathbf{p}s}e^{ipx}, \qquad \frac{1}{\sqrt{V}}v_{\mathbf{p}s}e^{-ipx}, \quad s = 1, 2, \tag{2.14}$$

where $px = px - E_{\mathbf{p}}t$, $E_{\mathbf{p}} = \sqrt{\mathbf{p}^2 + m^2}$, and A_μ and $\underline{A}_\mu$ can be expanded in terms of the complete set

$$\frac{1}{\sqrt{2\omega_{\mathbf{k}}V}}e^{\lambda}_{\mathbf{k}\mu}e^{\pm ikx}, \tag{2.15}$$

where $kx = kx - \omega_{\mathbf{k}}t, \omega_{\mathbf{k}} =\mid k \mid, \lambda = 1, 2,$. To get a completeness relation, it is necessary to form a quartet of orthonormal 4-vectors [5].

$$e_k^1 = \left(\varepsilon_{\mathbf{k}}^1, 0\right), \; e_k^2 = \left(\varepsilon_{\mathbf{k}}^2, 0\right), \; e_k^3 = -\left[k + \eta\left(k\eta\right)\right]/k\eta, \; \eta = (0,0,0,i),$$

$$e_k^4 = i\eta, \quad \varepsilon_{\mathbf{k}}^{1,2} \cdot \mathbf{k} = \mathbf{0}. \qquad e_{\mathbf{k}}^{\lambda} e_{\mathbf{k}}^{\lambda'} = \delta_{\lambda\lambda'}, \qquad \sum_{\lambda=1}^{4} e_{\mathbf{k}\mu}^{\lambda} e_{\mathbf{k}\nu}^{\lambda} = \delta_{\mu\nu}.$$

3 Quantization for free fields

3.1 Field operators and equations of motion

We now regard ψ etc., as quantum fields. ψ, A_μ, $\underline{\psi}$ and $\underline{A}_\mu$ as the solutions of the equations of the quantum fields (2.11) – (2.12) can also be expanded in terms of the complete sets (2.14) and (2.15), respectively, only the expanding coefficients are all operators. Thus, for free fields we have

$$\psi_0\left(x\right) = \frac{1}{\sqrt{V}} \sum_{\mathbf{p}s} \left(\underline{I}_{\mathbf{p}} \lessdot a_{\mathbf{p}s}(t) \mid u_{\mathbf{p}s} e^{i\mathbf{p}\mathbf{x}} + \mid b_{\mathbf{p}s}(t) \gtrdot \underline{I}_{(-\mathbf{p})} v_{\mathbf{p}s} e^{-i\mathbf{p}\mathbf{x}}\right), \tag{3.1}$$

$$A_{0\mu}\left(x\right) = \frac{1}{\sqrt{V}} \sum_{\mathbf{k}} \frac{1}{\sqrt{2\omega_{\mathbf{k}}}} \sum_{\lambda=1}^{4} e_{\mathbf{k}\mu}^{\lambda} \left(\underline{j}_{\mathbf{k}} \lessdot c_{\mathbf{k}\lambda}(t) \mid e^{i\mathbf{k}\mathbf{x}} + \mid \bar{c}_{\mathbf{k}\lambda}(t) \gtrdot \underline{j}_{(-\mathbf{k})} e^{-i\mathbf{k}\mathbf{x}}\right), \tag{3.2}$$

$$\underline{\psi}_0\left(x\right) = \frac{1}{\sqrt{V}} \sum_{\mathbf{p}s} \left(\mid \underline{b}_{\mathbf{p}s}(t) \gtrdot I_{\mathbf{p}} u_{\mathbf{p}s} e^{i\mathbf{p}\mathbf{x}} + I_{(-\mathbf{p})} \lessdot \underline{a}_{\mathbf{p}s}(t) \mid v_{\mathbf{p}s} e^{-i\mathbf{p}\mathbf{x}}\right), \tag{3.3}$$

$$\underline{A}_{0\mu}\left(x\right) = \frac{1}{\sqrt{V}} \sum_{\mathbf{k}} \frac{1}{\sqrt{2\omega_{\mathbf{k}}}} \sum_{\lambda=1}^{4} e_{\mathbf{k}\mu}^{\lambda} \left(\mid \underline{\bar{c}}_{\mathbf{k}\lambda}(t) \gtrdot j_{(-\mathbf{k})} e^{i\mathbf{k}\mathbf{x}} + j_{\mathbf{k}} \lessdot \underline{c}_{\mathbf{k}\lambda}(t) \mid e^{-i\mathbf{k}\mathbf{x}}\right), \tag{3.4}$$

$$\pi_{0\psi} = i\psi_0^+\left(x\right) \equiv \frac{i}{\sqrt{V}} \sum_{\mathbf{p}s} \left(\mid a_{\mathbf{p}s}(t) \gtrdot \underline{I}_{\mathbf{p}}^+ u_{\mathbf{p}s}^+ e^{-i\mathbf{p}\mathbf{x}} + \underline{I}_{(-\mathbf{p})}^+ \lessdot b_{\mathbf{p}s}(t) \mid v_{\mathbf{p}s}^+ e^{i\mathbf{p}\mathbf{x}}\right), \tag{3.5}$$

$$\pi_{0\mu} = \dot{A}_{0\mu}\left(x\right) \equiv \frac{-i}{\sqrt{V}} \sum_{\mathbf{k}} \sqrt{\frac{\omega_{\mathbf{k}}}{2}} \sum_{\lambda=4}^{4} e_{\mathbf{k}\mu}^{\lambda} \left(\underline{j}_{\mathbf{k}} \lessdot c_{\mathbf{k}\lambda}(t) \mid e^{i\mathbf{k}\mathbf{x}} - \mid \bar{c}_{\mathbf{k}\lambda}(t) \gtrdot \underline{j}_{(-\mathbf{k})} e^{-i\mathbf{k}\mathbf{x}}\right), \tag{3.6}$$

$$\underline{\pi}_{0\psi} = -i\underline{\psi}_0^+(x) \equiv \frac{-i}{\sqrt{V}} \sum_{\mathbf{p}s} \left(I_{\mathbf{p}}^+ \leqslant \underline{b}_{\mathbf{p}s}(t) \mid u_{\mathbf{p}s}^+ e^{-i\mathbf{px}} + \mid \underline{a}_{\mathbf{p}s}(t) \geqslant I_{-\mathbf{p}}^+ v_{\mathbf{p}s}^+ e^{i\mathbf{px}} \right), \quad (3.7)$$

$$\underline{\pi}_{0\mu} = \dot{\underline{A}}_{0\mu}(x) \equiv \frac{-i}{\sqrt{V}} \sum_{\mathbf{k}} \sqrt{\frac{\omega_{\mathbf{k}}}{2}} \sum_{\lambda=1}^{4} e_{\mathbf{k}\mu}^{\lambda} \left(\mid \bar{\underline{c}}_{\mathbf{k}\lambda} \geqslant j_{(-\mathbf{k})} e^{i\mathbf{kx}} - j_{\mathbf{k}} \leqslant \underline{c}_{\mathbf{k}\lambda} \mid e^{-i\mathbf{kx}} \right), \quad (3.8)$$

$$\mid \bar{\underline{c}}_{\mathbf{k}\lambda} \geqslant = \begin{cases} \mid \underline{c}_{\mathbf{k}\lambda} \geqslant, \lambda = 1,2,3, \\ -\mid \underline{c}_{\mathbf{k}\lambda} \geqslant, \lambda = 4 \end{cases}, \mid \bar{c}_{\mathbf{k}\lambda} \geqslant = \begin{cases} \mid c_{\mathbf{k}\lambda} \geqslant, \lambda = 1,2,3, \\ -\mid c_{\mathbf{k}\lambda} \geqslant, \lambda = 4 \end{cases}, \quad (3.9)$$

$$\alpha_{\mathbf{p}s}(t) = \alpha_{\mathbf{p}s} e^{-i\omega_{\mathbf{p}} t}, \ \beta_{\mathbf{p}s}(t) = \beta_{\mathbf{p}s} e^{i\omega_{\mathbf{p}} t}, \ \zeta_{\mathbf{k}\lambda}(t) = \zeta_{\mathbf{k}\lambda} e^{-i\omega_{\mathbf{k}} t}, \ \eta_{\mathbf{k}\lambda}(t) = \eta_{\mathbf{k}\lambda} e^{i\omega_{\mathbf{k}} t}, \quad (3.10)$$

where $\alpha_{\mathbf{p}s} = \leqslant a_{\mathbf{p}s} \mid, \leqslant b_{\mathbf{p}s} \mid, \mid \underline{b}_{\mathbf{p}s} \geqslant, \mid \underline{a}_{\mathbf{p}s} \geqslant$, $\beta_{\mathbf{p}s} = \mid b_{\mathbf{p}s} \geqslant, \mid a_{\mathbf{p}s} \geqslant, \leqslant \underline{a}_{\mathbf{p}s} \mid, \leqslant \underline{b}_{\mathbf{p}s} \mid$, $\zeta_{\mathbf{k}\lambda} = \leqslant c_{\mathbf{k}\lambda} \mid, \mid \bar{\underline{c}}_{\mathbf{k}\lambda} \geqslant$, $\eta_{\mathbf{k}\lambda} = \mid \bar{c}_{\mathbf{k}\lambda} \geqslant, \leqslant \underline{c}_{\mathbf{k}\lambda} \mid$. Such an operator as $\leqslant \underline{a}_{\mathbf{p}s}(t) \mid$ changes with time, but $\underline{I}_{\mathbf{p}}$ and $j_{\mathbf{k}}$ etc. do not change. In the Heisenberg picture the evolution of a quantum field system as time is carried by the field operators according to the equations of motion

$$\dot{F} = -i\left[F, H_0\right] = -i\left[F, H_{0F}\right], \quad (3.11)$$

$$\dot{W} = i\left[W, H_0\right] = i\left[W, H_{0W}\right], \quad (3.12)$$

where $F = \psi_0(x), \psi_0^+(x), A_{0\mu}(x), \pi_{0\mu}(x), \mid a_{\mathbf{p}s}(t) \geqslant, \mid b_{\mathbf{p}s}(t) \geqslant, \mid c_{\mathbf{k}\lambda}(t) \geqslant, \leqslant a_{\mathbf{p}s}(t) \mid, \leqslant b_{\mathbf{p}s}(t) \mid$ and $\leqslant c_{\mathbf{k}\lambda}(t) \mid$, $W = \underline{\psi}_0(x), \underline{\psi}_0^+(x), \underline{A}_{0\mu}(x), \underline{\pi}_{0\mu}(x), \mid \underline{a}_{\mathbf{p}s}(t) \geqslant, \mid \underline{b}_{\mathbf{p}s}(t) \geqslant, \mid \underline{c}_{\mathbf{k}\lambda}(t) \geqslant, \leqslant \underline{a}_{\mathbf{p}s}(t) \mid, \leqslant \underline{b}_{\mathbf{p}s}(t) \mid$ and $\leqslant \underline{c}_{\mathbf{k}\lambda}(t) \mid$. The equation (3.11) is well-known as the Heisenberg equation, while (3.12) is a new equation of motion. We will see

$$\left[H_{0W}, H_{0F}\right] = \left[H_{0F}, H_0\right] = \left[H_{0W}, H_0\right] = 0, \quad (3.13)$$

hence H_{0F} and H_{0W} are the constants of motion. Thus, from $(3.11) - (3.13)$ we have

$$F(t) = e^{iH_0 t} F(0) e^{-iH_0 t} = e^{iH_{F0} t} F(0) e^{-iH_{F0} t}, \quad (3.14)$$

$$W(t) = e^{-iH_0 t} W(0) e^{iH_0 t} = e^{-iH_{W0} t} W(0) e^{iH_{W0} t}, \quad (3.15)$$

$(3.11) - (3.12)$ are consistent with $(2.11) - (2.12)$, and $(3.14) - (3.15)$ are consistent with (3.10).

3.2 Properties and multiplication rules of the transformation operators.

1. A transformation operator as $I_{\mathbf{p}} \leqslant \underline{a}_{\mathbf{p}s} \mid$ is regarded as a whole. Thus, though $I_{\mathbf{p}}$ and $\leqslant \underline{a}_{\mathbf{p}s} \mid$ can be separated, the order of its two parts cannot be reversed, say, $I_{\mathbf{p}} \leqslant \underline{a}_{\mathbf{p}s} \mid$ cannot be written as $\leqslant \underline{a}_{\mathbf{p}s} \mid I_{\mathbf{p}}$.

2. Commutators or anti-commutators of such operators as $\leqslant a_{\mathbf{p}s} \mid$ and $\mid \underline{c}_{\mathbf{k}\lambda} \geqslant$.

Such an operator in the form $\leqslant a_{\mathbf{p}s} \mid$ is equivalent to an annihilation operator $a_{\mathbf{p}s}$, and such an operator in the form $\mid a_{\mathbf{p}s} \geqslant$ is equivalent to an creation operator $a^{+}_{\mathbf{p}s}$ in the conventional QED. Thus, let $\alpha = a$, b, $\underline{a}$ and $\underline{b}$, $\gamma = c$ and $\underline{c}$, we have

$$\{\leqslant \alpha_{\mathbf{p}s}(t) \mid, \mid \alpha_{\mathbf{p}'s'}(t) \geqslant\} = \delta_{\alpha\alpha'}\delta_{\mathbf{p}\mathbf{p}'}\delta_{ss'} \tag{3.16}$$

$$[\leqslant \gamma_{\mathbf{k}\lambda}(t) \mid, \mid \gamma'_{\mathbf{k}'\lambda'}(t) \geqslant] = \begin{cases} \delta_{\gamma\gamma'}\delta_{\mathbf{k}\mathbf{k}'}\delta_{\lambda\lambda'}, \lambda = 1,2,3, \\ -\delta_{\gamma\gamma'}\delta_{\mathbf{k}\mathbf{k}'}\delta_{\lambda\lambda'}, \lambda = 4 \end{cases}, \tag{3.17}$$

The other equal-time commutators or anti-commutators are all zero.

3. States and inner products of states.

(3.16) and (3.17) are the same as the anti-commutation relations and the commutation relations of the conventional QED, respectively. As the conventional QED, from (3.16)-(3.17) we get free fermion states and n-photon states to be

$$\mid \alpha_{\mathbf{p}s}\rangle = \mid \alpha_{\mathbf{p}s} \geqslant \mid 0\rangle, \qquad \langle \alpha_{\mathbf{p}s} \mid = \langle 0 \mid \leqslant \alpha_{\mathbf{p}s} \mid, \tag{3.18}$$

$$\mid N_{\mathbf{k}\lambda}\rangle \equiv \frac{1}{\sqrt{n!}}(\mid \gamma_{\mathbf{k}\lambda} \geqslant)^n \mid 0\rangle,\ \langle N_{\mathbf{k}\lambda} \mid \equiv \frac{1}{\sqrt{n!}}\langle 0 \mid (\leqslant \gamma_{\mathbf{k}\lambda} \mid)^n, \tag{3.19}$$

where $N = n$, $\underline{n}$, $\gamma = c$ and $\underline{c}$. Considering (3.16)-(3.17), $\langle 0 \mid 0\rangle = 1$ and

$$\leqslant \alpha_{\mathbf{p}s} \mid 0\rangle = \leqslant \gamma_{\mathbf{k}\lambda} \mid 0\rangle = \langle 0 \mid \alpha_{\mathbf{p}s} \geqslant = \langle 0 \mid \gamma_{\mathbf{k}\lambda} \geqslant = 0, \tag{3.20}$$

we obtain the inner products of states to be

$$\langle \alpha_{\mathbf{p}s} \mid \cdot \mid \alpha'_{\mathbf{p}'s'}\rangle = \langle \alpha_{\mathbf{p}s} \mid \alpha'_{\mathbf{p}'s'}\rangle = \delta_{\alpha\alpha'}\delta_{\mathbf{p}\mathbf{p}'}\delta_{ss'}, \tag{3.21}$$

$$\langle \gamma_{\mathbf{k}\lambda} \mid \cdot \mid \gamma'_{\mathbf{k}'\lambda'}\rangle = \langle \gamma_{\mathbf{k}\lambda} \mid \gamma'_{\mathbf{k}'\lambda'}\rangle = \begin{cases} \delta_{\gamma\gamma'}\delta_{\mathbf{k}\mathbf{k}'}\delta_{\lambda\lambda'}, \lambda = 1,2,3, \\ -\delta_{\gamma\gamma'}\delta_{\mathbf{k}\mathbf{k}'}\delta_{\lambda\lambda'}, \lambda = 4 \end{cases} \tag{3.22}$$

$$\langle \beta_{\mathbf{p}s} \mid \cdot \mid \gamma_{\mathbf{k}\lambda}\rangle = 0. \tag{3.23}$$

4. Inner products of $I_{\mathbf{p}}$, $J_{\mathbf{p}}$,$\underline{I}_{\mathbf{p}}$, and $\underline{J}_{\mathbf{p}}$.

The original form of transformation operators is the same as $\mid \underline{a}_{\mathbf{p}s}\rangle \leqslant a_{\mathbf{p}s} \mid$, $\mid b_{\mathbf{p}s} \geqslant \langle \underline{b}_{\mathbf{p}s} \mid$ or $\mid c_{\mathbf{k}\lambda}\rangle \leqslant \underline{c}_{\mathbf{k}\lambda} \mid$, and their essential meaning is

$$\begin{aligned}
\mid \underline{a}_{\mathbf{p}'s'}\rangle \leqslant a_{\mathbf{p}s} \mid\mid a_{\mathbf{p}s}\rangle &= \mid \underline{a}_{\mathbf{p}s}\rangle \delta_{\mathbf{p}'\mathbf{p}}\delta_{s's}, \\
\langle \underline{b}_{\mathbf{p}'s'} \mid\mid \underline{b}_{\mathbf{p}s} \geqslant \langle b_{\mathbf{p}s} \mid &= \delta_{\mathbf{p}'\mathbf{p}}\delta_{s's}\langle b_{\mathbf{p}s} \mid \\
\mid c_{\mathbf{k}'\lambda'}\rangle \leqslant \underline{c}_{\mathbf{k}\lambda} \mid\mid \underline{c}_{\mathbf{k}\lambda}\rangle &= \mid c_{\mathbf{k}\lambda}\rangle \delta_{\mathbf{k}'\mathbf{k}}\delta_{\lambda'\lambda}.
\end{aligned} \tag{3.24}$$

By such transformation operators we can also construct a new QFT from which the same results as the present papers can be derived with more complicated discussion. But for convenience we rewrite such transformation operators in (3.24) as

$$\begin{aligned}
&\mid \underline{a}_{\mathbf{p}s}\rangle \leqslant a_{\mathbf{p}s}(t) \mid = \mid \underline{a}_{\mathbf{p}s}\rangle \underline{I}_{\mathbf{p}}^{+} \cdot \underline{I}_{\mathbf{p}} \leqslant a_{\mathbf{p}s}(t) \mid, \\
&\mid b_{\mathbf{p}s}(t) \geqslant \langle \underline{b}_{\mathbf{p}s} \mid = \mid b_{\mathbf{p}s}(t) \geqslant \underline{I}_{(-\mathbf{p})} \cdot \underline{I}_{(-\mathbf{p})}^{+} \langle \underline{b}_{\mathbf{p}s} \mid, \\
&\mid \underline{c}_{\mathbf{k}\lambda}\rangle \leqslant c_{\mathbf{k}\lambda}(t) \mid = \mid \underline{c}_{\mathbf{k}\lambda}\rangle \underline{J}_{\mathbf{k}}^{+} \cdot \underline{J}_{\mathbf{k}} \leqslant c_{\mathbf{k}\lambda}(t) \mid, \\
&\mid b_{\mathbf{p}s}\rangle \leqslant \underline{b}_{\mathbf{p}s}(t) \mid = \mid b_{\mathbf{p}s}\rangle I_{\mathbf{p}}^{+} \cdot I_{\mathbf{p}} \leqslant \underline{b}_{\mathbf{p}s}(t) \mid, \\
&\mid a_{\mathbf{p}s}\rangle \leqslant \underline{a}_{\mathbf{p}s}(t) \mid = \mid a_{\mathbf{p}s}\rangle I_{(-\mathbf{p})}^{+} \cdot I_{(-\mathbf{p})} \leqslant \underline{a}_{\mathbf{p}s}(t) \mid, \\
&\mid c_{\mathbf{k}\lambda}\rangle \leqslant \underline{c}_{\mathbf{k}\lambda}(t) \mid = \mid c_{\mathbf{k}\lambda}\rangle J_{\mathbf{k}}^{+} \cdot J_{\mathbf{k}} \leqslant \underline{c}_{\mathbf{k}\lambda}(t) \mid .
\end{aligned} \tag{3.25}$$

where $\underline{I}_{\mathbf{p}}^{+} \cdot \underline{I}_{\mathbf{p}} = \underline{J}_{\mathbf{k}}^{+} \cdot \underline{J}_{\mathbf{k}} = I_{\mathbf{p}}^{+} \cdot I_{\mathbf{p}} = J_{\mathbf{k}}^{+} \cdot J_{\mathbf{k}} = 1$. It is unnecessary to explain the physical meaning of $I_{\mathbf{p}}$ etc. in detail, since only for mathematical convenience $I_{\mathbf{p}}$ etc. are be introduced. In order to easily deal with problems, we divide such an operators into two parts. For example, we divide $\mid \underline{a}_{\mathbf{p}s}\rangle \underline{I}_{\mathbf{p}}^{+} \cdot \underline{I}_{\mathbf{p}} \leqslant a_{\mathbf{p}s}(t) \mid$ into $\mid \underline{a}_{\mathbf{p}s}\rangle \underline{I}_{\mathbf{p}}^{+}$ and $\underline{I}_{\mathbf{p}} \leqslant a_{\mathbf{p}s}(t) \mid$, leave such a part as $\mid \underline{\alpha}_{\mathbf{p}s}\rangle \underline{I}_{\mathbf{p}}^{+}$ to belong a coupling operator or a mass operator (see below), and leave such a part as $\underline{I}_{\mathbf{p}} \leqslant \alpha_{\mathbf{p}s} \mid$ to belong a field operator and also call it a transformation operator. Thus the field operators can be written as the form (3.1)-(3.8).

Their properties and the multiplication rules are as follows.

$$J_{-\mathbf{k}} = J_{\mathbf{k}}^{+}, \quad \underline{J}_{-\mathbf{k}} = \underline{J}_{\mathbf{k}}^{+} \tag{3.26}$$

Their inner products are defined as

$$\begin{aligned}
&I_{\mathbf{p}'}^{+} \cdot I_{\mathbf{p}} = I_{\mathbf{p}} \cdot I_{\mathbf{p}'}^{+} = \underline{I}_{\mathbf{p}'}^{+} \cdot \underline{I}_{\mathbf{p}} = \underline{I}_{\mathbf{p}} \cdot \underline{I}_{\mathbf{p}'}^{+} = \delta_{\mathbf{p}\mathbf{p}'}, \\
&J_{\mathbf{k}'}^{+} \cdot J_{\mathbf{k}} = \underline{J}_{\mathbf{k}'}^{+} \cdot \underline{J}_{\mathbf{k}} = \delta_{\mathbf{k}\mathbf{k}'},
\end{aligned} \tag{3.27}$$

the other inner products are all zero.

5.Multiplication rules and commutation or anti-commutation relations for the transformation operators.

Let $K = I_{\mathbf{p}}, I_{\mathbf{p}}^{+}, \underline{I}_{\mathbf{p}}, \underline{I}_{\mathbf{p}}^{+}, J_{\mathbf{k}}$ and $\underline{J}_{\mathbf{k}}$. To multiple a transformation operator containing a factor K by other operator containing a factor K, we define the product to be such an operator obtained after first achieving multiplication of the two $K's$, i.e.,

$$AK_A \cdot K_B B \equiv A(K_A \cdot K_B)B, \tag{3.28a}$$

$$K_B B \cdot AK_A \equiv \pm A(K_A \cdot K_B)B, \tag{3.28b}$$

$$K_B B \cdot K_A A = (K_B \cdot K_A)BA, \; BK_B \cdot AK_A = BA(K_B \cdot K_A), \tag{3.28c}$$

$$[A, K] = 0. \tag{3.28d}$$

where A, $B = \leqslant a_{\mathbf{p}s}(t) \mid$ etc. or $\mid b_{\mathbf{p}s}\rangle$ etc., when bath A and B are fermion operators, (3.28b) takes '-', and otherwise takes '+'. K can be constructed by states[3], but this is not necessary. A product of two F-transformation operators (two W-transformation operators) is a F-operators which transform a F-state into other F-state (a W-operators which transform a W-state into other W-state). It can be seen from (3.27) that the product of a F-transformation operator and a W-transformation operator must be equal to zero.

When many operators containing K multiply, associative law does no longer hold water. Hence we should appoint the associative order of such the operators. The complexity cannot appear in fact, since after completing products of two field operators and products of field operators and coupling operators or mass operators (see the following paper), the Lagrangian or Hamiltonian density does no longer contain K so that multiplication of many operators containing K will not appear. In interaction parts of Lagrangian or Hamiltonian density every field operator will directly multiply a coupling operator or a mass operator.

When a transformation operator and a operator not containing K multiply, the multiplication rule is the same as usual.

From (3.16)-(3.17), (3.27)-(3.28) and (3.1)-(3.8), we easily derive all commutation or anti-commutation relations of the operators containing K to be zero, e.g.,

$$\begin{aligned} &\{\underline{I}_{\mathbf{p}} \leqslant a_{\mathbf{p}s}(t) \mid, \mid a_{\mathbf{p}'s'}(t) \geqslant \underline{I}_{\mathbf{p}'}^{+}\} \\ &\quad = \{\underline{I}_{-\mathbf{p}}^{+} \leqslant b_{\mathbf{p}s}(t) \mid, \mid b_{\mathbf{p}'s'}(t) \geqslant \underline{I}_{-\mathbf{p}'}\} \\ &\quad = [\underline{J}_{\mathbf{k}} \leqslant c_{\mathbf{k}\lambda}(t) \mid, \mid \bar{c}_{\mathbf{k}'\lambda'}(t) \geqslant \underline{J}_{\mathbf{k}'}^{+}] = 0, \end{aligned} \tag{3.29}$$

$$\begin{aligned} &\{I_{-\mathbf{p}}^{+} \leqslant \underline{a}_{\mathbf{p}s}(t) \mid, \mid \underline{a}_{\mathbf{p}'s'}(t) \geqslant I_{-\mathbf{p}'}\} \\ &\quad = \{I_{\mathbf{p}} \leqslant \underline{b}_{\mathbf{p}s}(t) \mid, \mid \underline{b}_{\mathbf{p}'s'}(t) \geqslant I_{\mathbf{p}'}^{+} \\ &\quad = [J_{\mathbf{k}} \leqslant \underline{c}_{\mathbf{k}\lambda}(t) \mid, \mid \underline{\bar{c}}_{\mathbf{k}'\lambda'}(t) \geqslant J_{\mathbf{k}'}^{+}] = 0, \end{aligned} \tag{3.30}$$

$$\{\psi_{0\alpha}(\mathbf{x}, t), \psi_{0\beta}^{+}(\mathbf{y}, t)\} = \{\psi_{0\alpha}(\mathbf{x}, t), \psi_{0\beta}(\mathbf{y}, t)\} = \{\psi_{0\alpha}^{+}(\mathbf{x}, t), \psi_{0\beta}^{+}(\mathbf{y}, t)\} = 0, \tag{3.31}$$

$$[A_{0\mu}(\mathbf{x}, \mathbf{t}), \pi_{0\nu}(\mathbf{y}, \mathbf{t})] = [A_{0\mu}(\mathbf{x}, \mathbf{t}), A_{0\nu}(\mathbf{y}, \mathbf{t})] = [\pi_{0\mu}(\mathbf{x}, \mathbf{t}), \pi_{0\nu}(\mathbf{y}, \mathbf{t})] = 0, \tag{3.32}$$

$$\{\underline{\psi}_{0\alpha}(\mathbf{x},t),\underline{\psi}^+_{0\beta}(\mathbf{y},t)\}=\{\underline{\psi}_{0\alpha}(\mathbf{x},t),\underline{\psi}_{0\beta}(\mathbf{y},t)\}=\{\underline{\psi}^+_{0\alpha}(\mathbf{x},t),\underline{\psi}^+_{0\beta}(\mathbf{y},t)\}=0, \quad (3.33)$$

$$[\underline{A}_{0\mu}(\mathbf{x},\mathbf{t}),\underline{\pi}_{0\nu}(\mathbf{y},\mathbf{t})]=[\underline{A}_{0\mu}(\mathbf{x},\mathbf{t}),\underline{A}_{0\nu}(\mathbf{y},\mathbf{t})]=[\underline{\pi}_{0\mu}(\mathbf{x},\mathbf{t}),\underline{\pi}_{0\nu}(\mathbf{y},\mathbf{t})]=0. \quad (3.34)$$

The commutation or anti-commutation relations are different from those of the conventional QED.

The new QFT seem to be more complicated than the conventional QFT from the rules above, in fact it is not true since regularization and counter-terms are no longer necessary in the new QFT.

4 The energies and charges of particles

From $(2.7)-(2.9)$, $(3.1)-(3.8)$ and $(3.26)-(3.28)$ we obtain

$$H_{F0}=\sum_{\mathbf{p}s}E_{\mathbf{p}}\left(\mid a_{\mathbf{p}s}\gg\ll a_{\mathbf{p}s}\mid+\mid b_{\mathbf{p}s}\gg\ll b_{\mathbf{p}s}\mid\right)$$

$$+\sum_{\mathbf{k}}\omega_{\mathbf{k}}\left(\sum_{\lambda=1}^{3}\mid c_{\mathbf{k}\lambda}\gg\ll c_{\mathbf{k}\lambda}\mid-\mid c_{\mathbf{k}4}\gg\ll c_{\mathbf{k}4}\mid\right), \quad (4.1)$$

$$H_{W0}=\sum_{\mathbf{p}s}E_{\mathbf{p}}\left(\mid \underline{b}_{\mathbf{p}s}\gg\ll \underline{b}_{\mathbf{p}s}\mid+\mid \underline{a}_{\mathbf{p}s}\gg\ll \underline{a}_{\mathbf{p}s}\mid\right)$$

$$+\sum_{\mathbf{k}}\omega_{\mathbf{k}}\left(\sum_{\lambda=1}^{3}\mid \underline{c}_{\mathbf{k}\lambda}\gg\ll \underline{c}_{\mathbf{k}\lambda}\mid-\mid \underline{c}_{\mathbf{k}4}\gg\ll \underline{c}_{\mathbf{k}4}\mid\right), \quad (4.2)$$

$$Q_F=\sum_{\mathbf{p}s}\left(\mid a_{\mathbf{p}s}\gg\ll a_{\mathbf{p}s}\mid-\mid b_{\mathbf{p}s}\gg\ll b_{\mathbf{p}s}\mid\right), \quad (4.3)$$

$$Q_W=\sum_{\mathbf{p}s}\left(-\mid \underline{b}_{\mathbf{p}s}\gg\ll \underline{b}_{\mathbf{p}s}\mid+\mid \underline{a}_{\mathbf{p}s}\gg\ll \underline{a}_{\mathbf{p}s}\mid\right). \quad (4.4)$$

From (4.1) and (4.2) we see that energies are positive-definite and (3.11) and (3.12) are consistent with (3.10), respectively. It is easily seen from $(4.1)-(4.4)$ that

$$\langle\underline{\sigma}\mid H_0\mid\underline{\sigma}\rangle=\langle\sigma\mid H_0\mid\sigma\rangle, \quad (4.5)$$

$$\langle \underline{\sigma} \mid Q \mid \underline{\sigma} \rangle = \langle \sigma \mid Q \mid \sigma \rangle, \tag{4.6}$$

where $\sigma = a_{\mathbf{p}s},\ b_{\mathbf{p}s},\ c_{\mathbf{k}\lambda}$.

The Hamiltonian and charge operators can also be written as

$$H_{F0} = \int d^3x : [\psi_0'^+ \hat{H}_0 \psi_0' + \frac{1}{2}\left(\dot{A}_{0\mu}' \dot{A}_{0\mu}' + \partial_j A_{0\nu}' \partial_j A_{0\nu}'\right)] :, \tag{4.7}$$

$$H_{W0} = -\int d^3x : [(\underline{\psi}_0'^+ \hat{H}_0 \underline{\psi}_0' - \frac{1}{2}(\dot{\underline{A}}_{0\mu}' \dot{\underline{A}}_{0\mu}' + \partial_j \underline{A}_{0\nu}' \partial_j \underline{A}_{0\nu}')] :, \tag{4.8}$$

$$Q_F = \int d^3x : \psi_0'^+ \psi_0' :, \quad Q_F = \int d^3x : \underline{\psi}_0'^+ \underline{\psi}_0' :, \tag{4.9}$$

where the double-dot notation : $\cdots$: is known as normal ordering. An operator product is in normal ordered form if all operators as $\mid \alpha \gg$ stand to the left of all operators as $\ll \alpha \mid$. In (4.7)-(4.9),

$$\psi_0'(x) = \frac{1}{\sqrt{V}} \sum_{\mathbf{p}s} \left(\ll a_{\mathbf{p}s}(t) \mid u_{\mathbf{p}s} e^{i\mathbf{px}} + \mid b_{\mathbf{p}s}(t) \gg v_{\mathbf{p}s} e^{-i\mathbf{px}}\right), \tag{4.10}$$

$$A_{0\mu}'(x) = \frac{1}{\sqrt{V}} \sum_{\mathbf{k}} \frac{1}{\sqrt{2\omega_{\mathbf{k}}}} \sum_{\lambda=1}^{4} e_{\mathbf{k}\mu}^{\lambda} \left(\ll c_{\mathbf{k}\lambda}(t) \mid e^{i\mathbf{kx}} + \mid \bar{c}_{\mathbf{k}\lambda}(t) \gg e^{-i\mathbf{kx}}\right), \tag{4.11}$$

$$\underline{\psi}_0'(x) = \frac{1}{\sqrt{V}} \sum_{\mathbf{p}s} \left(\mid \underline{b}_{\mathbf{p}s}(t) \gg u_{\mathbf{p}s} e^{i\mathbf{px}} + \ll \underline{a}_{\mathbf{p}s}(t) \mid v_{\mathbf{p}s} e^{-i\mathbf{px}}\right), \tag{4.12}$$

$$\underline{A}_{0\mu}'(x) = \frac{1}{\sqrt{V}} \sum_{\mathbf{k}} \frac{1}{\sqrt{2\omega_{\mathbf{k}}}} \sum_{\lambda=1}^{4} e_{\mathbf{k}\mu}^{\lambda} \left(\mid \underline{\bar{c}}_{\mathbf{k}\lambda}(t) \gg e^{i\mathbf{kx}} + \ll \underline{c}_{\mathbf{k}\lambda}(t) \mid e^{-i\mathbf{kx}}\right), \tag{4.13}$$

$$\pi_{0\psi}' = i\psi_{0(x)}'^+ = \frac{i}{\sqrt{V}} \sum_{\mathbf{p}s} \left(\mid a_{\mathbf{p}s}(t) \gg u_{\mathbf{p}s}^+ e^{-i\mathbf{px}} + \ll b_{\mathbf{p}s}(t) \mid v_{\mathbf{p}s}^+ e^{i\mathbf{px}}\right) \tag{4.14}$$

$$\pi'_{0\mu} = \dot{A}'_{0\mu}(x) = \frac{-i}{\sqrt{V}}\sum_{\mathbf{k}}\sqrt{\frac{\omega_{\mathbf{k}}}{2}}\sum_{\lambda=1}^{4} e^{\lambda}_{\mathbf{k}\mu}\left(\leqslant c_{\mathbf{k}\lambda}(t)\mid e^{i\mathbf{kx}} - \mid \bar{c}_{\mathbf{k}\lambda}(t)\geqslant e^{-i\mathbf{kx}}\right), \quad (4.15)$$

$$\pi'_{0\psi} = -i\underline{\psi}'^{+}_{0}(x) = \frac{-i}{\sqrt{V}}\sum_{\mathbf{p}s}\left(\leqslant \underline{b}_{\mathbf{p}s}(t)\mid u^{+}_{\mathbf{p}s}e^{-i\mathbf{px}} + \mid \underline{a}_{\mathbf{p}s}(t)\geqslant v^{+}_{\mathbf{p}s}e^{i\mathbf{px}}\right), \quad (4.16)$$

$$\underline{\pi}'_{0\mu} = \underline{\dot{A}}'_{0\mu} = \frac{-i}{\sqrt{V}}\sum_{\mathbf{k}}\sqrt{\frac{\omega_{\mathbf{k}}}{2}}\sum_{\lambda=1}^{4} e^{\lambda}_{\mathbf{k}\mu}\left(\mid \underline{\bar{c}}_{\mathbf{k}\lambda}(t)\geqslant e^{i\mathbf{kx}} - \leqslant \underline{c}_{\mathbf{k}\lambda}(t)\mid e^{-i\mathbf{kx}}\right), \quad (4.17)$$

where the operators $\mid a_{\mathbf{p}s}(t)\geqslant$ etc., are the same as (3.10). From (3.16)-(3.17) and (4.10)-(4.17) we have

$$\{\psi'_{0\alpha}(\mathbf{x},t), \psi'^{+}_{0\beta}(\mathbf{y},t)\} = \{\underline{\psi}'_{0\alpha}(\mathbf{x},t), \underline{\psi}'^{+}_{0\beta}(\mathbf{y},t)\} = \delta(\mathbf{x}-\mathbf{y})\delta_{\alpha\beta}, \quad (4.18)$$

$$[A'_{0\mu}(\mathbf{x},t), \pi'_{0\nu}(\mathbf{y},t)] = [\underline{A}'_{0\mu}(\mathbf{x},t), \underline{\pi}'_{0\nu}(\mathbf{y},t)] = i\delta(\mathbf{x}-\mathbf{y})\delta_{\mu\nu}. \quad (4.19)$$

All other equal-time anti-commutators and commutators are zero. (4.18)-(4.19) are the same as those in the conventional QED.

In contrast with the conventional QFT, (4.1)-(4.4) or (4.7)-(4.9) are the deductions from the multiplication rules (3.28) and are determined by transformation operator such as $\underline{I}_{\mathbf{p}} \leqslant a_{\mathbf{p}s}(t)\mid$, but propagators can be deduce from (3.16)-(3.17) or (4.18)-(4.19) (see the following paper or [3]) and are determined by only such operator as $A'_{0\mu}(x,t)$ or $\leqslant c_{\mathbf{k}\lambda}(t)\mid$. Hence in present theory, (4.1)-(4.4) or (4.7)-(4.9) (thereby $\langle 0 \mid H \mid 0\rangle = 0$) and (3.16)-(3.17) or (4.18)-(4.19) are self-consistent. In the conventional QFT, both propagators and Hamiltonian are deduced from (4.18)-(4.19) or (3.16)-(3.17), hence it is inevitable that $\langle 0 \mid H \mid 0\rangle$ is divergent except to redefine H as a normal product. But that H is redefined as a normal product in the conventional QED, in fact, is equivalent to demand

$$\{a_{\mathbf{p}s}, a^{+}_{\mathbf{p}s}\} = \{b_{\mathbf{p}s}, b^{+}_{\mathbf{p}s}\} = [c_{\mathbf{k}\lambda}, c^{+}_{\mathbf{k}\lambda}] = \{\psi'_{0\alpha}(\mathbf{x},t), \psi'^{+}_{0\beta}(\mathbf{y},t)\}$$
$$= [A'_{0\mu}(\mathbf{x},t), \pi'_{0\nu}(\mathbf{y},t)] = 0.$$

In the case, all propagators will be zero. Thus the conventional QFT is not self-consistent.

5 Subsidiary condition

After the Maxwell field is quantized, the Lorentz condition (2.13) is no longer applicable. From (4.11) and (4.13) we have

$$(\partial_\mu A'_\mu)^+ = \frac{i}{\sqrt{V}} \sum_{\mathbf{k}} \frac{|\,\mathbf{k}\,|}{\sqrt{2\omega_{\mathbf{k}}}} (\leqslant c_{\mathbf{k}3} \mid -i \leqslant c_{\mathbf{k}4} \mid) e^{ikx}, \tag{5.1}$$

$$(\partial_\mu \underline{A}'_\mu)^- = -\frac{i}{\sqrt{V}} \sum_{\mathbf{k}} \frac{|\,\mathbf{k}\,|}{\sqrt{2\omega_{\mathbf{k}}}} (\leqslant \underline{c}_{\mathbf{k}3} \mid -i \leqslant \underline{c}_{\mathbf{k}4} \mid) e^{-ikx}, \tag{5.2}$$

Thus we define the subsidiary condition to be

$$(\partial_\mu A'_\mu)^+ \mid c_p\rangle = 0, \tag{5.3}$$

$$(\partial_\mu \underline{A}'_\mu)^- \mid \underline{c}_p\rangle = 0. \tag{5.4}$$

$\mid c_p\rangle$ and $\mid \underline{c}_p\rangle$ are known as F-physics state ket and W-physics state ket, respectively. From $(5.1) - (5.4)$ we obtain

$$\mid c_p\rangle = \mid c_T\rangle\{1 + \sum_{\mathbf{k}} f(\mathbf{k}) \mid c_{p\mathbf{k}}\rangle + \cdots + \sum_{\mathbf{k}_1\cdots\mathbf{k}_n} f(\mathbf{k}_1\cdots\mathbf{k}_n) \mid c_{p\mathbf{k}_1}\cdots c_{p\mathbf{k}_n}\rangle\}, \tag{5.5}$$

$$\mid \underline{c}_p\rangle = \mid \underline{c}_T\rangle\{1 + \sum_{\mathbf{k}} \underline{f}(\mathbf{k}) \mid \underline{c}_{p\mathbf{k}}\rangle + \cdots$$
$$+ \sum_{\mathbf{k}_1\cdots\mathbf{k}_n} \underline{f}(\mathbf{k}_1\cdots\mathbf{k}_n) \mid \underline{c}_{p\mathbf{k}_1}\cdots \underline{c}_{p\mathbf{k}_n}\rangle\}, \tag{5.6}$$

where $\mid c_T\rangle$ and $\mid \underline{c}_T\rangle$ are states containing only transverse photons, and

$$\mid c_{p\mathbf{k}}\rangle = \mid c_{\mathbf{k}3}\rangle + i \mid c_{\mathbf{k}4}\rangle, \tag{5.7}$$

$$\mid \underline{c}_{p\mathbf{k}}\rangle = \mid \underline{c}_{\mathbf{k}3}\rangle + i \mid \underline{c}_{\mathbf{k}4}\rangle. \tag{5.8}$$

From (4.1)-(4.2) and (5.5)-(5.8) we obtain

$$\begin{aligned}\langle c_{p\mathbf{k}} \mid c_{p\mathbf{k}'}\rangle &= \langle \underline{c}_{p\mathbf{k}} \mid \underline{c}_{p\mathbf{k}'}\rangle \\ &= \langle c_{p\mathbf{k}} \mid H_0 \mid c_{p\mathbf{k}}\rangle = \langle \underline{c}_{p\mathbf{k}} \mid H_0 \mid \underline{c}_{p\mathbf{k}}\rangle = 0,\end{aligned} \tag{5.9}$$

$$\langle c_p \mid c_{p'}\rangle = \langle c_T \mid c_{T'}\rangle,\ \langle \underline{c}_p \mid \underline{c}_{p'}\rangle = \langle \underline{c}_T \mid \underline{c}_{T'}\rangle, \tag{5.10}$$

$$\begin{aligned}\langle c_p \mid H_0 \mid c_p\rangle &= \langle c_T \mid H_0 \mid c_T\rangle, \\ \langle \underline{c}_p \mid H_0 \mid \underline{c}_p\rangle &= \langle \underline{c}_T \mid H_0 \mid \underline{c}_T\rangle,\end{aligned} \tag{5.11}$$

6 The equations of motion

From (3.1) -(3.4) , (3.6) , (3.8) , (4.1) and (4.2) , we have

$$i\frac{\partial\psi_0}{\partial t} = [\psi_0, H_{F0}] = \hat{H}_0\psi_0, \tag{6.1}$$

$$i\frac{\partial\underline{\psi}_0}{\partial t} = -[\underline{\psi}_0, H_{W0}] = \hat{H}_0\underline{\psi}_0, \tag{6.2}$$

$$\frac{\partial A_{0\mu}}{\partial t} = -i\left[A_{0\mu}, H_{F0}\right], \qquad \frac{\partial \dot{A}_{0\mu}}{\partial t} = -i[\dot{A}_{0\mu}H_{F0}] = \nabla^2 A_{0\mu}, \tag{6.3}$$

$$\frac{\partial \underline{A}_{0\mu}}{\partial t} = i[\underline{A}_{0\mu}, H_{W0}], \qquad \frac{\partial \underline{\dot{A}}_{0\mu}}{\partial t} = i[\underline{\dot{A}}_{0\mu}, H_{W0}] = \nabla^2 \underline{A}_{0\mu}. \tag{6.4}$$

$$i\frac{\partial\psi_0'}{\partial t} = \left[\psi_0', H_{F0}\right] = \hat{H}_0\psi_0', \tag{6.5}$$

$$i\frac{\partial\underline{\psi}_0'}{\partial t} = -[\underline{\psi}_0', H_{W0}] = \hat{H}_0\underline{\psi}_0', \tag{6.6}$$

$$\frac{\partial A_{0\mu}'}{\partial t} = -i\left[A_{0\mu}', H_{F0}\right], \qquad \frac{\partial \dot{A}_{0\mu}'}{\partial t} = -i[\dot{A}_{0\mu}'H_{F0}] = \nabla^2 A_{0\mu}', \tag{6.7}$$

$$\frac{\partial \underline{A}'_{0\mu}}{\partial t}=i[\underline{A}'_{0\mu},H_{W0}],\qquad \frac{\partial \dot{\underline{A}}'_{0\mu}}{\partial t}=i[\dot{\underline{A}}'_{0\mu},H_{W0}]=\nabla^2\underline{A}'_{0\mu}. \tag{6.8}$$

Since $[H_0,H_{F0}]=[H_0,H_{W0}]=0$, H_{F0} and H_{W0} are the constants of motion. Thus we obtain (3.11)-(3.12) and

$$\psi'_0\left(\mathbf{x},t\right)=e^{iH_{F0}t}\psi'_0\left(\mathbf{x},\mathbf{0}\right)e^{-iH_{F0}t}, \tag{6.9}$$

$$\underline{\psi}'_0\left(\mathbf{x},t\right)=e_0^{-iH_{W0}t}\underline{\psi}'_0\left(\mathbf{x},\mathbf{0}\right)e^{iH_{W0}t}, \tag{6.10}$$

$$A'_{0\mu}\left(\mathbf{x},t\right)=e^{iH_{F0}t}A'_{0\mu}\left(\mathbf{x},\mathbf{0}\right)e^{-iH_{F0}t}, \tag{6.11}$$

$$\underline{A}'_{0\mu}\left(\mathbf{x},t\right)=e^{-iH_{W0}t}\underline{A}'_{0\mu}\left(\mathbf{x},\mathbf{0}\right)e^{iH_{W0}t}, \tag{6.12}$$

As seen the equations $(6.1)-(6.4)$ are consistent with $(2.11)-(2.12)$, respectively. From (4.7), (4.9), (4.10)-(4.11), (4.18)-(4.19), (6.5) and (6.7) we see that H_F, Q_F, ψ', A'_μ, the commutators or anti-commutators and equations of ψ' and A'_μ are the same as those of the conventional QED.

7 The physical meanings of that the energy of the vacuum state is equal to zero

From (2.6), (4.1) and (4.2) we obtain that the energy of the vacuum state,

$$E_0=\langle 0\mid (H_{0F}+H_{0W})\mid 0\rangle=E_{0F}+E_{0W}=0. \tag{7.1}$$

It is easily seen that (7.1) is not relative to the definition for multiplication of transformation operators. (7.1) holds water provided H_0 is composed of transformation operators. We may arbitrarily choose the zero point of energy in quantum field theory. But in the theory of gravitation, if $E_0\neq 0$, E_0 will have gravitational effect. Hence we are not at liberty to redefine $E_0=0$. Thus the knotty problem of the cosmological constant arises in the conventional QFT and the relativistic theory of gravitation [6]. In the present theory $E_0=0$, hence the density of the energy of the vacuum state $\rho_{vac}=0$. Thus, it is seem that from the equation of gravitation field

$$R_{\mu\nu}-\frac{1}{2}g_{\mu\nu}R-\lambda g_{\mu\nu}=-8\pi G\{(T_{f\mu\nu}+T_{w\mu\nu})-\rho_{vac}g_{\mu\nu})\},$$

and astronomical observation values we can easily determine the cosmological constant λ. We will discuss the cosmological constant problem in another paper in detail.

We second simply discuss the correction originating from $E_0 = 0$ to a non-perturbational method in quantum field theory. When one evaluates the energy of a system by a non-perturbational method, e.g., a Hartree-type approximation[7], it is necessary to subtract the zero-point energy E_0[8]. According to the conventional quantum field theory $E_0 \neq 0$, while according to the present theory $E_0 = 0$, hence we will obtain different results in nature.

8 Summary

We have presented a new conjecture. According to the conjectures, there are F-particles and W-particles which are symmetric. From this we have presented a new Lagrangian density and a new quantization method for QED. That the energy of the vacuum state is equal to zero is naturally obtained. From this the cosmological constant is easily determined by astronomical observation values and it is possible to correct non-perturbational methods which depend on the energy of the ground state in quantum field theory.

Acknowledgement

I am very grateful to professor Zhan-yao Zhao for best support and professor Zhao-yan Wu for helpful discussions.

References

[1] G.Scharf, *Finite Quantum Electrodynamics*, Second Edition, Springer- Verlag (1995).

[2] Shi-Hao Chen, *Physica Energiae Fortis et Physica Nuclearis*, V9, no 6, 686 (1985).

[3] Shi-Hao Chen, *Quantum Field Theory Without Divergence A*, hep-th/0203220. Shi-Hao Chen, *Significance of Negative Energy State in Quantum Field Theory*, hep-th/0203230.

[4] Shi-Hao Chen, *A Possible Candidate for Dark Matter*, hep-th/0103234.

[5] David Lurie, *Particles and Fields*, p41-42, New York .London. Sydney (1968).

[6] Yu Yun Qiang, *An Introduction to General Relativity*, Second Edition, (1997), Peking University, Beijing.

[7] T. Kinoshita and Y. Nambu, *Phys. Rev.* 94 (1954) 598 ; A.L. Fetter and J.D.Walecka, *Quantum Theory of Many-Particle Systems*, McGraw-Hill, New York (1971).

[8] Shau-Jin Chang and Jon A. Wright, *Phys. Rev. D*, 12 (1975), 1595.

In: Quantum Field Theory: New Research
Editor: O. Kovras, pp. 123-142

ISBN 1-59454-509-X

Chapter 4

QUANTUM FIELD THEORY WITHOUT DIVERGENCE: QUANTIZATION OF INTERACTING FIELDS

Shi-Hao Chen*
Department of Physics,
Harbin Institute of Technology, Harbin 150006;
Institute of Theoretical Physics,
Northeast Normal University, Changchun 130024, P. R. China

Abstract

On the basis of preceding paper we discuss quantization for interacting fields, construct the coupling operators and mass operators, derive scattering operators and Feynman rules. We see that though independent of each other before quantization, $\mathcal{L}_f$ and $\mathcal{L}_w$ are dependent on each other after quantization. In contrast with the conventional QED, in the present theory, there is only one sort of parameters which are all finite and measurable, there are two sorts of corrections originating S_f and S_w, and all Feynman integrals are convergent.

Keywords: Coupling operators; Scattering operators; Propagators
PACS numbers: 11.10.Ef, 11.30.Ly, 12.20, 11.55.Ds, 11.90.+t

*E-mail: shchen@nenu.edu.cn

1 Introduction

In the preceding paper[1], we have presented a new Lagrangian density $\mathcal{L} = \mathcal{L}_f + \mathcal{L}_w$, have defined the transformation operators and have quantized free fields by the transformation operators. Consequentially, in order to quantize interacting fields, it is necessary to transform coupling coefficients and masses respectively into coupling operators and mass operators. Thus, though $\mathcal{L}_f$ and $\mathcal{L}_w$ are independent of each other before quantization, both must be dependent on each other after quantization, since $g_f(p_2, p_1)$ and $m_{ef}(p_2, p_1)$ are determined by S_w and $g_w(p_2, p_1)$ and $m_{ew}(p_2, p_1)$ are determined by S_f. S_f and S_w both determine scattering amplitudes. Thus, all scattering amplitudes will be convergent and it is unnecessary to introduce regularization and counter-terms. In the present paper we construct coupling operators and mass operators, derive scattering operators S_w, S_f and Feynman rules.

We think that for a self-consistent theory, there should be only one sort of physical parameters which are measurable and finite. The mass m_{e0} and the coupling constant g_0 defined at the so-called subtraction point are such parameters. From this we can determine $\mathcal{L}_f^{(0-loop)}$ and $\mathcal{L}_w^{(0-loop)}$, thereby determine scattering operators $S_f^{(0-loop)}$ and $S_w^{(0-loop)}$. Both $S_f^{(0-loop)}$ and $S_w^{(0-loop)}$ determine the one-loop corrections to the coupling constants and the masses, thereby determine the one-loop corrections to scattering amplitudes as well. Thus we can derive $S_f^{(1-loop)}$, $S_w^{(1-loop)}$, and $S_f^{(n-loop)}$ and $S_w^{(n-loop)}$ order by order.

2 Interaction Lagrangian density, Hamiltonian density and equations of motion

From (2.1) – (2.3) in [1] we can construct the Lagrangian density of the new QED

$$\mathcal{L} = \mathcal{L}_{f0} + \mathcal{L}_{w0} + \mathcal{L}_{fI} + \mathcal{L}_{wI}, \tag{2.1}$$

$$\mathcal{L}_{f0} = -\overline{\psi}(x)(\gamma_\mu \partial_\mu + m)\psi(x) - \frac{1}{2}\partial_\mu A_\nu \partial_\mu A_\nu, \quad \mathcal{L}_{fI} = ig\overline{\psi}\gamma_\mu A_\mu \psi, \tag{2.2}$$

$$\mathcal{L}_{w0} = \overline{\underline{\psi}}(x)(\gamma_\mu \partial_\mu + m)\underline{\psi}(x) - \frac{1}{2}\partial_\mu \underline{A}_\nu \partial_\mu \underline{A}_\nu, \quad \mathcal{L}_{wI} = ig\overline{\underline{\psi}}\gamma_\mu \underline{A}_\mu \underline{\psi}, \tag{2.3}$$

which is invariant under the following global gauge transformation.

$$\psi \to \psi' = e^{i\theta}\psi, \qquad \overline{\psi} \to \overline{\psi}' = \overline{\psi}e^{-i\theta}, \tag{2.4}$$

$$A_\mu \to A_\mu' = A_\mu + \partial_\mu \theta, \tag{2.5}$$

$$\underline{\psi} \to \underline{\psi}' = e^{-i\theta}\underline{\psi}, \qquad \overline{\underline{\psi}} \to \overline{\underline{\psi}}' = \overline{\underline{\psi}}e^{i\theta}, \tag{2.6}$$

$$\underline{A}_\mu \to \underline{A}'_\mu = \underline{A}_\mu + \partial_\mu\theta, \tag{2.7}$$

where ψ, A_μ, $\underline{\psi}$ and $\underline{A}_\mu$ are regarded as the classical fields, and g and m are constants. After quantization, as mentioned [1], field operators are composed of transformation operators, hence g and m must become respectively a coupling operator and a mass operator, i.e., in (2.2) and (2.3) ,

$$m \to M'_F = m + \left(M'_F - m\right) \equiv m + M_F, \quad g \to G_F\,;$$

$$m \to M'_W = m + \left(M'_W - m\right) \equiv m + M_W; \quad g \to G_W;$$

respectively, here all M_F, G_F , M_W and G_W are operators. They are determined on the basis of the gauge and Lorentz invariance of the Lagrangian density (2.1) . Thus we have

$$\mathcal{L}_{fI} = i\overline{\psi}\gamma_\mu \cdot G_F \cdot A_\mu\psi - \overline{\psi} \cdot M_F \cdot \psi, \tag{2.8}$$

$$\mathcal{L}_{wI} = i\overline{\underline{\psi}}\gamma_\mu \cdot G_W \cdot \underline{A}_\mu\underline{\psi} + \overline{\underline{\psi}} \cdot M_W \cdot \underline{\psi}, \tag{2.9}$$

In (2.8)-(2.9) a coupling operator or a mass operator directly multiplies by every field operator. From (2.1), (2.8) and (2.9) we obtain the Hamiltonian to be

$$H = H_F + H_W, \tag{2.10}$$

$$H_F = H_{F0} + H_{FI}, \quad H_W = H_{W0} + H_{WI}, \tag{2.11}$$

$$H_{FI} = \int d^3x \mathcal{H}_{fI} \equiv -\int d^3x \mathcal{L}_{fI}, \tag{2.12}$$

$$H_{WI} = \int d^3x \mathcal{H}_{wI} \equiv -\int d^3x \mathcal{L}_{wI}. \tag{2.13}$$

H_{F0} and H_{W0} are the same as (2.7)-(2.8) in [1]. The Euler-Lagrange equations of motion can be derived from (2.1), (2.8) and (2.9).

$$i\frac{\partial}{\partial t}\psi = \gamma_4\left(\gamma_j\partial_j - i\gamma_\mu G_F \cdot A_\mu + m + M_F\cdot\right)\psi, \tag{2.14}$$

$$\Box A_\mu = -i\overline{\psi}\gamma_\mu \cdot G_F \cdot \psi, \tag{2.15}$$

$$i\frac{\partial}{\partial t}\underline{\psi} = \gamma_4\left(\gamma_j\partial_j + i\gamma_\mu G_W \cdot \underline{A}_\mu + m + M_W\cdot\right)\underline{\psi}, \tag{2.16}$$

$$\Box \underline{A}_\mu = -i\underline{\overline{\psi}}\gamma_\mu \cdot G_W \cdot \underline{\psi}, \tag{2.17}$$

In the Heisenberg picture the evolution of a quantum field system as time is carried by the field operators according to the equations of motion as well,

$$\dot{F} = -i\left[F, H\right] = -i\left[F, H_F\right], \tag{2.18}$$

$$\dot{W} = i\left[W, H\right] = i\left[W, H_W\right], \tag{2.19}$$

where $F = \psi(x)$, $\psi^{+}(x)$, $A_\mu(x)$, $\pi_\mu(x)$, $\mid a_{\mathbf{p}s}(t) \gg$, $\mid b_{\mathbf{p}s}(t) \gg$, $\mid c_{\mathbf{k}\lambda}(t) \gg$,, $\ll a_{\mathbf{p}s}(t) \mid$, $\ll b_{\mathbf{p}s}(t) \mid$ and $\ll c_{\mathbf{k}\lambda}(t) \mid$, and $W = \underline{\psi}(x)$, $\underline{\psi}^{+}(x)$, $\underline{A}_\mu(x)$, $\underline{\pi}_\mu(x)$, $\mid \underline{a}_{\mathbf{p}s}(t) \gg$, $\mid \underline{b}_{\mathbf{p}s}(t) \gg$, $\mid \underline{c}_{\mathbf{k}\lambda}(t) \gg$, $\ll \underline{a}_{\mathbf{p}s}(t) \mid$, $\ll \underline{b}_{\mathbf{p}s}(t) \mid$ and $\ll \underline{c}_{\mathbf{k}\lambda}(t) \mid$. It can be proven that (2.18) and (2.19) are consistent with (2.14) – (2.17), respectively (see appendix A). The equal-time anticommutation and commutation relations are the same as [1] – (3.16) – (3.17) and [1] – (3.29) – (3.34), respectively. The equation (2.18) is well-known as the Heisenberg equation, while (2.19) is a new equation of motion. It is easily seen from (2.10) – (2.13) that

$$\left[H_F, H\right] = \left[H_W, H\right] = 0, \tag{2.20}$$

hence both H_F and H_W are the constants of motion. Thus, from (2.18) and (2.19) we have

$$F\left(\mathbf{x},t\right) = e^{iHt}F\left(\mathbf{x},0\right)e^{-iHt} = e^{iH_Ft}F\left(\mathbf{x},0\right)e^{-iH_Ft}, \tag{2.21}$$

$$W\left(\mathbf{x},t\right) = e^{-iHt}W\left(\mathbf{x},0\right)e^{iHt} = e^{-iH_Wt}W\left(\mathbf{x},0\right)e^{iH_Wt}. \tag{2.22}$$

At a given time, say $t = 0$, we can still expand the field operators in terms of their Fourier components as $[1] - (3.1) - (3.8)$, provided let $t = 0$ in $[1] - (3.1) - (3.8)$. Of course, in this case we cannot interpret $\leqslant \underline{a}_{\mathbf{p}s}(t) \mid, \mid b_{\mathbf{p}s}(t) \geqslant$, etc., as single-particle annihilation or creation operators. Passage from time $t = 0$ to t involves the replacements $[1]-(3.1)-(3.8)$ by $(2.21) - (2.22)$.

3 Coupling operators and mass operators

The coupling operators G_F, G_W and the mass operators M_F and M_W should satisfy the following demands.

1. After multiplied by field operators, a coupling operator and a mass operator should become a coupling coefficient and a mass, respectively.

2. The coupling operators and the mass operators possess the same symmetry as those satisfied by the Lagrangian density containing them, e.g., the Lorentz invariance, the symmetry between F-particles and W-particles, particle-antiparticle symmetry, etc..

In order to construct the coupling operators, we first define the coupling coefficients. Let $A_{gf}\left(\mid a_{\mathbf{p}_1 s_1} c_{\mathbf{k}\lambda}\rangle \rightarrow \mid a_{\mathbf{p}_2 s_2}\rangle\right)$ be a transition amplitude of an initial state $\mid a_{\mathbf{p}_1 s_1} c_{\mathbf{k}\lambda}\rangle$ to a final state $\mid a_{\mathbf{p}_2 s_2}\rangle$, here it is not necessary that p_1, p_2 and k satisfy the mass shell restrictions. We define the F-coupling constant as

$$g_f(\mid a_{\mathbf{p}_1 s_1} c_{\mathbf{k}\lambda}\rangle \rightarrow \mid a_{\mathbf{p}_2 s_2}\rangle) = \frac{A_{gf}\left(\mid a_{\mathbf{p}_1 s_1} c_{\mathbf{k}\lambda}\rangle \rightarrow \mid a_{\mathbf{p}_2 s_2}\rangle\right)}{A'_{gf}\left(\mid a_{\mathbf{p}_1 s_1} c_{\mathbf{k}\lambda}\rangle \rightarrow \mid a_{\mathbf{p}_2 s_2}\rangle\right)}$$

$$= \frac{\langle a_{\mathbf{p}_2 s_2} \mid S_f \mid a_{\mathbf{p}_1 s_1} c_{\mathbf{k}\lambda}\rangle}{A'_{gf}\left(\mid a_{\mathbf{p}_1 s_1} c_{\mathbf{k}\lambda}\rangle \rightarrow \mid a_{\mathbf{p}_2 s_2}\rangle\right)} = g_f\left(p_2, p_1\right), \tag{3.1}$$

where S_f is the scattering operator for F-states.

$$A'_{gf}\left(\mid a_{\mathbf{p}_1 s_1} c_{\mathbf{k}\lambda}\rangle \rightarrow \mid a_{\mathbf{p}_2 s_2}\rangle\right)$$

$$= \langle a_{\mathbf{p}_2 s_2} \mid \left(-\int d^4x : \overline{\psi}' \gamma_\mu A'_\mu \psi' :\right) \mid a_{\mathbf{p}_1 s_1} c_{\mathbf{k}\lambda}\rangle$$

$$= -\left(2\pi\right)^4 \delta^4\left(p_2 - p_1 - k\right) \frac{1}{V} \overline{u}_{\mathbf{p}_2 s_2} \gamma_\mu u_{\mathbf{p}_1 s_1} \frac{1}{\sqrt{2\omega_k V}} e^\lambda_{\mathbf{k}\mu}. \tag{3.2}$$

where $k = p_2 - p_1$, ψ' and A'_μ are the same as $[1] - (4.10) - (4.11)$ in form, but do not satisfy the equations for free particle when p_2, p_1 and k are not in mass shell. The act of A'_{gf} is only to eliminate the external-line factors of A_{gf}.

Why a coupling constant $g\left(k^2\right))$ or a mass $m\left(k^2\right))$ can be a constant for a given k^2 is because the corresponding interaction have some symmetries. Conversely, from the symmetries of interaction we can determine the symmetries of the coupling constant and the corresponding coupling operator. Considering the Lorentz invariance and that an outgoing

$\mid b_{(-\mathbf{p})}\rangle$ is equivalent to an ingoing $\mid a_{\mathbf{p}}\rangle$, and an outgoing $\mid c_{(-\mathbf{k})}\rangle$ is equivalent to an ingoing $\mid c_{\mathbf{k}}\rangle$, we have

$$\begin{aligned}
& g_f\left(p_2, p_1\right) \\
& = g_f\left(\mid c_{\mathbf{k}\lambda}\rangle \rightarrow\mid b_{(-\mathbf{p}_1 s_1)} a_{\mathbf{p}_2 s_2}\rangle\right) = g_f\left(\mid a_{\mathbf{p}_1 s_1} b_{(-\mathbf{p}_2 s_2)}\rangle \mid c_{\mathbf{k}\lambda}\rangle \rightarrow\mid 0\rangle\right) \\
& = g_f\left(\mid b_{(-\mathbf{p}_2 s_2)} c_{\mathbf{k}\lambda}\rangle \rightarrow\mid b_{(-\mathbf{p}_1 s_1)}\rangle\right) = g_f\left(\mid a_{\mathbf{p}_1 s_1}\rangle \rightarrow\mid c_{(-\mathbf{k}\lambda)} a_{\mathbf{p}_2 s_2}\rangle\right) \\
& = g_f\left(\mid 0\rangle \rightarrow\mid c_{(-\mathbf{k}\lambda)} b_{(-\mathbf{p}_1 s_1)} a_{\mathbf{p}_2 s_2}\rangle\right) = g_f\left(\mid a_{\mathbf{p}_1 s_1} b_{(-\mathbf{p}_2 s_2)}\rangle \rightarrow\mid c_{(-\mathbf{k}\lambda)}\rangle\right) \\
& = g_f\left(\mid b_{(-\mathbf{p}_2 s_2)}\rangle \rightarrow\mid c_{(-\mathbf{k}\lambda)} b_{(-\mathbf{p}_1 s_1)}\rangle\right) = g_f[(p_2 - p_1)^2] = g_f\left(-\mu^2\right).
\end{aligned} \tag{3.3}$$

Similarly, we can define the W-coupling constant

$$\begin{aligned}
g_w\left(p_2, p_1\right) &= g_w\left(\mid \underline{a}_{\mathbf{p}_1 s_1} \underline{c}_{\mathbf{k}\lambda}\rangle \rightarrow\mid \underline{a}_{\mathbf{p}_2 s_2}\rangle\right) \\
&= \frac{A_{gw}\left(\mid \underline{a}_{\mathbf{p}_1 s_1} \underline{c}_{\mathbf{k}\lambda}\rangle \rightarrow\mid \underline{a}_{\mathbf{p}_2 s_2}\rangle\right)}{A'_{gw}\left(\mid \underline{a}_{\mathbf{p}_1 s_1} \underline{c}_{\mathbf{k}\lambda}\rangle \rightarrow\mid \underline{a}_{\mathbf{p}_2 s_2}\rangle\right)} \\
&= \frac{\langle \underline{a}_{p_2 s_2} \mid S_w \mid \underline{a}_{\mathbf{p}_1 s_1} \underline{c}_{\mathbf{k}\lambda}\rangle}{A'_{gw}\left(\mid \underline{a}_{\mathbf{p}_2 s_2} \underline{c}_{\mathbf{k}\lambda}\rangle \rightarrow\mid \underline{a}_{\mathbf{p}_2 s_2}\rangle\right)}
\end{aligned} \tag{3.4}$$

$$\begin{aligned}
& A'_{gw}\left(\mid \underline{a}_{\mathbf{p}_1 s_1} \underline{c}_{\mathbf{k}\lambda}\rangle \rightarrow\mid \underline{a}_{\mathbf{p}_2 s_2}\rangle\right) \\
& = \langle \underline{a}_{\mathbf{p}_2 s_2} \mid \int d^4x : \underline{\overline{\psi}}' \gamma_\mu \underline{A}'_\mu \underline{\psi}' :\mid \underline{a}_{\mathbf{p}_1 s_1} \underline{c}_{\mathbf{k}\lambda}\rangle \\
& = (2\pi)^4 \delta^4\left(p_2 - p_1 - k\right) \frac{1}{V} \overline{v}_{\mathbf{p}_1 s_1} \gamma_\mu v_{\mathbf{p}_2 s_2} \frac{1}{\sqrt{2\omega_k V}} e^{\lambda}_{\mathbf{k}\mu},
\end{aligned} \tag{3.5}$$

Considering the symmetry of the F-particles and the W-particles, we have

$$g_f\left(p_2, p_1\right) = g_w\left(p_2, p_1\right) \equiv g\left(p_2, p_1\right) = g[(p_2 - p_1)^2] = g\left(-\mu^2\right). \tag{3.6}$$

What relation is there between $g_f\left(p_2, p_1\right)$ and G_F? We analyse G_F as follows.

Replacing $[1]-(3.10)$ or $[1]-(3.14)-(3.15)$ by (2.21)-(2.22), we obtain the expansions of ψ, A_μ, $\underline{\psi}$ and $\underline{A}_\mu$ which are the same as $[1]-(3.1)-(3.4)$ in form. Substituting the expansions into (2.12), (2.13), we obtain the expansions of the coupling terms H_{FI} and H_{WI}. Without loss of generality, we take a term in (2.12)

$$\mid a_{\mathbf{p}_2 s_2}(t) \gg I^+_{\mathbf{p}_2} \cdot G_F \mid \cdot I_{\mathbf{p}_1} \ll a_{\mathbf{p}_1 s_1}(t) \mid \underline{J}_{\mathbf{k}} \ll c_{\mathbf{k}\lambda}(t) \mid \tag{3.7}$$

as an example to illuminate the structure of G_F. The c-number part relating to external lines in (3.7) is ignored. Recalling [1] – (3.25) – (3.28), from the factor $I^+_{\mathbf{p}_2} G_F I_{\mathbf{p}_1} \underline{J}_{\mathbf{k}}$ we can see that the corresponding part in G_F can be written as

$$\underline{I}_{\mathbf{p}_2} \langle \underline{a}_{\mathbf{p}_2 s_2} \mid G'_F \mid \underline{a}_{\mathbf{p}_1 s_1} \underline{c}_{\mathbf{k}\lambda} \rangle \underline{I}^+_{\mathbf{p}_1} \underline{J}^+_{\mathbf{k}}. \tag{3.8}$$

Because $\langle \underline{a}_{\mathbf{p}_2 s_2} \mid$ and $\mid \underline{a}_{\mathbf{p}_1 s_1} \underline{c}_{\mathbf{k}\lambda} \rangle$ can be regarded as a final W-state and an initial W-state, $\langle \underline{a}_{\mathbf{p}_2 s_2} \mid G'_F \mid \underline{a}_{\mathbf{p}_1 s_1} \underline{c}_{\mathbf{k}\lambda} \rangle$ must be directly proportional to the scattering amplitude $A_{gw}\left(\mid \underline{a}_{\mathbf{p}_1 s_1} \underline{c}_{\mathbf{k}\lambda} \rangle \rightarrow \mid \underline{a}_{\mathbf{p}_2 s_2} \rangle\right)$. Comparing with (3.4), we define

$$\begin{aligned} \langle \underline{a}_{\mathbf{p}_2 s_2} \mid G'_F \mid \underline{a}_{\mathbf{p}_1 s_1} \underline{c}_{\mathbf{k}\lambda} \rangle &\equiv g_f\left(p_2, p_1\right) \\ &\equiv \frac{\langle \underline{a}_{\mathbf{p}_2 s_2} \mid S_w \mid \underline{a}_{\mathbf{p}_1 s_1} \underline{c}_{\mathbf{k}\lambda} \rangle}{A'_{gw}\left(\mid \underline{a}_{\mathbf{p}_2 s_2} \underline{c}_{\mathbf{k}\lambda} \rangle \rightarrow \mid \underline{a}_{\mathbf{p}_2 s_2} \rangle\right)}, \end{aligned} \tag{3.9a}$$

as a coupling coefficient. From (3.4) and (3.9a) we can anew obtain (3.6). This implies (3.9a) is consistent with (3.6). In general cases $p_2 \neq m^2$ or $p_1^2 \neq m^2$ in $g_f\left(p_2, p_1\right)$. From (3.8) and (3.9a) we can write (3.7) as

$$\mid a_{\mathbf{p}_2 s_2}(t) \geqslant g_f\left(p_2, p_1\right) \leqslant a_{\mathbf{p}_1 s_1}(t) \mid \leqslant c_{\mathbf{k}\lambda}(t) \mid . \tag{3.9b}$$

The momenta in $g_f\left(p_2, p_1\right)$ are equal to the momenta of propagators or external lines joining to $g_f\left(p_2, p_1\right)$. Thus we determine $g_f\left(p_2, p_1\right)$ and obtain

$$\begin{aligned} G_F &= \sum_{\mathbf{p}_2} \sum_{\mathbf{p}_1} g_f\left(p_2, p_1\right) \left\{ \underline{I}_{\mathbf{p}_2} \underline{I}^+_{\mathbf{p}_1} + \underline{I}_{\mathbf{p}_2} \underline{I}^+_{(-\mathbf{p}_1)} + \underline{I}_{(-\mathbf{p}_2)} \underline{I}^+_{\mathbf{p}_1} + \underline{I}_{(-\mathbf{p}_2)} \underline{I}^+_{(-\mathbf{p}_1)} \right\} \underline{J}^+_{\mathbf{k}} \\ &= \sum_{\mathbf{p}_2} \sum_{\mathbf{p}_1} g_f\left(p_2, p_1\right) \underline{I}_{\mathbf{p}_2} \underline{I}^+_{\mathbf{p}_1} \underline{J}_{(-\mathbf{k})}. \end{aligned} \tag{3.10}$$

For the initial W-state $\mid a_{\mathbf{p}_1 s_1} c_{\mathbf{k}\lambda} \rangle$ and the final W-state $\mid a_{\mathbf{p}_2 s_2} \rangle$, $g_f(p_2, p_1)$ is precise. If for arbitrary p_2 and p_1 we can also determine $g(p_2, p_1)$, (3.10) is the precise coupling operator. In fact it is impossible to determine all $g_f\left(p_2, p_1\right)$. We can only accurately determine some $g_f\left(p_1, p_2\right)$, e.g., $g_f\left(q_2, q_1\right)$, where q_2 and q_1 are the momenta at the so-called subtraction point which satisfy the restrictions

$$i\gamma q_1 + m_0 = i\gamma q_2 + m_0 = 0, \quad q' = q_2 - q_1, \quad q'^2 = 0. \tag{3.11}$$

Defining

$$g_f\left(q_2, q_1\right) = g_{f0} \tag{3.12}$$

and replacing $g_f\left(p_2, p_1\right)$ by g_{f0}, we obtain a approximate coupling operator

$$G_F^{(0)} = g_{f0} \sum_{\mathbf{p}_2} \sum_{\mathbf{p}_1} \underline{I}_{\mathbf{p}_2} \underline{I}^+_{\mathbf{p}_1} \underline{J}^+_{\mathbf{k}}. \tag{3.13}$$

Analogously to $G_F(p_2, p_1)$ and $G_F^{(0)}$, and considering the symmetry between $\mathcal{L}_f$ and $\mathcal{L}_w$, from (3.9) we have

$$\langle a_{\mathbf{p}_2 s_2} \mid G'_W \mid a_{\mathbf{p}_1 s_1} c_{\mathbf{k}\lambda} \rangle \equiv \frac{\langle a_{\mathbf{p}_2 s_2} \mid S_f \mid a_{\mathbf{p}_1 s_1} c_{\mathbf{k}\lambda} \rangle}{A'_{gf} \left(\mid a_{\mathbf{p}_1 s_1} c_{\mathbf{k}\lambda} \rangle \to \mid a_{\mathbf{p}_2 s_2} \rangle \right)}$$

$$\equiv g_w(p_2, p_1) = g_f(p_2, p_1), \tag{3.14}$$

$$G_W = \sum_{\mathbf{p}_2} \sum_{\mathbf{p}_1} g_w(p_2, p_1) \, I_{\mathbf{p}_2} I^+_{\mathbf{p}_1} \underline{J}^+_{\mathbf{k}}, \tag{3.15}$$

$$G_W^{(0)} = g_{w0} \sum_{\mathbf{p}_2} \sum_{\mathbf{p}_1} I_{\mathbf{p}_2} I^+_{\mathbf{p}_1} J^+_{\mathbf{k}}, \quad g_{w0}(q_2, q_1) = g_{f0} = g_0. \tag{3.16}$$

Let m_{ef} be the mass originating from the electromagnetic interaction, m'_f be the mass originating from the other interactions, $m_f = m'_f + m_{ef}$ is the total mass of a F-electron. Analogously to g_f, we define

$$m_{ef} \left(\mid a_{\mathbf{p}_1 s_1} \rangle \to \mid a_{\mathbf{p}_2 s_2} \rangle \right) = \frac{A_{mf} \left(\mid a_{\mathbf{p}_1 s_1} \rangle \to \mid a_{\mathbf{p}_2 s_2} \rangle \right)}{A'_{mf} \left(\mid a_{\mathbf{p}_1 s_1} \rangle \to \mid a_{\mathbf{p}_2 s_2} \rangle \right)}$$

$$= \frac{\langle a_{\mathbf{p}_2 s_2} \mid S_f \mid a_{\mathbf{p}_1 s_1} \rangle}{\langle a_{\mathbf{p}_2 s_2} \mid \left(-i \int d^4x : \overline{\psi}' \psi' : \right) \mid a_{\mathbf{p}_1 s_1} \rangle}, \tag{3.17}$$

$$A'_{mf} \left(\mid a_{\mathbf{p}_1 s_1} \rangle \to \mid a_{\mathbf{p}_2 s_2} \rangle \right) = \langle a_{\mathbf{p}_2 s_2} \mid \left(-i \int d^4x : \overline{\psi}' \psi' : \right) \mid a_{\mathbf{p}_1 s_1} \rangle$$

$$= -i \, (2\pi)^4 \, \delta^4 \left(p_2 - p_1 \right) \frac{1}{V} \overline{u}_{\mathbf{p}_2 s_2} u_{\mathbf{p}_1 s_1}. \tag{3.18}$$

Because of the symmetry of $\mid a_{\mathbf{p}_1 s_1} \rangle$ and $\mid b_{\mathbf{p}_1 s_1} \rangle$, we have

$$m_{ef} \left(\mid a_{\mathbf{p}_1 s_1} \rangle \to \mid a_{\mathbf{p}_2 s_2} \rangle \right) = m_{ef} \left(\mid b_{\mathbf{p}_1 s_1} \rangle \to \mid b_{\mathbf{p}_2 s_2} \rangle \right) = m_{ef} \left(p_1 \right). \tag{3.19}$$

Similarly, we can define the electromagnetic mass of a W-electron as

$$m_{ew} \left(p_1 \right) = \frac{A_{mw} \left(\mid \underline{a}_{\mathbf{p}_1 s_1} \rangle \to \mid \underline{a}_{\mathbf{p}_2 s_2} \rangle \right)}{A'_{mw} \left(\mid \underline{a}_{\mathbf{p}_1 s_1} \rangle \to \mid \underline{a}_{\mathbf{p}_2 s_2} \rangle \right)}$$

$$= \frac{\langle \underline{a}_{\mathbf{p}_2 s_2} \mid S_w \mid \underline{a}_{\mathbf{p}_1 s_{11}} \rangle}{\langle \underline{a}_{\mathbf{p}_2 s_2} \mid -i \int d^4x : \underline{\overline{\psi}'_0} \underline{\psi'_0} : \mid \underline{a}_{\mathbf{p}_1 s_{11}} \rangle}, \tag{3.20}$$

$$A'_{mw}\left(| \underline{a}_{\mathbf{p}_1 s_1}\rangle \rightarrow | \underline{a}_{\mathbf{p}_2 s_2}\rangle\right) = \langle \underline{a}_{\mathbf{p}_2 s_2} | -i \int d^4x : \overline{\underline{\psi}}'_0 \underline{\psi}'_0 :| \underline{a}_{\mathbf{p}_1 s_{11}}\rangle$$
$$= -i\left(2\pi\right)^4 \delta^4\left(p_1 - p_2\right) \frac{1}{V} \overline{v}_{\mathbf{p}_1 s_1} v_{\mathbf{p}_1 s_1}, \qquad (3.21)$$

Considering the symmetry of $\mathcal{L}_f$ and $\mathcal{L}_w$, we have

$$m_{ew}\left(p\right) = m_{ef}\left(p\right) \equiv m_e\left(p\right). \qquad (3.22)$$

Without loss of generality, we take a term in (2.12)

$$| a_{\mathbf{p}_2 s_2}(t) \geqslant I^+_{\mathbf{p}_2} \cdot M_F \cdot I_{\mathbf{p}_1} \leqslant a_{\mathbf{p}_1 s_1}(t) | \qquad (3.23)$$

as an example to illuminate the structure of M_F. Recalling [1] – (3.25) – (3.28), we can know that the part in M_F corresponding to $I^+_{\mathbf{p}_2} \cdot M_F \cdot I_{\mathbf{p}_1}$ should be written as

$$I_{\mathbf{p}_2} \langle \underline{a}_{\mathbf{p}_2 s_2} | M'_F | \underline{a}_{\mathbf{p}_1 s_1}\rangle I^+_{\mathbf{p}_1} \qquad (3.24)$$

Because $\langle \underline{a}_{\mathbf{p}_2 s_2}|$ and $| \underline{a}_{\mathbf{p}_1 s_1}\rangle$ may be regarded a initial W-state and a final W-state, respectively, $\langle \underline{a}_{\mathbf{p}_2 s_2} | M'_F | \underline{a}_{\mathbf{p}_1 s_1}\rangle$ must be directly proportional to the scattering amplitude $A_{mw}\left(| \underline{a}_{\mathbf{p}_1 s_1}\rangle \rightarrow | \underline{a}_{\mathbf{p}_2 s_2}\rangle\right)$. Comparing $\langle \underline{a}_{\mathbf{p}_2 s_2} | M'_F | \underline{a}_{\mathbf{p}_1 s_1}\rangle$ with (3.20), we can define $\langle \underline{a}_{\mathbf{p}_2 s_2} | M'_F | \underline{a}_{\mathbf{p}_1 s_1}\rangle$ as the electromagnetic mass of a F-electron,

$$\langle \underline{a}_{\mathbf{p}_2 s_2} | M'_F | \underline{a}_{\mathbf{p}_1 s_1}\rangle$$
$$\equiv \frac{\langle \underline{a}_{\mathbf{p}_2 s_2} | S_w | \underline{a}_{\mathbf{p}_1 s_{11}}\rangle}{\langle \underline{a}_{\mathbf{p}_2 s_2} | -i \int d^4x : \overline{\underline{\psi}}'_0 \underline{\psi}'_0 :| \underline{a}_{\mathbf{p}_1 s_{11}}\rangle} \equiv m_{ef}\left(p_1\right), \qquad (3.25)$$

where $p_2 = p_1$. From (3.20) and (3.25) we can anew obtain (3.22). It is seen that (3.25) is consistent with (3.22). Substituting (3.25) into (3.24), considering

$$\langle \underline{a}_{\mathbf{p}_2 s_2} | M'_F | \underline{a}_{\mathbf{p}_1 s_1}\rangle = \langle \underline{b}_{\mathbf{p}_2 s_2} | M'_F | \underline{b}_{\mathbf{p}_1 s_1}\rangle = m_{ef}\left(p_1\right)$$

and the expansions of $\overline{\underline{\psi}}$ and $\underline{\psi}$, we have

$$M_F = \sum_{\mathbf{p}_2}\sum_{\mathbf{p}_1} m_{ef}(p_1) \underline{I}_{\mathbf{p}_2} \underline{I}^+_{\mathbf{p}_1}. \qquad (3.26)$$

For some p, e.g., $p = q$, we can determine $m_{ef}\left(q\right)$. Replacing $m_{ef}\left(p_1\right)$ in (3.26) by $m_{ef}\left(q\right)$, we obtain a approximate mass operator

$$M^{(0)}_F = m_{ef0} \sum_{\mathbf{p}_2}\sum_{\mathbf{p}_1} \underline{I}_{\mathbf{p}_2} \underline{I}^+_{\mathbf{p}_1}, \qquad m_{ef0} \equiv m_{ef}\left(q\right). \qquad (3.27)$$

Analogously to (3.26) and (3.27) and considering the symmetry between $\mathcal{L}_f$ and $\mathcal{L}_w$, we have

$$\langle a_{\mathbf{p}_2 s_2} \mid M_W' \mid a_{\mathbf{p}_1 s_1} \rangle \equiv \frac{\langle a_{\mathbf{p}_2 s_2} \mid S_f \mid a_{\mathbf{p}_1 s_1} \rangle}{\langle a_{\mathbf{p}_2 s_2} \mid \left(-i \int d^4x : \overline{\psi}' \psi' : \right) \mid a_{\mathbf{p}_1 s_1} \rangle}$$

$$\equiv m_{ew}(p_1) = m_{ef}(p_1) = \langle \underline{a}_{p_2 s_2} \mid M_F' \mid \underline{a}_{p_1 s_1} \rangle, \tag{3.28}$$

$$M_W = \sum_{\mathbf{p}_2} \sum_{\mathbf{p}_1} m_{ew}(p_1) I_{\mathbf{p}_2} I_{\mathbf{p}_1}^+, \tag{3.29}$$

$$M_W^{(0)} = m_{ew0} \sum_{\mathbf{p}_2} \sum_{\mathbf{p}_1} I_{\mathbf{p}_2} I_{\mathbf{p}_1}^+, \quad m_{ew0} \equiv m_{ew}(q) = m_{ef0} \equiv m_{e0} \,. \tag{3.30}$$

Because we cannot differentiate m_{ef0} from m'_{f0} in $m_{f0} = m'_{f0} + m_{ef0}$, for convenience, we define

$$m_{ef0} = m_{ew0} = m_{e0} = 0, \qquad m_{f0} = m'_{f0} = m_{w0} = m'_{w0} = m_0. \tag{3.31}$$

Of course, for an interacting field operator $p^2 - p_0^2 \neq -m^2$ and $k^2 \neq 0$. When $p_2 = q_2$ and $p_1 = q_1$, both g_0 and m_{e0} are accurate. When $p_2 \neq q_2$ or $p_1 \neq q_1$, both g_0 and m_{e0} are approximate. If the subtraction point is a nonphysical point for a coupling constant, we assume that g can analytically expand from the nonphysical point into physical regions.

4 Expansion of the Hamiltonian

When multiplication of two transformation operators and multiplication of transformation operators and a coupling operator or a mass operator are accomplished, $\mathcal{L}$ can no longer contain factor K ($K = I_{\mathbf{p}}, I_{\mathbf{p}}^+, \underline{I}_{\mathbf{p}}, \underline{I}_{\mathbf{p}}^+, J_{\mathbf{k}}$ and $\underline{J}_{\mathbf{k}}$). Consequentially, Hamiltonian operator H and scattering operator S do not contain K as well. The essence of matter is just to derive such H and S which are composed of only such operator as $\mid \alpha \gg$ and $\ll \alpha \mid$. When many transformation operators multiply, associative law does no longer hold water, but the problem of associative order is easily solved owing to the reasons above. In fact, only when transformation operators are multiplied by a coupling operator or a mass operator, the problem arises. In this case, we define the order to be that the coupling operator or the mass operator directly multiply every transformation operator.

Thus substituting the expansions of ψ, $\overline{\psi}$, A_μ, $\underline{\psi}$, $\underline{\overline{\psi}}$ and $\underline{A}_\mu$ and (3.10), (3.15), (3.26) and (3.29) into (2.11)-(2.13), we obtain

$$H_{F0} = \sum_{\mathbf{p}s} \{ | a_{\mathbf{p}s}(t) \gg\ll a_{\mathbf{p}s}(t) | u^{+}_{\mathbf{p}s}\gamma_4 (i\gamma_j p_j + m) u_{\mathbf{p}s}$$
$$+ \ll b_{(-\mathbf{p})s}(t) |\ll a_{\mathbf{p}s}(t) | v^{+}_{(-\mathbf{p})s}\gamma_4 (i\gamma_j p_j + m) u_{\mathbf{p}s}$$
$$+ | a_{(-\mathbf{p})s}(t) \gg| b_{\mathbf{p}s}(t) \gg u^{+}_{(-\mathbf{p})s}\gamma_4 (-i\gamma_j p_j + m) v_{\mathbf{p}s}$$
$$- | b_{\mathbf{p}s}(t) \gg\ll b_{\mathbf{p}s}(t) | v^{+}_{\mathbf{p}s}\gamma_4 (-i\gamma_j p_j + m) v_{\mathbf{p}s}\}$$
$$+ \sum_{\mathbf{k}} \frac{\omega_{\mathbf{k}}^2 + \mathbf{k}^2}{2\omega_{\mathbf{k}}} \cdot$$
$$\{ \sum_{\lambda=1}^{3} | c_{\mathbf{k}\lambda}(t) \gg\ll c_{\mathbf{k}\lambda}(t) | - | c_{\mathbf{k}4}(t) \gg\ll c_{\mathbf{k}4}(t) | \}$$
$$- \sum_{\mathbf{k}} \frac{\omega_{\mathbf{k}}^2 - \mathbf{k}^2}{4\omega_{\mathbf{k}}} \cdot$$
$$\{ \sum_{\lambda=1}^{3} (\ll c_{\mathbf{k}\lambda}(t) |\ll c_{-\mathbf{k}\lambda}(t) | + | c_{\mathbf{k}\lambda}(t) \gg| c_{-\mathbf{k}\lambda}(t) \gg)$$
$$-(\ll c_{\mathbf{k}4}(t) |\ll c_{-\mathbf{k}4}(t) | + | c_{\mathbf{k}4}(t) \gg| c_{-\mathbf{k}4}(t) \gg)\}, \tag{4.1}$$

$$H_{FIM} = \sum_{\mathbf{p}s} m_{ef}(p) \{ | a_{\mathbf{p}s}(t) \gg\ll a_{\mathbf{p}s}(t) | u^{+}_{\mathbf{p}s}\gamma_4 u_{\mathbf{p}s}$$
$$+ \ll b_{(-\mathbf{p})s}(t) |\ll a_{\mathbf{p}s}(t) | v^{+}_{(-\mathbf{p})s}\gamma_4 u_{\mathbf{p}s}$$
$$+ | a_{(-\mathbf{p})s}(t) \gg| b_{\mathbf{p}s}(t) \gg u^{+}_{(-\mathbf{p})s}\gamma_4 v_{\mathbf{p}s}$$
$$- | b_{\mathbf{p}s}(t) \gg\ll b_{\mathbf{p}s}(t) | v^{+}_{\mathbf{p}s}\gamma_4 v_{\mathbf{p}s}\}, \tag{4.2}$$

$$H_{FIG} = -\frac{i}{\sqrt{V}} \sum_{\mathbf{p}_2 s_2} \sum_{\mathbf{p}_1 s_1} \{ | a_{\mathbf{p}_2 s_2}(t) \gg\ll a_{\mathbf{p}_1 s_1}(t) | \overline{u}_{\mathbf{p}_2 s_2}\gamma_\mu u_{\mathbf{p}_1 s_1}$$
$$+ \ll b_{(-\mathbf{p}_2)s_2}(t) |\ll a_{\mathbf{p}_1 s_1}(t) | \overline{v}_{(-\mathbf{p}_2)s_2}\gamma_\mu u_{\mathbf{p}_1 s_1}$$
$$+ | a_{\mathbf{p}_2 s_2}(t) \gg| b_{(-\mathbf{p}_1)s_1}(t) \gg \overline{u}_{\mathbf{p}_2 s_2}\gamma_\mu v_{(-\mathbf{p}_1)s_1}$$
$$- | b_{(-\mathbf{p}_1)s_1}(t) \gg\ll b_{(-\mathbf{p}_2)s_2}(t) | \overline{v}_{(-\mathbf{p}_2)s_2}\gamma_\mu v_{(-\mathbf{p}_1)s_1}\} g(p_2, p_1) \frac{1}{\sqrt{2\omega_{\mathbf{k}}}}$$
$$\cdot \sum_{\lambda=1}^{4} \left(e^{\lambda}_{\mathbf{k}\mu} \ll c_{\mathbf{k}\lambda}(t) | + e^{\lambda}_{(-\mathbf{k}\mu)} | \overline{c}_{(-\mathbf{k}\lambda)}(t) \gg \right), \tag{4.3}$$

where $k = p_2 - p_1$,

$$H_{W0} = \sum_{\mathbf{p}s}\{\mid \underline{b}_{\mathbf{p}s}(t) \gg\ll \underline{b}_{\mathbf{p}s}(t) \mid u^+_{\mathbf{p}s}\gamma_4 (i\gamma_j p_j + m) u_{\mathbf{p}s}$$
$$- \mid \underline{a}_{(-\mathbf{p})s}(t) \gg\mid \underline{b}_{\mathbf{p}s}(t) \gg v^+_{(-\mathbf{p})s}\gamma_4 (i\gamma_j p_j + m) u_{\mathbf{p}s}$$
$$- \ll \underline{b}_{(-\mathbf{p})s}(t) \mid\ll \underline{a}_{\mathbf{p}s}(t) \mid u^+_{(-\mathbf{p})s}\gamma_4 (-i\gamma_j p_j + m) v_{\mathbf{p}s}$$
$$- \mid \underline{a}_{\mathbf{p}s}(t) \gg\ll \underline{a}_{\mathbf{p}s}(t) \mid v^+_{\mathbf{p}s}\gamma_4 (-i\gamma_j p_j + m) v_{\mathbf{p}s}\}$$
$$+ \sum_{\mathbf{k}} \frac{\omega^2_{\mathbf{k}} + \mathbf{k}^2}{2\omega_{\mathbf{k}}}.$$
$$\{\sum_{\lambda=1}^{3} \mid \underline{c}_{\mathbf{k}\lambda}(t) \gg\ll \underline{c}_{\mathbf{k}\lambda}(t) \mid - \mid \underline{c}_{\mathbf{k}4}(t) \gg\ll \underline{c}_{\mathbf{k}4}(t) \mid\}$$
$$- \sum_{\mathbf{k}} \frac{\omega^2_{\mathbf{k}} - \mathbf{k}^2}{4\omega_{\mathbf{k}}}.$$
$$\{\sum_{\lambda=1}^{3}(\ll \underline{c}_{\mathbf{k}\lambda}(t) \mid\ll \underline{c}_{-\mathbf{k}\lambda}(t) \mid + \mid \underline{c}_{\mathbf{k}\lambda}(t) \gg\mid \underline{c}_{-\mathbf{k}\lambda}(t) \gg)$$
$$-(\ll \underline{c}_{\mathbf{k}4}(t) \mid\ll \underline{c}_{-\mathbf{k}4}(t) \mid + \mid \underline{c}_{\mathbf{k}4}(t) \gg\mid \underline{c}_{-\mathbf{k}4}(t) \gg)\}, \tag{4.4}$$

$$H_{WIM} = \sum_{\mathbf{p}s} m_{ew}(p)\{\mid \underline{b}_{\mathbf{p}s}(t) \gg\ll \underline{b}_{\mathbf{p}s}(t) \mid u^+_{\mathbf{p}s}\gamma_4 u_{\mathbf{p}s}$$
$$- \mid \underline{a}_{(-\mathbf{p})s}(t) \gg\mid \underline{b}_{\mathbf{p}s}(t) \gg v^+_{(-\mathbf{p})s}\gamma_4 u_{\mathbf{p}s}$$
$$- \ll \underline{b}_{(-\mathbf{p})s}(t) \mid\ll \underline{a}_{\mathbf{p}s}(t) \mid u^+_{(-\mathbf{p})s}\gamma_4 v_{\mathbf{p}s}$$
$$- \mid \underline{a}_{\mathbf{p}s}(t) \gg\ll \underline{a}_{\mathbf{p}s}(t) \mid v^+_{\mathbf{p}s}\gamma_4 v_{\mathbf{p}s}\}, \tag{4.5}$$

$$H_{WIG} = \frac{i}{\sqrt{V}} \sum_{\mathbf{p}_2 s_2}\sum_{\mathbf{p}_1 s_1}\{\mid \underline{b}_{\mathbf{p}_2 s_2}(t) \gg\ll \underline{b}_{\mathbf{p}_1 s_1}(t) \mid u^+_{\mathbf{p}_1 s_1}\gamma_4\gamma_\mu u_{\mathbf{p}_2 s_2}$$
$$- \mid \underline{a}_{(-\mathbf{p}_1 s_1)}(t) \gg\mid \underline{b}_{\mathbf{p}_2 s_2}(t) \gg v^+_{-\mathbf{p}_1 s_1}\gamma_4\gamma_\mu u_{\mathbf{p}_2 s_2}$$
$$- \ll \underline{b}_{\mathbf{p}_1 s_1}(t) \mid\ll \underline{a}_{(-\mathbf{p}_2 s_2)}(t) \mid u^+_{\mathbf{p}_1 s_1}\gamma_4\gamma_\mu v_{-\mathbf{p}_2 s_2}$$
$$- \mid \underline{a}_{(-\mathbf{p}_1 s_1)}(t) \gg\ll \underline{a}_{(-\mathbf{p}_2 s_2)}(t) \mid v^+_{-\mathbf{p}_1 s_1}\gamma_4\gamma_\mu v_{-\mathbf{p}_2 s_2}\} g(p_2, p_1) \frac{1}{\sqrt{2\omega_{\mathbf{k}}}}$$
$$\sum_{\lambda=1}^{4}(e^{\lambda}_{(-\mathbf{k})\mu} \mid \overline{\underline{c}}_{(-\mathbf{k})\lambda}(t) \gg + e^{\lambda}_{\mathbf{k}\mu} \ll \underline{c}_{\mathbf{k}\lambda}(t) \mid). \tag{4.6}$$

From (4.1)-(4.6) we can prove (2.18)-(2.19) to be consistent with (2.14)-(2.17) (see appendix A).

In fact, we can only obtain an approximate Hamiltonian in which the coupling constants and masses are approximately regarded as the same, i.e., $g(p_2, p_1) = g_0$ and $m_e(p) = 0$. In this case, we can write H_F and H_W as

$$H_F^{(0-loop)}(g_0, m_{e0}) \equiv H_F^{(0)}(g_0, m_{e0})$$
$$= \int d^3x : [\psi'^{+}\gamma_4(\gamma_j\partial_j - ig_0\gamma_\mu A'_\mu + m)\psi' + \frac{1}{2}\left(\dot{A}'_\mu\dot{A}'_\mu + \partial_j A'_\nu \partial_j A'_\nu\right)] :, \tag{4.7}$$

$$H_W^{(0-loop)}(g_0, m_{e0}) \equiv H_W^{(0)}(g_0, m_{e0})$$
$$= \int d^3x : [-\underline{\psi}'^{+}\gamma_4(\gamma_j\partial_j + ig_0\gamma_\mu \underline{A}'_\mu + m)\underline{\psi}' + \frac{1}{2}(\underline{\dot{A}}'\underline{\dot{A}}' + \partial'_j \underline{A}'_\nu \underline{A}'_\nu)] : \tag{4.8}$$

here the expansions of the field operators $\psi'(\mathbf{x}, t)$ etc. are the same as $[1]-(4.10)-(4.17)$ in form, but the operators $\leqslant a_{\mathbf{p}s}(t) \mid$ etc. in $[1]-(4.10)-(4.17)$ or $[1]-(3.14)-(3.15)$ must be replaced by (2.21)-(2.22). (4.7) is the full same as that of the conventional QED. When $p_2 = q_2$ and $p_1 = q_1$, both $H_F^{(0)}(g_0, m_{e0})$ and $H_W^{(0)}(g_0, m_{e0})$ are accurate. When $p_2 \neq q_2$ or $p_1 \neq q_1$, both $H_F^{(0)}(g_0, m_{e0})$ and $H_W^{(0)}(g_0, m_{e0})$ are approximate. The equal-time anticommulation and commulation relations for the operators $\leqslant \underline{b}_{\mathbf{p}s}(t) \mid$ and $\psi'_\rho(\mathbf{x}, t)$, etc., are the same as $[1]-(3.16)-(3.17)$ and $[1]-(4.18)-(4.19)$, respectively. In this case, the Heisenberg equations are

$$\dot{F} = -i\left[F, H_F^{(0)}\right] = -i\left[F, H^{(0)}\right], \tag{4.9}$$

$$\dot{W} = i[W, H_W^{(0)}] = i[W, H^{(0)}], \tag{4.10}$$

where $H^{(0)} = H_F^{(0)} + H_W^{(0)}$, $F = \psi', A'_\mu, \psi, A_\mu, \leqslant a_{\mathbf{p}s}(t) \mid, \leqslant b_{\mathbf{p}s}(t) \mid, \leqslant c_{\mathbf{k}\lambda}(t) \mid$; $W = \underline{\psi}', \underline{A}'_\mu, \underline{\psi}, \underline{A}_\mu, \leqslant \underline{a}_{\mathbf{p}s}(t) \mid, \leqslant \underline{b}_{\mathbf{p}s}(t) \mid, \leqslant \underline{c}_{\mathbf{k}\lambda}(t) \mid$. From (4.9) – (4.10) we obtain (2.14) – (2.17) (where $M_F \to M_F^{(0)}$, $G_F \to G_F^{(0)}$, $M_W \to M_W^{(0)}$, $G_W \to G_W^{(0)}$) and

$$i\frac{\partial}{\partial t}\psi' = \gamma_4(\gamma_j\partial_j - i\gamma_\mu g_0 A_\mu + m)\psi', \tag{4.11}$$

$$\square A'_\mu = -i\overline{\psi}'\gamma_\mu g_0 \psi', \tag{4.12}$$

$$i\frac{\partial}{\partial t}\underline{\psi}' = \gamma_4(\gamma_j\partial_j + i\gamma_\mu g_0 \underline{A}'_\mu + m)\underline{\psi}', \tag{4.13}$$

$$\Box \underline{A}'_{\mu} = -i\underline{\overline{\psi}}'\gamma_{\mu}g_0\underline{\psi}', \tag{4.14}$$

$$\psi'(\mathbf{x},t) = e^{iH^{(0)}t}\psi'(\mathbf{x},0)\, e^{-iH^{(0)}t} = e^{iH_F^{(0)}t}\psi'(\mathbf{x},0)\, e^{-iH_F^{(0)}t}, \tag{4.15}$$

$$A'_{\mu}(\mathbf{x},t) = e^{iH^{(0)}t}A'_{\mu}(\mathbf{x},0)\, e^{-iH^{(0)}t} = e^{iH_F^{(0)}t}A'_{\mu}(\mathbf{x},0)\, e^{-iH_F^{(0)}t}, \tag{4.16}$$

$$\underline{\psi}'(\mathbf{x},t) = e^{-iH^{(0)}t}\underline{\psi}'(\mathbf{x},0)\, e^{iH^{(0)}t} = e^{-iH_W^{(0)}t}\underline{\psi}'(\mathbf{x},0)\, e^{iH_W^{(0)}t}, \tag{4.17}$$

$$\underline{A}'_{\mu}(\mathbf{x},t) = e^{-iH^{(0)}t}\underline{A}'_{\mu}(\mathbf{x},0)\, e^{iH^{(0}t} = e^{-iH_W^{(0)}t}\underline{A}'_{\mu}(\mathbf{x},0)\, e^{iH_W^{(0)}t}, \tag{4.18}$$

(4.11)-(4.12) and (4.15)-(4.16) are the same as those of the conventional QED, (4.13)-(4.14) and (4.17)-(4.18) are different from those of the conventional QED. It is seen from the $\mathcal{L}_f$ we can also obtain the results of the conventional QED.

5 Scattering operators and Feynman rules

As the conventional QED, transforming the Heisenberg picture into the interaction picture, we can derive the scattering operator S_f and S_w from (4.2)-(4.3), (4.5)-(4.6), (4.7) and (4.8),

$$S_f = 1 + \sum_{n=1}^{\infty} \frac{(-i)^n}{n!} \int_{-\infty}^{\infty} d^4x_1 .. \int_{-\infty}^{\infty} d^4x_n T : \mathcal{H}_{fI}(g,m_e,x) .. \mathcal{H}_{fI}(g,m_e,x) \tag{5.1}$$

$$S_w = 1 + \sum_{n=1}^{\infty} \frac{i^n}{n!} \int_{-\infty}^{\infty} d^4x_1 ... \int_{-\infty}^{\infty} d^4x_n T : \mathcal{H}_{wI}(g,m_e,x) ... \mathcal{H}_{wI}(g,m_e,x) \tag{5.2}$$

$$S_f^{(0)}(g_0, m_{e0}) = 1 + \sum_{n=1}^{\infty} \frac{(-i)^n}{n!} \int_{-\infty}^{\infty} d^4x_1 ... \int_{-\infty}^{\infty} d^4x_n T : \mathcal{H}_{fI}^{(0)} ... \mathcal{H}_{fI}^{(0)} \tag{5.3}$$

$$S_w^{(0)}(g_0, m_{e0}) = 1 + \sum_{n=1}^{\infty} \frac{i^n}{n!} \int_{-\infty}^{\infty} d^4x_1 ... \int_{-\infty}^{\infty} d^4x_n T : \mathcal{H}_{wI}^{(0)} ... \mathcal{H}_{wI}^{(0)} \tag{5.4}$$

$$\mathcal{H}_{fI} = -i\overline{\psi}\gamma_{\mu} \cdot G_F \cdot A_{\mu}\psi + \overline{\psi} \cdot M_F \cdot \psi, \tag{5.5}$$

$$\mathcal{H}_{wI} = -i\underline{\overline{\psi}}\gamma_{\mu} \cdot G_W \underline{A}_{\mu}\underline{\psi} - \underline{\overline{\psi}} \cdot M_W \cdot \underline{\psi}, \tag{5.6}$$

$$\mathcal{H}_{fI}^{(0)} = \mathcal{H}_{fI}^{(0-loop)}(g_0,m_{e0},x) = -ig_0 : \psi'^{+}\gamma_4\gamma_{\mu}A'_{\mu}\psi' :, \tag{5.7}$$

$$\mathcal{H}_{wI}^{(0)} = \mathcal{H}_{wI}^{(0-loop)}(g_0,m_{e0},x) = -ig_0 : \underline{\psi}'^{+}\gamma_4\gamma_{\mu}\underline{A}'_{\mu}\underline{\psi}' :, \tag{5.8}$$

where all field operators in (5.5)-(5.8) satisfy free-field equations as the conventional QED, G_F and M_F are respectively determined by (3.10) and (3.26), G_W and M_W are respectively determined by (3.15) and (3.29), the symbol T denotes that the products are in time-ordered form.

If for arbitrary momenta p_1 and p_2 we could determine the accurate coupling constants $g\left(p_1, p_2\right)$ and the masses $m_e\left(p\right)$, we could evaluate accurate scattering amplitudes by only tree diagrams determined by $S_f\left(g, m_e\right)$ or $S_w\left(g, m_e\right)$. But this is impossible. It should be pointed that in the meaning of perturbation theory, for an initial state and a final state with given momenta, e.g., the momenta at the subtraction point, we can give the precise coupling coefficient g_0 and mass m_{e0}. From this we can determine $\mathcal{L}_f^{(0-loop)}$ and $\mathcal{L}_w^{(0-loop)}$, thereby determine scattering operators $S_f^{(0-loop)}$ and $S_w^{(0-loop)}$. Both $S_f^{(0-loop)}$ and $S_w^{(0-loop)}$ determine the one-loop corrections to the coupling constants and the masses, thereby determine the one-loop corrections to scattering amplitudes as well. Thus we can derive $S_f^{(1-loop)}$, $S_w^{(1-loop)}$, and $S_f^{(n-loop)}$ and $S_w^{(n-loop)}$ order by order. Because for arbitrary initial states and final states, we cannot give the precise coupling coefficients, masses, $\mathcal{H}_{fI}\left(g,m_e,x\right)$ and $\mathcal{H}_{wI}\left(g,m_e,x\right)$, the two scattering operators S_f and S_w are not practical to evaluate scattering amplitudes. We can evaluate Feynman amplitudes by only $S_f^{(0)}$ and $S_w^{(0)}$ and perturbation approximation.

The scattering operator $S_f^{(0)}\left(g_0, m_{e0}\right)$ is the same as the scattering operator of the conventional QED. $S_w^{(0)}$ differ from $S_f^{(0)}$ only in the sign before i in form. Hence we can evaluate scattering amplitudes by $S_f^{(0)}$ and $S_w^{(0)}$ in the same method as is used by the conventional QED.

In order to simplify $S_f^{(0)}$ and $S_w^{(0)}$, we must decompose the time-ordered products appearing in $S_f^{(0)}$ and $S_w^{(0)}$ into normal-ordered products. Considering the expansions of $\psi'\left(x\right)$ and $A'_\mu\left(x\right)$ to be the same as those of the free fields of the conventional QED and $\underline{A'_\mu}\left(x\right)$ and $\underline{\psi'}\left(x\right)$ to have the similar expansions as the conventional QED, we obtain propagators to be

$$\begin{aligned}&\langle 0 \mid T\psi'_\alpha\left(x_1\right)\overline{\psi}'_\beta\left(x_2\right) \mid 0\rangle \\ &= \frac{-i}{(2\pi)^4}\int d^4p\frac{(m - ip\gamma)_{\alpha\beta}}{p^2 + m^2 - i\varepsilon}e^{ip(x_1 - x_2)} \equiv S_{Ff}\left(x_1 - x_2\right),\end{aligned} \tag{5.9}$$

$$\begin{aligned}&\langle 0 \mid TA'_\mu\left(x_1\right)A'_\nu\left(x_2\right) \mid 0\rangle \\ &= \delta_{\mu\nu}\frac{-i}{(2\pi)^4}\int d^4k\frac{1}{k^2 - i\varepsilon}e^{ik(x_1 - x_2)} \equiv \delta_{\mu\nu}D_{Ff}\left(x_1 - x_2\right),\end{aligned} \tag{5.10}$$

$$
\begin{aligned}
&\langle 0 \mid T\underline{\psi}'_{\alpha}(x_1)\,\overline{\underline{\psi}}'_{\beta}(x_2) \mid 0\rangle \\
&= \frac{-i}{(2\pi)^4}\int d^4p \frac{(m-ip\gamma)_{\alpha\beta}}{p^2+m^2+i\varepsilon} e^{ip(x_1-x_2)} \equiv S_{Fw}(x_1-x_2), \qquad (5.11)
\end{aligned}
$$

$$
\begin{aligned}
&\langle 0 \mid T\underline{A}'_{\mu}(x_1)\,\underline{A}'_{\nu}(x_2) \mid 0\rangle \\
&= \delta_{\mu\nu}\frac{i}{(2\pi)^4}\int d^4k \frac{1}{k^2+i\varepsilon} e^{ik(x_1-x_2)} \equiv \delta_{\mu\nu} D_{Fw}(x_1-x_2), \qquad (5.12)
\end{aligned}
$$

where $\varepsilon \to 0^+$, the integral contours are shown in Fig.1. The other contractions are all equal to zero. Comparing (5.11)-(5.12) with (5.9)-(5.10), we find the differences and the common properties among the four propagators as follows.

1. The places of the polar points of D_{Fw} and S_{Fw} are opposite to those of D_{Fw} and S_{Fw}, respectively. The polar points of D_{Fw} and S_{Fw} are in the first and third quadrants, the polar points of D_{Ff} and S_{Ff} are in the second and the fourth quadrants (see Fig.1-A and Fig.1-B).

2. Neglecting ε, $D_{Ff} = -D_{Fw}$ and $S_{Ff} = S_{Fw}$.

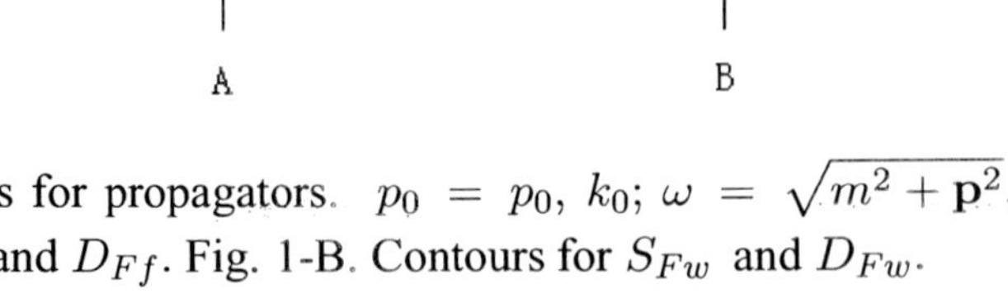

Figure 1: Contours for propagators. $p_0 = p_0$, k_0; $\omega = \sqrt{m^2+\mathbf{p}^2}$, $|\,\mathbf{k}\,|$. Fig. 1-A. Contours for S_{Ff} and D_{Ff}. Fig. 1-B. Contours for S_{Fw} and D_{Fw}.

It can be seen that the Wick theorem still applicable to the present theory. Decomposing the time-ordered products appearing in (5.3) and (5.4) into normal-ordered products, we

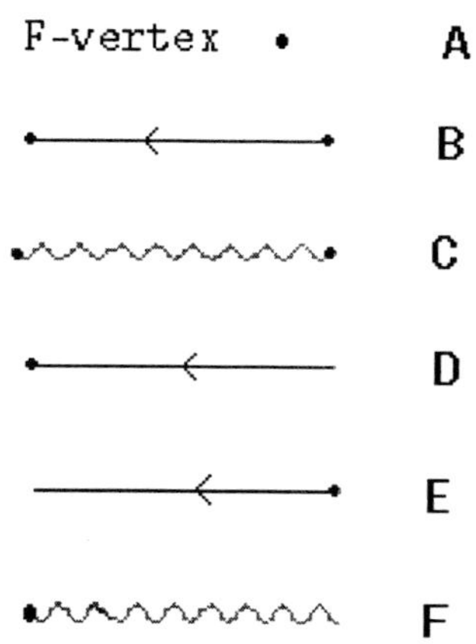

Figure 2: The Feynman rules for S_f. There is an minus sign corresponding to a closed fermion loop. A. $-g_0\gamma_\mu\,(2\pi)^4\,\delta^4\,(\Sigma P)$; B. $\frac{-i}{(2\pi)^4}\frac{(m-ip\gamma)_{\alpha\beta}}{p^2+m^2-i\varepsilon}$ with $\int d^4p$; C. $\delta_{\mu\nu}\frac{-i}{(2\pi)^4}\frac{1}{k^2-i\varepsilon}$ with $\int d^4k$; D. $\frac{1}{\sqrt{V}}u_{\mathbf{p}s}$ (ingoing) or $\frac{1}{\sqrt{V}}\overline{v}_{\mathbf{p}s}$ (outgoing); E. $\frac{1}{\sqrt{V}}\overline{u}_{\mathbf{p}s}$ (outgoing) or $\frac{1}{\sqrt{V}}v_{\mathbf{p}s}$ (ingoing); F. $\frac{1}{\sqrt{V\omega_{\mathbf{k}}}}e^{\lambda}_{\mathbf{k}\mu}$, $\lambda = 1, 2$.

can evaluate S-matrix elements approximate to tree-diagrams. It is readily proven the S-matrix elements $\langle F_f \mid S_f^{(0)}\,(g_0, m_{e0}) \mid F_i\rangle$ approximate to tree-diagrams are the same as those obtained by the conventional QED. From the S-matrix elements $\langle F_f \mid S_f\,(g_0, m_{e0}) \mid F_i\rangle$ and $\langle W_f \mid S_w\,(g_0, m_{e0}) \mid W_i\rangle$ approximate to tree-diagrams we can obtain the Feynman rules in the momentum space (see Fig. 2 and Fig. 3).

In addition to the rules given by Fig. 1 and Fig. 2-3, there is an overall minus sign corresponding to a closed fermion loop and three supplementary Feynman rules (see the following paper). The rules fully determine the method evaluating a F-amplitude or a W-amplitude.

6 Summary

On the basis of [1] we discuss quantization for interacting fields. Since we quantize fields by the transformation operators replacing creation and annihilation operators in the conventional QED, it is necessary to replace coupling constants and masses by coupling operators and mass operators. We construct the coupling operators and mass operators, derive Feynman rules and scattering operators. We see that $\mathcal{L}_f$ and $\mathcal{L}_w$ are independent of each other

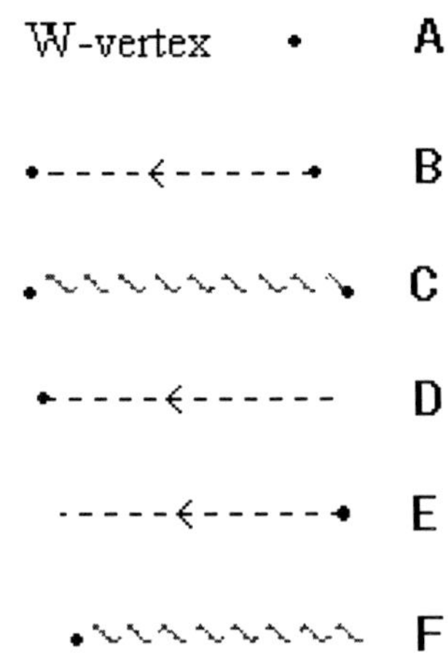

Figure 3: The Feynman rules for S_w. There is an minus sign corresponding to a closed fermion loop.A. $g_0\gamma_\mu\left(2\pi\right)^4\delta^4\left(P\right)$; B. $\frac{-i}{(2\pi)^4}\frac{(m-ip\gamma)_{\alpha\beta}}{p^2+m^2+i\varepsilon}$ with $\int d^4p$; C. $\delta_{\mu\nu}\frac{i}{(2\pi)^4}\frac{1}{k^2+i\varepsilon}$ with $\int d^4k$; D. $\frac{1}{\sqrt{V}}v_{\mathbf{p}s}$ (ingoing) or $\frac{1}{\sqrt{V}}\overline{u}_{\mathbf{p}s}$ (outgoing); E. $\frac{1}{\sqrt{V}}\overline{v}_{\mathbf{p}s}$ (outgoing) or $\frac{1}{\sqrt{V}}u_{\mathbf{p}s}$ (ingoing); F. $\frac{1}{\sqrt{V\omega_{\mathbf{k}}}}e^{\lambda}_{\mathbf{k}\mu}$, $\lambda=1,2$.

before quantization and dependent on each other after quantization. In contrast with the conventional QED, in the present theory, there is only one sort of parameters which are all finite and measurable and there are the two sorts of corrections originating S_f and S_w. We will see that the integrands causing divergence which originate from S_f and S_w cancel each other out and all Feynman integrals are convergent.

Appendix A

The equal-time anticommutation or commutation relations of such operators as $\lessdot a_{\mathbf{p}s}(t)\mid$ are the same as $[1]-(3.16)-(3.17)$. From $[1]-(3.16)-(3.17)$ and $[1]-(3.28)$ we have

$$\begin{aligned}&[\underline{I}_{\mathbf{p}}\lessdot a_{\mathbf{p}s}(t)\mid,\mid a_{\mathbf{p}_2s_2}(t)\gtrdot\lessdot a_{\mathbf{p}_1s_1}(t)\mid]\\&=\underline{I}_{\mathbf{p}}\lessdot a_{\mathbf{p}_1s_1}(t)\mid\delta_{\mathbf{p}\mathbf{p}_2}\delta_{ss_2},\end{aligned}\tag{A.1}$$

$$\begin{aligned}&[\mid b_{\mathbf{p}s}(t)\gtrdot\underline{I}_{(-\mathbf{p})},\mid b_{(-\mathbf{p}_1)s_1}(t)\gtrdot\lessdot b_{(-\mathbf{p}_2)s_2}(t)\mid]\\&=-\delta_{\mathbf{p}(-\mathbf{p}_2)}\delta_{ss_2}\mid b_{(-\mathbf{p}_1)s_1}(t)\gtrdot\underline{I}_{(-\mathbf{p})},\end{aligned}\tag{A.2}$$

$$[\mid b_{\mathbf{p}s}(t) \gg \underline{I}_{(-\mathbf{p})}, \ll b_{(-\mathbf{p}_2)s_2}(t) \mid \ll a_{\mathbf{p}_1 s_1}(t) \mid]$$
$$= \underline{I}_{(-\mathbf{p})} \ll a_{\mathbf{p}_1 s_1}(t) \mid \delta_{\mathbf{p}(-\mathbf{p}_2)}\delta_{ss_2}, \tag{A.3}$$

$$[\underline{I}_{\mathbf{p}} \ll a_{\mathbf{p}s}(t) \mid, \mid a_{\mathbf{p}_2 s_2}(t) \gg \mid b_{(-\mathbf{p}_1)s_1}(t) \gg]$$
$$= \delta_{\mathbf{p}\mathbf{p}_2}\delta_{ss_2} \mid b_{(-\mathbf{p}_1)s_1}(t) \gg \underline{I}_{\mathbf{p}}, \tag{A.4}$$

$$[\underline{I}_{\mathbf{p}} \ll a_{\mathbf{p}s}(t) \mid, \mid b_{(-\mathbf{p}_1)s_1}(t) \gg \ll b_{(-\mathbf{p}_2)s_2}(t) \mid]$$
$$= [\mid b_{\mathbf{p}s}(t) \gg \underline{I}_{(-\mathbf{p})}, \mid a_{\mathbf{p}_2 s_2}(t) \gg \ll a_{\mathbf{p}_1 s_1}(t) \mid]$$
$$= [\underline{I}_{\mathbf{p}} \ll a_{\mathbf{p}s}(t) \mid, \ll b_{(-\mathbf{p}_2)s_2}(t) \mid \ll a_{\mathbf{p}_1 s_1}(t) \mid]$$
$$= [\mid b_{\mathbf{p}s}(t) \gg \underline{I}_{(-\mathbf{p})}, \mid a_{\mathbf{p}_2 s_2}(t) \gg \mid b_{(-\mathbf{p}_1)s_1}(t) \gg] = 0. \tag{A.5}$$

$$\sum_s (u_{\mathbf{p}s}u^+_{\mathbf{p}s} + v_{(-\mathbf{p})s}v^+_{(-\mathbf{p})s}) = 1 \tag{A.6}$$

Substituting (4.1)-(4.3), (A.1)-(A.6) and

$$\psi(x) = \frac{1}{\sqrt{V}}\sum_{\mathbf{p}s}\left(\underline{I}_{\mathbf{p}} \ll a_{\mathbf{p}s}(t) \mid u_{\mathbf{p}s}e^{i\mathbf{p}\mathbf{x}} + \mid b_{\mathbf{p}s}(t) \gg \underline{I}_{(-\mathbf{p})}v_{\mathbf{p}s}e^{-i\mathbf{p}\mathbf{x}}\right), \tag{A.7}$$

into (2.18), i.e.,

$$\dot{\psi}(x) = -i[\psi(x), H] = -i[\psi(x), H_F], \tag{A.8}$$

we obtain (2.14).

From (2.20) we have

$$[\underline{j}_{\mathbf{k}} \ll c_{\mathbf{k}\lambda}(t) \mid, \mid \bar{c}_{(-\mathbf{k}'\lambda')}(t) \gg] = \underline{j}_{\mathbf{k}}\delta_{\mathbf{k}(-\mathbf{k}')}\delta_{\lambda\lambda'}, \tag{A.9}$$

$$[\mid \bar{c}_{\mathbf{k}\lambda}(t) \gg \underline{j}_{(-\mathbf{k}')}, \ll c_{\mathbf{k}'\lambda'}(t) \mid] = -\underline{j}_{(-\mathbf{k}')}\delta_{\mathbf{k}(-\mathbf{k}')}\delta_{\lambda\lambda'}, \tag{A.10}$$

$$[\underline{j}_{\mathbf{k}} \ll c_{\mathbf{k}\lambda}(t) \mid, \ll c_{\mathbf{k}'\lambda'}(t) \mid]$$
$$= [\mid \bar{c}_{\mathbf{k}\lambda}(t) \gg \underline{j}_{(-\mathbf{k}')}, \mid \bar{c}_{(-\mathbf{k}'\lambda')}(t) \gg] = 0. \tag{A.11}$$

$$[\underline{j}_{\mathbf{k}} \ll c_{\mathbf{k}\lambda}(t) \mid, \mid \bar{c}_{\mathbf{k}'\lambda'}(t) \gg \ll c_{\mathbf{k}'\lambda'}(t) \mid]$$
$$= \underline{j}_{\mathbf{k}} \ll c_{\mathbf{k}'\lambda'}(t) \mid \underline{j}_{\mathbf{k}}\delta_{\mathbf{k}\mathbf{k}'}\delta_{\lambda\lambda'} \tag{A.12}$$

$$[\mid \bar{c}_{\mathbf{k}\lambda}(t) \gg \underline{j}_{(-\mathbf{k}')}, \mid \bar{c}_{\mathbf{k}'\lambda'}(t) \gg \ll c_{\mathbf{k}'\lambda'}(t) \mid]$$
$$= -\underline{j}_{(-\mathbf{k}')} \mid \bar{c}_{\mathbf{k}'\lambda'}(t) \gg \delta_{\mathbf{k}\mathbf{k}'}\delta_{\lambda\lambda'} \tag{A.13}$$

$$\sum_{\lambda=1}^{4} e_{\mathbf{k}\mu}^{\lambda} e_{\mathbf{k}\nu}^{\lambda} = \delta_{\mu\nu} \tag{A.14}$$

Substituting (4.1), (4.3), (A.9)-(A.13) and

$$\begin{aligned} A_{\mu}(x) = \frac{1}{\sqrt{V}} \sum_{\mathbf{k}} \frac{1}{\sqrt{2\omega_{\mathbf{k}}}} \sum_{\lambda=1}^{4} (e_{\mathbf{k}\mu}^{\lambda} \underline{j}_{\mathbf{k}} \leqslant c_{\mathbf{k}\lambda}(t) \mid e^{i\mathbf{kx}} \\ + \mid \bar{c}_{\mathbf{k}\lambda}(t) \geqslant \underline{j}_{(-\mathbf{k})} e^{-i\mathbf{kx}}), \end{aligned} \tag{A.15}$$

$$\begin{aligned} \pi_{\mu} = \dot{A}_{\mu}(x) \equiv \frac{-i}{\sqrt{V}} \sum_{\mathbf{k}} \sqrt{\frac{\omega_{\mathbf{k}}}{2}} \sum_{\lambda=4}^{4} e_{\mathbf{k}\mu}^{\lambda} (\underline{j}_{\mathbf{k}} \leqslant c_{\mathbf{k}\lambda}(t) \mid e^{i\mathbf{kx}} \\ - \mid \bar{c}_{\mathbf{k}\lambda}(t) \geqslant \underline{j}_{(-\mathbf{k})} e^{-i\mathbf{kx}}), \end{aligned} \tag{A.16}$$

into (2.18), i.e.,

$$\dot{A}_{\mu}(x) = -i[A_{\mu}(x), H_F], \ \dot{\pi}_{\mu} = \ddot{A}_{\mu} = -i[\pi_{\mu}(x), H_F], \tag{A.17}$$

we obtain (2.15). It is seen that (2.18) is consistent with (2.14)-(2.15). Analogously, from (4.4)-(4.6) we can prove (2.19) to be consistent with (2.16)-(2.17).

Acknowledgement

I am very grateful to Professor Zhan-yao Zhao for best support and professor Zhao-yan Wu for helpful discussions.

References

[1] Shi-Hao Chen, *Quantum Field Theory Without Divergence A*, hep-th/0203220.

In: Quantum Field Theory: New Research
Editor: O. Kovras, pp. 143-170

ISBN 1-59454-509-X

Chapter 5

QUANTUM FIELD THEORY WITHOUT DIVERGENCE: PERTURBATION

Shi-Hao Chen*
Department of Physics,
Harbin Institute of Technology, Harbin 150006;
Institute of Theoretical Physics,
Northeast Normal University, Changchun 130024, P. R. China

Abstract

The present paper takes one-loop correction as example to illustrate the perturbation method in the Quantum Field Theory Without Divergence, and to show that there are two sorts of corrections originating from S_f and S_w, Feynman integrals of loop-diagrams are all determined by the sum of integrands originating from S_f and S_w and are all convergent, thus it is unnecessary to introduce regularization and counter-terms. Three supplementary Feynman rules are given. On the same basis as the new QED, we obtain naturally a new generalized SU(2)XU(1) electroweak unified model which is left-right symmetric and does not contain unknown massive particles. Thus, the world is left-right symmetric in principle, but the part observed by us is asymmetric because $\mathcal{L}_w$ and $\mathcal{L}_f$ are all asymmetric. If the interaction between the W-matter and the F-matter is gravitation, W-matter is the candidate for dark matter.

Keywords: Feynman integrals; Feynman rules; Two sorts of correction
PACS numbers: 11.10, 12.20.-m, 11.30.Rd, 11.90.+t, 11.55.Bq, 12.10.-g,12.60.-i

*E-mail: shchen@nenu.edu.cn

1 Introduction

We have constructed a new Lagrangian density of free fields and quantized the free field by the transformation operators in [1], have discussed quantization for interacting fields, have derived the scattering operators S_f and S_w and the Feynman rules in [2]. In present paper we evaluate one-loop correction to the coupling coefficients and the masses in detail, supplementary three Feynman rules, and derive the method evaluating n-loop correction, and discuss the possibility that W-matter is the candidate for dark matter.. On the same basis as the new QED, we obtain naturally a new generalized SU(2)XU(1) electroweak unified model which is left-right symmetric.

If g_0 and m_{e0} are regarded constants, $\mathcal{L}_f$ and $\mathcal{L}_w$ were fully independent. In this case from the new QED we can only obtain one new result i.e., $\langle 0 \mid H \mid 0 \rangle = 0$. But in fact, because g and m_e must be transformed into coupling operator and mass operator, after quantization, though there is no coupling between the F-field and the W-field, $\mathcal{L}_f$ and $\mathcal{L}_w$ are dependent on each other, since $g_f(p_2, p_1)$ and $m_{ef}(p)$ are determined by S_w and $g_w(p_2, p_1)$ and $m_{ew}(p)$ are determined by S_f. Both S_f and S_w determine scattering amplitudes. Thus, the integrands causing divergence in a total correction will cancel each other out, all Feynman integrals are convergent, and it is unnecessary to introduce regularization and counter-terms.

From this we can determine $\mathcal{L}_f^{(0-loop)}$ and $\mathcal{L}_w^{(0-loop)}$, thereby determine scattering operators $S_f^{(0-loop)}$ and $S_w^{(0-loop)}$. Both $S_f^{(0-loop)}$ and $S_w^{(0-loop)}$ determine the one-loop corrections to the coupling constants and the masses, thereby determine the one-loop corrections to scattering amplitudes as well. Thus we can derive $S_f^{(1-loop)}$, $S_w^{(1-loop)}$, and $S_f^{(n-loop)}$,$S_w^{(n-loop)}$ order by order.

2 Two sorts of correction

When the momenta meeting at a single vertex $p_2 = q_2, p_1 = q_1$ (q_1 and q_2 are the momenta at the subtraction point), both $g_0(q_2, q_1)$ and $m_{e0}(q_1)$ are accurate, hence scattering amplitudes $A_{gf}^{(0-loop)}(q_2, q_1)$, $A_{gw}^{(0-loop)}(q_2, q_1)$, $A_{mf}^{(0-loop)}(q_1)$ and $A_{mf}^{(0-loop)}(q_1)$ evaluated by $S_f^{(0)}(g_0, m_{e0})$ and $S_w^{(0)}(g_0, m_{e0})$ with tree diagrams are also all accurate (it is possible that there is no real process for a single vertex). When $p_2 \neq q_2, p_1 \neq q_1$, e.g., for a Feynman diagram with many vertices, g_0, m_{e0} and the scattering amplitudes obtained by $S_f^{(0)}$ and $S_w^{(0)}$ with tree diagrams are no longer accurate and must be corrected. According to the perturbation theory, Feynman diagrams with the same initial state and final state , no matter whether or not $p_1 = q_1$ and $p_2 = q_2$, , the tree diagrams and all diagrams with n-loop must exist and must simultaneously be considered. It is obvious that corrections must begin with one–loop diagrams. The coupling constants, the masses and scattering amplitudes corrected to n-loop diagrams can be written as

$$Z^{(n-loop)}\left(p_2, p_1, k\right) = Z_0 + \sum_{i=1}^{n} Z^{(i)}\left(p_2, p_1, k\right), \tag{2.1}$$

where $Z = g_f,\ g_w,\ m_{ef},\ m_{ew},\ A_{gf},\ A_{mf},\ A_{gw},\ A_{mw}$, the superscript i denotes only diagrams with i loops to be evaluated. Because of the gauge invariance of the Lagrangian density, there is no correction of the mass of a free F-photon and W-photon.

We consider that a self-consistent theory should satisfy the following demands:

1. There is only one sort of physical parameters which are measurable and finite, e.g., there are only g_0 and m_{e0} in the present theory, and there is no other sort of parameters as the bare mass and the bare charge in the conventional QED which are unmeasured and divergent.

2. $Z^{(n-loop)}\left(p_2, p_1, k\right)$ and $Z^{(i)}\left(p_2, p_1, k\right)$ must be finite and must tend to zero as $p_2 \to q_2, p_1 \to q_1$ and $k \to q'$, i.e.,

$$Z^{(i)}\left(q_2, q_1, q'\right) = 0, \qquad Z^{(n-loop)}\left(q_2, q_1, q'\right) = Z_0. \tag{2.2}$$

3. $Z^{(n-loop)}\left(p_2, p_1, k\right)$ should be consistent with the results obtained by the given QED.

According to the conventional QED, the 1-loop corrections to $g_{f0}(q_2, q_1)$ and $m_{ef0}(q)$ are all divergent. This is because there is only one sort of corrections originating S_f. In order to remove divergence, it is necessary to introduce regularization and counter-terms. For instance, in order to remove divergence of the one-loop correction of the mass of a free electron

$$\delta m = m^{(1)}_{eff}(q) = \frac{3\alpha}{4\pi^2} m \left(\frac{1}{i\pi^2}\int d^4k \frac{1}{(k^2+m^2)^2} + \frac{3}{2}\right) \equiv A,$$

the counter-term $A\overline{\psi}\psi$ must be introduced, here A is a divergent constant[3]. Thus, there are two sorts of parameters in the conventional QED, i.e., the physical mass and charge(the so-called bare mass and bare charge). It is noteworthy that in order to determine A we must firstly carry out integration over k. Consequently regularization must be introduced.

As the conventional QED, it can be proven from the Feynman rules that the one-loop corrections only originating from $S^{(0)}_f\left(g_0, m_{e0}\right)$ or $S^{(0)}_w\left(g_0, m_{e0}\right)$ are all divergent and do not tend to zero as $p_2 \to q_2$ and $p_1 \to q_1$ (first sort of corrections). This implies that there must be another sort of corrections (second sort of corrections) which cancels out the first sort of corrections as $p_2 \to q_2$ and $p_1 \to q$. In contrast with the conventional QED, in the present theory, there is the second sort of corrections (originating from $\S_f$ or S_w). Both $\S_f$ and S_w determine $Z^{(i)}\left(p_2, p_1, k\right)$ which satisfy the demands above.

We first take one-loop correction as an example to discuss the first sort of correction. As the conventional QED, there are the one-loop corrections $A^{(1)}_{gff}(p_2, p_1)$ to $A^{(0-loop)}_{gf}(p_2, p_1)$

and $A^{(1)}_{mff}(p_2,p_1)$ to $A^{(0-loop)}_{mf}(p_2,p_1)$ originating from $S^{(0)}_f(g_0,m_{e0})$, and the one-loop corrections $A^{(1)}_{gww}(p_2,p_1)$ to $A^{(0-loop)}_{gw}(p_2,p_1)$ and $A^{(1)}_{mww}(p_2,p_1)$ to $A^{(0-loop)}_{mw}(p_2,p_1)$ originating from $S^{(0)}_w(g_0,m_{e0})$. From the definition $[2]-(3.1)$ we see that $A^{(1)}_{gff}$ firstly correct the amplitude $A^{(0)}_{gf}(p_2,p_1)$ and thereby corrects g_{f0}, hence the momenta in $A^{(1)}_{gff}(p_2,p_1)$ and $g^{(1)}_{ff}(p_2,p_1)$ must be the same as those in $A^{(0)}_{gf}(p_2,p_1)$. We can evaluate $g^{(1)}_{ff}(p_2,p_1)$ by $S^{(1)}_f(g_0,m_{e0})$ as the conventional QED. Thus from $[2]-(3.1)$ we have

$$g^{(1)}_{ff}=g^{(1)}_{ff}(p_2,p_1)=\frac{\langle a_{p_2s_2}\mid S^{(1)}_f(g_0,m_{e0})\mid a_{p_1s_1}c_{k\lambda}\rangle}{\langle a_{p_2s_2}\mid S^{(0)}_f(g_0=1,m_{e0}=0)\mid a_{p_1s_1}c_{k\lambda}\rangle}, \tag{2.3}$$

where p may be a momentum of an internal line and does not satisfy the mass shell restriction, $S^{(1)}_f$ is the scattering operator approximate to one-loop. Analogously to $g^{(1)}_{ff}$, from $[2]-(3.17)$, $[2]-(3.4)$ and $[2]-(3.20)$ we have

$$m^{(1)}_{eff}(p_1)=\frac{\langle a_{p_2s_2}\mid S^{(1)}_f(g_0,m_{e0})\mid a_{p_1s_1}\rangle}{\langle a_{p_2s_2}\mid S^{(0)}_f(g_0=1,m_{e0}=0)\mid a_{p_1s_1}\rangle}, \tag{2.4}$$

$$g^{(1)}_{ww}(p_2,p_1)=\frac{\langle \underline{a}_{p_2s_2}\mid S^{(1)}_w(g_0,m_{e0})\mid \underline{a}_{p_1s_1}\underline{c}_{k\lambda}\rangle}{\langle \underline{a}_{p_2s_2}\mid S^{(0)}_w(g_0=1,m_{e0}=0)\mid \underline{a}_{p_1s_1}\underline{c}_{k\lambda}\rangle}, \tag{2.5}$$

$$m^{(1)}_{eww}(p_1)=\frac{\langle \underline{a}_{p_2s_2}\mid S^{(1)}_w(g_0,m_{e0})\mid \underline{a}_{p_1s_1}\rangle}{\langle \underline{a}_{p_2s_2}\mid S^{(0)}_w(g_0=1,m_{e0}=0)\mid \underline{a}_{p_1s_1}\rangle}. \tag{2.6}$$

where the denominators of (2.3)-(2.6) are the same as $[2]-(3.2)$, $[2]-(3.18)$, $[2]-(3.5)$ and $[2]-(3.21)$, respectively. (2.3)-(2.6) are the first sort of corrections.

Secondly, we consider the second sort of one-loop corrections. It is seen from $[2]-(3.9a)$ that $A^{(1)}_{gww}$ originating from S_w not only corrects $A^{(0-loop)}_{gw}$ and g_{w0}, but also corrects g_{f0} and m_{ef0}. We denote the sort of one-loop correction to g_{f0} originating from S_w by $g^{(1)}_{fw}$. In contrast with the first sort of corrections, the corrections of the second sort are to directly correct the coupling constants and the masses. Because $g_0(q_2,q_1)$ and $m_{e0}(q)$ are defined at the subtraction point, the second sort of corrections must also be defined at the subtraction point, i.e. $g^{(1)}_{fw}=g^{(1)}_{fw}(q_2,q_1)$. Considering

$$g^{(1)}_f(p_2,p_1)\equiv g^{(1)}_{ff}(p_2,p_1)+g^{(1)}_{fw}(q_2,q_1) \tag{2.7}$$

should be finite, from $[2]-(3.9a)$ and (2.5) we define

$$g^{(1)}_{fw}=g^{(1)}_{fw}(q_2,q_1)\equiv -g^{(1)}_{ww}(q_2,q_1), \tag{2.8}$$

Analogously to $g_{fw}^{(1)}$, from [2] – (3.25) and (2.6) we define

$$m_{efw}^{(1)} = m_{efw}^{(1)}(q) \equiv -m_{eww}^{(1)}(q), \quad m_{ef}^{(1)}(p) \equiv m_{eff}^{(1)}(p) + m_{efw}^{(1)}(q). \tag{2.9}$$

Analogously to $g_{fw}^{(1)}$ and $m_{efw}^{(1)}$, there are the corrections $g_{wf}^{(1)}$ and $m_{ewf}^{(1)}$ originating from S_f to g_{w0} and m_{ew0}. From [2] – (3.14), (2.3), [2] – (3.28) and (2.4) we define

$$g_{wf}^{(1)} = g_{wf}^{(1)}(q_2, q_1) \equiv -g_{ff}^{(1)}(q_2, q_1), \; g_{w}^{(1)}(p_2, p_1) = g_{ww}^{(1)}(p_2, p_1) + g_{wf}^{(1)}(q_2, q_1), \tag{2.10}$$

$$m_{ewf}^{(1)} = m_{ewf}^{(1)}(q) \equiv -m_{eff}^{(1)}(q), \quad m_{ew}^{(1)}(p) \equiv m_{eww}^{(1)}(p) + m_{ewf}^{(1)}(q). \tag{2.11}$$

(2.8)-(2.11) are the second sort of 1-loop corrections. (2.3)-(2.11) can be generalized to n-loop diagrams. Since there must be the two sorts of corrections simultaneously, both must simultaneously be considered and be approximated to the same loop-number, i.e., after their integrands are added up, the corresponding integral is completed. Thus the integrands causing divergences will cancel each other out, consequently $\langle F_f \mid S_f \mid F_i \rangle$ and $\langle W_f \mid S_w \mid W_i \rangle$ will be all convergent, and it is unnecessary to introduce regularization and counter-terms. For example, in the new QED, we have [1] – (1.1). From (2.7)-(2.11) we see that if we let $g_{fw}^{(1)} = g_{fw}^{(1)}(p_2, p_1)$, the total sum of corrections of the first and second sorts must be zero. This is equivalent to redefine the point with the momenta p_2 and p_1 as the subtraction point and $g_f(p_2, p_1)$ is regarded as an accurate value. In fact, $g_f(p_2, p_1)$ is unknown, and our aim is to evaluate an approximate $g_f(p_2, p_1)$ from the accurate $g_0(q_2, q_1)$ and $m_{e0}(q_1)$. In meaning of perturbation theory, $g_0(q_2, q_1)$ as an accurate value already contains $g_{ff}^{(1)}(q_2, q_1)$ and $g_{fw}^{(1)}(q_2, q_1)$, i.e., $g_f^{(1)}(q_2, q_1) = g_{ff}^{(1)}(q_2, q_1) + g_{fw}^{(1)}(q_2, q_1) = 0$. From the F-W symmetry and (2.7)-(2.11) we can prove $g_f^{(1)}(q_2, q_1) = 0$. When $g_{ff}^{(1)}(q_2, q_1)$ becomes $g_{ff}^{(1)}(p_2, p_1)$, $g_{ff}^{(1)}(p_2, p_1) + g_{fw}^{(1)}(q_2, q_1)$ is not equal to zero and is finite. Analogous analysis holds water for $m_{efw}^{(1)}(q)$, $g_{wf}^{(1)}(q_2, q_1)$ and $m_{ewf}^{(1)}(q)$ and

$$g_{w}^{(1)}(q_2, q_1) = m_{ew}^{(1)}(q_1) = m_{ef}^{(1)}(q_1) = 0. \tag{2.12}$$

For a free particle, $p = q$ or $k = q'$ and $m_{ew}^{(1)}(q) = m_{ef}^{(1)}(q) = 0$. When $p \neq q$, $m_{ef}^{(1)}(p) = m_{ew}^{(1)}(p) \neq 0$. In this case $m_{ef}^{(1)}(p)$ or $m_{ew}^{(1)}(p)$ must join one or two vertexes, hence we can regard $m_{ef}^{(1)}(p)$ or $m_{ew}^{(1)}(p)$ as a part of corrections of the vertexes. We can regard specially a correction to a propagator (according to conventional QFT) as the sum of partial corrections to the two vertexes joining to the propagator. Both views are obviously equivalent. The correction to every vertex joining the propagator is the same, hence this correction is half of the correction to the propagator. Analogously, we regard correction to an external line as partial correction to a vertex. We can prove that these results hold water for n-loop diagrams (see section 4.5). Thus, in present theory there is no correction to an external line and a propagator, there is only correction to a vertex.

As mentioned above, we see that ψ' and A'_μ are the same as ψ and A_μ in the conventional QED. Formulating the new QED by ψ' , A'_μ, $\underline{\psi}'$ and $\underline{A}'_\mu$, the new QED will be the same as the conventional QED in form. The essential differences between the new QED and the conventional QED are that the Lagrangian density of the conventional QED is replaced by $\mathcal{L} = \mathcal{L}_f + \mathcal{L}_w$ and S_f and S_w. Both determine correction to a scattering amplitude $\langle F_f \mid S_f \mid F_i \rangle$ and $\langle W_f \mid S_w \mid W_i \rangle$. Thus, though $\mathcal{L}_f$ and $\mathcal{L}_w$ are independent of each other in classical meanings after quantization, both are dependent on each other.

3 The first sort of 1-loop corrections

3.1 The first sort of one-loop corrections originating from $S_f\left(g_0, m_{e0}\right)$.

By $S_f\left(g_0, m_{e0}\right)$ (see [2] – (5.3)) we can evaluate the 1-loop correction to the scattering amplitude and the electromagnetic mass m_{e0} of a free F-electron corresponding to figure 1 A[3],

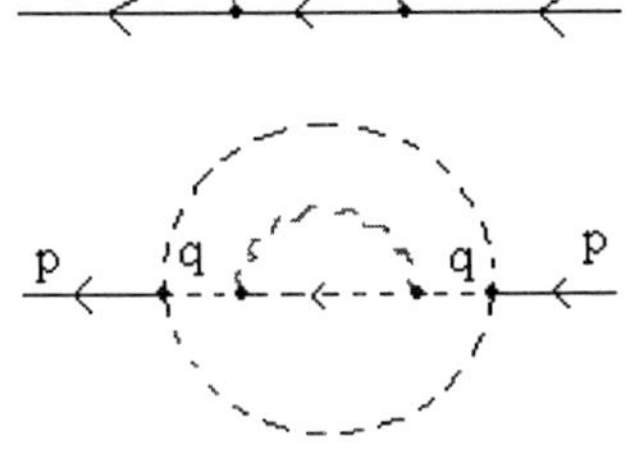

Figure 1: A WFDG1L representing the two sorts of corrections to the mass of a free F-electrons. Fig. 1A originates from S_f, Fig. 1B originates from S_w, and the dotted- line circle in Fig. 1B represents $A'^{-1}_{mw}\left(\mid \underline{a}_{q_1 s_1}\rangle \rightarrow \mid \underline{a}_{q_2 s_2}\rangle\right)$.

$$A^{(1)}_{mff}\left(q_1\right) = \langle a_{\mathbf{q}_2 s_2} \mid S^{(1)}_f\left(g_0, m_{e0}\right) \mid a_{\mathbf{q}_1 s_1}\rangle$$
$$= \delta^4\left(q_2 - q_1\right)\frac{1}{V}\overline{u}_{\mathbf{q}_2 s_2}\Sigma^{(1)}_{ff}\left(q_1\right) u_{\mathbf{q}_1 s_1}, \quad (3.1)$$

$$\Sigma_{ff}^{(1)}(q_1) = g_0^2 \int d^4k \frac{-i}{k^2 - i\varepsilon} r_\mu \frac{-i\left[m - i\left(q_1 - k\right)\gamma\right]}{\left(q_1 - k\right)^2 + m^2 - i\varepsilon} r_\mu$$
$$= -i\left(2\pi\right)^4 A + BS_{Ff}^{-1}(q_1) + S_{Ff}^{-1}(q_1)\,\Sigma_{fc}^{(1)}(q_1)\,S_{Ff}^{-1}(q_1), \qquad (3.2)$$

$$A \equiv \frac{\alpha}{2\pi} m\left(\frac{3}{2}D + \frac{9}{4}\right), \quad D \equiv \frac{1}{i\pi^2}\int d^4k \frac{1}{(k^2 + m^2)^2}, \qquad (3.3)$$

$$B \equiv -\frac{\alpha}{4\pi}\left(D - 4\int_0^1 \frac{dx}{x} + \frac{11}{2}\right), \qquad (3.4)$$

$$\overline{u}_{\mathbf{q}_2 s_2} S_{Ff}^{-1}(q_1) = S_{Ff}^{-1}(q_1)\, u_{\mathbf{q}_1 s_1} = \Sigma_{fc}^{(1)}(q_1) = 0, \qquad (3.5)$$

where A and B are divergent, $\alpha = g_0^2/4\pi$. From (2.4) we have

$$m_{eff}^{(1)}(q) = \frac{\left\langle a_{\mathbf{q}_2 s_2} \mid S_f^{(1)}(g_0, m_{e0}) \mid a_{\mathbf{q}_1 s_1}\right\rangle}{\left\langle a_{\mathbf{q}_2 s_2} \mid -i\int d^4x : \overline{\psi'}\psi' : \mid a_{\mathbf{q}_1 s_1}\right\rangle} = A \qquad (3.6)$$

The 1-loop correction of the F-electron propagator with its two vertices shown in figure 2 is

$$(-g_0\gamma_\mu) S_{Fff}^{(1)}(p)\,(-g_0\gamma_\nu) = g_0^2 \gamma_\mu S_{Ff}(p)\,\Sigma_f^{(1)}(p)\,S_{Ff}(p)\,\gamma_\nu, \qquad (3.7)$$

where the factors $(2\pi)^4 \delta(p_2 - p + k_2)$ and $(2\pi)^4 \delta(p - p_1 - k_1)$ are ignored, $\Sigma_{fc}^{(1)}(p)$ is finite, $S_{Ff}^{-1}(p) = i(2\pi)^4 (ip\gamma + m)$. It is not necessary to evaluate the integral, because the integrands in A and B will be cancelled out by the second integrand in the total scattering amplitude. Because a propagator must join its two vertexes, (3.7) may also be regarded as the sum of corrections to the two vertices shown in the figure 2. Because the corrections to the two vertexes must be the same, we have

$$\Lambda_{ff1\mu}^{(1)L}(p) \equiv -\frac{1}{2} g_0 \gamma_\mu S_{Ff}(p)\,\Sigma_f^{(1)}(p), \qquad (3.8)$$

$$\Lambda_{ff1\nu}^{(1)R}(p) \equiv -\frac{1}{2}\Sigma_f^{(1)}(p)\,S_{Ff}(p)\,g_0\gamma_\nu. \qquad (3.9)$$

(3.8) and (3.9) are respectively shown in the figure $2 - L$ and $2 - R$. We always regard $\Lambda_{ff1\mu}^{(1)L}(p)$ and $\Lambda_{ff1\nu}^{(1)R}(p)$ as a whole.The sort of corrections analogous to (3.8)-(3.9) is the first sort of partial corrections to a vertex. We will see the total correction to the mass of a free particle to be zero. Thus, in addition to the Feynman rules in the fifth section in [2], from (3.8), (3.9), the figure $2 - L$ and the figure $2 - R$ we obtain the first supplementary Feynman rule.

The first supplementary Feynman rule There is no correction to propagator and external lines. There are only correction to vertexes and correction to the mass of a free particle (which must be zero). A correction to a propagator

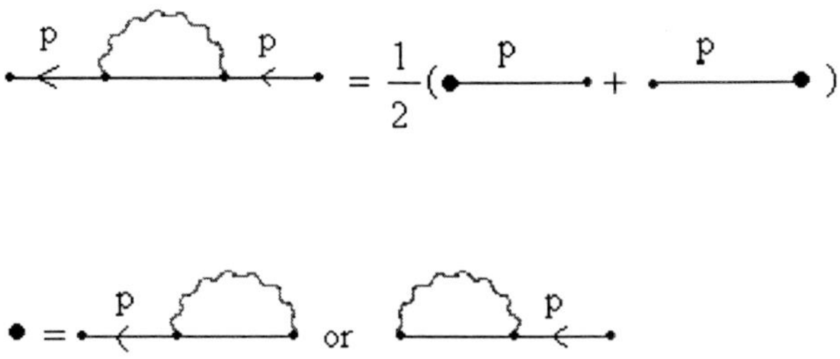

Figure 2: Fig. 2-4 are composed of the two simplest WFDG1Ls respectively representing the one-loop corrections to the two vertices joining a F-electron propagator. Fig. 2 represents that the one-loop correction to a propagator may be regarded as the sum of one-loop correction to the two vertices joining the propagator. Fig. 2L represents the contribution of $\Lambda^{(1)L}_{ff1\mu}$. Fig. 2R represents the contribution of $\Lambda^{(1)R}_{ff1\mu}$.

can be regarded the sum of partial corrections to the two vertexes joining the propagator, a correction to an external line can be regarded the partial corrections to the vertex joining the external line.

Operating $\Lambda^{(1)L}_{ff1\mu}(q)$ on $u_{\mathbf{q}s}$ and $\Lambda^{(1)R}_{ff1\nu}(q)$ on $\overline{u}_{\mathbf{q}s}$, considering (3.5), from (3.8) and (3.9) we have

$$\Lambda^{(1)L}_{ff1\mu}u_{\mathbf{q}s} = -\frac{1}{2}g_0\gamma_\mu[-i(2\pi)^4 AS_{Ff}(q) + B]u_{\mathbf{q}s}, \tag{3.10}$$

$$\overline{u}_{\mathbf{q}s}\Lambda^{(1)R}_{ff1\nu} = -\overline{u}_{\mathbf{q}s}\frac{1}{2}[-i(2\pi)^4 AS_{Ff}(q) + B]g_0\gamma_\nu. \tag{3.11}$$

From (3.10) or (3.11) we observe that the rule above naturally eliminates the ambiguity of corrections to external lines in the conventional QED [3].

Because of the gauge invariance of the Lagrangian density, there is no correction to the mass of a free F-photon or a W-photon. The one-loop contribution of $S_f(g_0, m_{e0})$ to the F-photon propagator with its two vertices can be represented by the Feynman diagram shown in figure $5-A$.

Considering the current to be conservational, by the Feynman rules we have [3]

$$(-g_0\gamma_\mu)D^{(1)}_{Fff\mu\nu}(k)(-g_0\gamma_\nu) = g_0\gamma_\mu D_{Ff}(k)\Pi^{(1)}_{f\mu\nu}(k)D_{Ff}(k)g_0\gamma_\nu, \tag{3.12}$$

$$\begin{aligned}\Pi^{(1)}_{f\mu\nu}(k) &= g_0^2 \int d^4pTr\gamma_\mu \frac{m-ip\gamma}{p^2+m^2-i\varepsilon}\gamma_\nu \frac{m-i(p-k)\gamma}{(p-k)^2+m^2-i\varepsilon} \\ &= \left(\delta_{\mu\nu}-\frac{k_\mu k\nu}{k^2}\right)\left[CD^{-1}_{Ff}(k)+\Pi^{(1)}_{fc}(k)D^{-2}_{Ff}(k)\right] \\ &= \delta_{\mu\nu}\left[CD^{-1}_{Ff}(k)+\Pi^{(1)}_{fc}(k)D^{-2}_{Ff}(k)\right],\end{aligned} \tag{3.13}$$

where $D^{-1}_{Ff}(k)=i(2\pi)^4k^2$,

$$C=-\frac{\alpha}{3\pi}\left(D+\frac{5}{6}\right). \tag{3.14}$$

C is logarithmically divergent , $\Pi^{(1)}_{fc}(k)$ is finite and $\Pi^{(1)}_{fc}(q')=0$.

Analogously to discussion for (3.8) and (3.9), from (3.12) and (3.13) we reach the second sort of one-loop partial correction $\Lambda^{(1)}_{ff2\nu}$ to a F-vertex to be

$$\begin{aligned}\Lambda^{(1)}_{ff2\nu}(k) &= -\frac{1}{2}g_0\gamma_\mu D_{Ff}(k)\Pi^{(1)}_{f\mu\nu}(k) \\ &= -\frac{1}{2}g_0\gamma_\mu\left(\delta_{\mu\nu}-\frac{k_\mu k\nu}{k^2}\right)\left[C+\Pi^{(1)}_{fc}(k)D^{-1}_{Ff}(k)\right].\end{aligned} \tag{3.15}$$

Considering $q'^2=0$ for external photon lines, from (3.15) we get

$$\Lambda^{(1)}_{ff2\mu}(q')\frac{1}{\sqrt{2\omega_{\mathbf{q}}V}}e^{\lambda}_{\mathbf{q}\mu}=-\frac{1}{2}g_0\gamma_\mu\delta_{\mu\nu}C\frac{1}{\sqrt{2\omega_{\mathbf{q}}V}}e^{\lambda}_{\mathbf{q}\nu}. \tag{3.16}$$

From (3.16) and (2.3) we obtain the second sort of the one-loop partial corrections originating from $S^{(1)}_f(g_0,m_{e0})$ to the coupling constant to be

$$\begin{aligned}&g^{(1)}_{ff2}(p_2,p_1) \\ &= \frac{(2\pi)^4\delta^4(p_2-k_1-p_1)V^{-3/2}\overline{u}_{\mathbf{p}_2s_2}\Lambda^{(1)}_{ff2\nu}(k)u_{\mathbf{p}_1s_1}e^{\lambda}_{\mathbf{k}_1\nu}(2\omega_{\mathbf{k}_1})^{-1/2}}{\langle a_{\mathbf{p}_2s_2}\mid -\int d^4x:\overline{\psi}'\gamma_\mu A'_\mu\psi':\mid a_{\mathbf{p}_1s_1}c_{\mathbf{k}_1\lambda}\rangle} \\ &= \frac{1}{2}g_0\left\{C+\Pi^{(1)}_{fc}(k)D^{-1}_{Ff}(k)\right\},\end{aligned} \tag{3.17}$$

$$g^{(1)}_{ff2}(q_2,q_1)=\frac{1}{2}g_0C, \tag{3.18}$$

where the numerator in (3.17) corresponds to Fig. $8-A$ to be the one part of the scattering amplitude $\langle a_{\mathbf{p}s}\mid S^{(1)}_f(g_0,m_{e0})\mid a_{\mathbf{p}_1s_1}\rangle\mid c_{\mathbf{k}_1\lambda}\rangle$. The first supplementary Feynman rule still applies to this case.

The third sort of one-loop partial contribution $A^{(1)}_{gff3}$ of the scattering operator $S_f(g_0, m_{e0})$ to the scattering amplitude $A_{gf}(p_2, p_1)$ is represented by the Feynman diagram shown in figure $9-A$. Applying the Feynman rules we have[3]

$$
\begin{aligned}
A^{(1)}_{gff3}(p_2,p_1) &= \langle a_{\mathbf{p}_2 s_2} \mid S^{(1)}_{f3}(g_0, m_{e0}) \mid a_{\mathbf{p}_1 s_1} c_{\mathbf{k}\lambda} \rangle \\
&= -g_0 (2\pi)^4 \delta^4 (p_2 - p_1 - k) \\
&\cdot \frac{1}{V} \overline{u}_{\mathbf{p}_2 s_2} \Lambda^{(1)}_{\mu,ff3}(p_2,p_1) u_{\mathbf{p}_1 s_1} \frac{1}{\sqrt{2\omega_{\mathbf{k}} V}} e^{\lambda}_{\mathbf{k}\mu},
\end{aligned}
\tag{3.19}
$$

$$
\begin{aligned}
\Lambda^{(1)}_{\mu,ff3}(p_2,p_1) &= \frac{i g_0^2}{(2\pi)^4} \int \frac{d^4 k}{k^2 - i\varepsilon} \gamma_\nu \frac{m - i(p_2 - k)\gamma}{(p_2 - k)^2 + m^2 - i\varepsilon} \\
&\cdot \gamma_\mu \frac{m - i(p_1 - k)\gamma}{(p_1 - k)^2 + m^2 - i\varepsilon} \gamma_\nu \\
&= L\gamma_\mu + \Lambda^{(1)}_{\mu,ff3c}(p_2,p_1),
\end{aligned}
\tag{3.20}
$$

where $L = -B$, is logarithmically divergent, $\Lambda^{(1)}_{\mu,ff3}(p_2,p_1)$ is finite and $\Lambda^{(1)}_{\mu,ff3}(q_2,q_1) = 0$. From (3.19) and (2.3) we get the third sort of the one-loop partial corrections originating from $S^{(1)}_f(g_0, m_{e0})$ to the coupling constant g_{f0} to be

$$
g^{(1)}_{ff3}(p_2, p_1) = g_0 \frac{\overline{u}_{\mathbf{p}_2 s_2} \Lambda^{(1)}_{\nu,ff3c}(p_2,p_1) \gamma_\nu u_{\mathbf{p}_1 s_1} e^{\lambda}_{\mathbf{k}_1 \nu}}{\overline{u}_{\mathbf{p}_2 s_2} \gamma_\mu u_{\mathbf{p}_1 s_1} e^{\lambda}_{\mathbf{k}_1 \mu}} + g_0 L,
\tag{3.21}
$$

$$
g^{(1)}_{ff3}(q_2, q_1) = g_0 L.
\tag{3.22}
$$

(3.1)-(3.7), (3.12)-(3.14) and (3.19)-(3.20) are the same as those of the conventional QED, respectively[3].

3.2 The first sort of one-loop corrections originating from $S_w(g_0, m_{e0})$

We can obtain the Feynman diagrams determined by $S_w(g_0, m_{e0})$ corresponding to those determined by $S_f(g_0, m_{e0})$, provided we transform real lines into the dotted lines corresponding to them. Analogously to computation of (3.1) -(3.22), and paying attention to the differences between the vertex, the propagators and the external lines of $\langle F_f \mid S_f(g_0, m_{e0}) \mid F_i \rangle$ and those of $\langle W_f \mid S_w(g_0, m_{e0}) \mid W_i \rangle$, we reach the results corresponding to (3.1) -(3.22).

$$A^{(1)}_{mww}(q_1) = \langle \underline{a}_{\mathbf{q}_2 s_2} \mid S^{(1)}_w(g_0, m_{e0}) \mid \underline{a}_{\mathbf{q}_1 s_1} \rangle$$
$$= \delta^4(q_2 - q_1)\frac{1}{V}\overline{v}_{\mathbf{q}_2 s_2}\Sigma^{(1)}_{ww}(p)\, v_{\mathbf{q}_1 s_1}, \tag{3.23}$$

$$\Sigma^{(1)}_{ww}(q_1) = g_0^2 \int d^4k \frac{i}{k^2 + i\varepsilon} r_\mu \frac{-i\,[m - i\,(q_1 - k)\,\gamma]}{(q_1 - k)^2 + m^2 + i\varepsilon} r_\mu$$
$$= -i\,(2\pi)^4 A + BS^{-1}_{Fw}(q_1) + S^{-1}_{Fw}(q_1)\,\Sigma^{(1)}_{wc}(q_1)\,S^{-1}_{Fw}(q_1)$$
$$= \Sigma^{(1)}_{ff}(q_1), \tag{3.24}$$

$$\Sigma^{(1)}_{wc}(q_1) = \Sigma^{(1)}_{fc}(q_1) = 0, \qquad S^{-1}_{Fw}(q_1) = S^{-1}_{Ff}(q_1). \tag{3.25}$$

Substituting $A^{(1)}_{mww}(p_1)$ into (2.6), we obtain the one-loop correction originating from $S_w(g_0, m_{e0})$ to the mass of a free W-electron to be

$$m^{(1)}_{eww}(q) = A. \tag{3.26}$$

The one-loop contribution for the W-electron propagator with its two vertices originating $S_w(g_0, m_{e0})$ is

$$g_0\gamma\mu S^{(1)}_{Fw,ww}(p)\, g_0\gamma_\nu = g_0^2\gamma_\mu S_{Fw}(p)\,\Sigma^{(1)}_{ww}(p)\, S_{Fw}(p)\,\gamma_\nu. \tag{3.27}$$

From above we obtain the first sort of one-loop partial corrections to a W-vertex to be

$$\Lambda^{(1)L}_{ww1\mu} = \frac{1}{2} g_0\gamma\mu S_{Fw}(p)\,\Sigma^{(1)}_{ww}(p) = -\Lambda^{(1)L}_{ff1\mu}, \tag{3.28}$$

$$\Lambda^{(1)R}_{ww1\nu} = \frac{1}{2}\Sigma^{(1)}_{ww}(p)\, S_{Fw}(p)\, g_0\gamma_\nu = -\Lambda^{(1)R}_{ff1\nu}. \tag{3.29}$$

Consequently,

$$\Lambda^{(1)L}_{ww1\mu}(q)\, v_{\mathbf{q}s}\frac{1}{\sqrt{V}} = \frac{1}{2} g_0\gamma\mu[-i\,(2\pi)^4 A S_{Fw}(p) + B] v_{\mathbf{q}s}\frac{1}{\sqrt{V}}, \tag{3.30}$$

$$\frac{1}{\sqrt{V}}\overline{v}_{\mathbf{q}s}\Lambda^{(1)R}_{ww1\nu}(q) = \frac{1}{\sqrt{V}}\overline{v}_{\mathbf{q}s}\frac{1}{2}[-i\,(2\pi)^4 A S_{Fw}(p) + B] g_0\gamma_\nu. \tag{3.31}$$

The one-loop contribution of the scattering operator $S_w(g_0, m_{e0})$ for the W-photon propagator with its two vertices is

$$g_0\gamma_\mu D^{(1)}_{Fw\mu\nu}(k)\, g_0\gamma_\nu = g_0\gamma_\mu D_{Fw}(k)\, \Pi^{(1)}_{w\mu\nu}(k)\, D_{Fw}(k)\, g_0\gamma_\nu, \tag{3.32}$$

$$\begin{aligned}\Pi^{(1)}_{w\mu\nu}(k) &= g_0^2 \int d^4p Tr\left\{r_\mu \frac{m-ip}{p^2+m^2+i\varepsilon} r_\nu \frac{m-i(p-k)}{(p-k)^2+m^2+i\varepsilon}\right\} \\ &= \left(\delta_{\mu\nu} - \frac{k_\mu k\nu}{k^2}\right)\left[CD^{-1}_{Fw}(k) + \Pi^{(1)}_{wc}(k)\, D^{-2}_{Fw}(k)\right] \\ &= -\Pi^{(1)}_{f\mu\nu}(k),\end{aligned} \tag{3.33}$$

$$\Pi^{(1)}_{wc}(k) = -\Pi^{(1)}_{fc}(k), \qquad D^{-1}_{Fw}(k) = -D^{-1}_{Ff}(k). \tag{3.34}$$

Analogously to (3.15), from (3.32) we obtain the second sort of one-loop partial corrections $\Lambda^{(1)}_{ww2}$ for a W-vertex to be

$$\begin{aligned}\Lambda^{(1)}_{ww2\nu}(k) &= \frac{1}{2} g_0\gamma\mu D_{Fw}(k)\, \Pi^{(1)}_{w\mu\nu}(k) \\ &= \frac{1}{2} g_0\gamma\mu\left(\delta_{\mu\nu} - \frac{k_\mu k\nu}{k^2}\right)\left[C + \Pi^{(1)}_{wc}(k)\, D^{-1}_{Fw}(k)\right].\end{aligned} \tag{3.35}$$

Considering $q'^2 = 0$ for external photon lines, from (3.35) we have

$$\Lambda^{(1)}_{ww2\mu}(q')\frac{1}{\sqrt{2\omega_{\mathbf{q}'}V}} e^\lambda_{\mathbf{q}'\mu} = \frac{1}{2} g_0\gamma\mu\left(\delta_{\mu\nu} - \frac{q'_\mu q'\nu}{q'^2}\right) C \frac{1}{\sqrt{2\omega_{\mathbf{q}'}V}} e^\lambda_{\mathbf{q}'\nu}. \tag{3.36}$$

From (3.35) and (2.5) we obtain the second sort of the one-loop partial corrections originating from $S^{(1)}_w(g_0, m_{e0})$ to the coupling constant to be

$$\begin{aligned}g^{(1)}_{ww2}(p_2, p_1) &= \frac{(2\pi)^4\, \delta^4(p_2 - k_1 - p_1)\, V^{-3/2}\overline{v}_{\mathbf{p}_2 s_2}\Lambda^{(1)}_{ww2\nu}(k)\, v_{\mathbf{p}_1 s_1} e^\lambda_{\mathbf{k}_1\nu}(2\omega_{\mathbf{k}_1})^{-1/2}}{\langle \underline{a}_{\mathbf{p}_2 s_2} \mid \int d^4x : \underline{\overline{\psi}'}\gamma_\mu \underline{A'_\mu}\underline{\psi'} :\mid \underline{a}_{\mathbf{p}_1 s_1}\underline{c}_{\mathbf{k}_1\lambda}\rangle} \\ &= \frac{1}{2} g_0\left\{C + \Pi^{(1)}_{wc}(k)\, D^{-1}_{Fw}(k)\right\}.\end{aligned} \tag{3.37}$$

$$g^{(1)}_{ww2}(q_2, q_1) = \frac{1}{2} g_0 C. \tag{3.38}$$

Let $A^{(1)}_{gww3}(p_2,p_1)$ be the third sort of one-loop partial contributions originating from $S_w(g_0, m_{e0})$ for the scattering amplitude $A^{(1)}_{gw3}(p_2,p_1)$. Analogously to $A^{(1)}_{gff3}(p_2,p_1)$, by the Feynman rules we have

$$\begin{aligned}A^{(1)}_{gww3}(p_2,p_1) &= \langle \underline{a}_{\mathbf{p}_2 s_2} \mid S^{(1)}_w(g_0, m_{e0}) \mid \underline{a}_{\mathbf{p}_1 s_1} \underline{c}_{\mathbf{k}\lambda}\rangle \\ &= g_0 (2\pi)^4 \delta^4(p_2 - p_1 - k) \frac{1}{V} \overline{v}_{\mathbf{p}_2 s_2} \Lambda^{(1)}_{\mu,ww3}(p_2,p_1) v_{\mathbf{p}_1 s_1} \frac{1}{\sqrt{2\omega_{\mathbf{k}} V}} e^{\lambda}_{\mathbf{k}\mu},\end{aligned} \tag{3.39}$$

$$\begin{aligned}&\Lambda^{(1)}_{\mu,ww3}(p_2,p_1) \\ &\quad = \frac{g_0^2}{(2\pi)^4} \int d^4k \frac{i}{k^2 + i\varepsilon} \gamma_\nu \frac{-i[m - i(p_2 - k)\gamma]}{(p_2 - k)^2 + m^2 + i\varepsilon} \gamma_\mu \frac{-i[m - i(p_1 - k)\gamma]}{(p_1 - k)^2 + m^2 + i\varepsilon} \gamma_\nu \\ &\quad = L\gamma_\mu + \Lambda^{(1)}_{\mu,ww3c}(p_2,p_1) = \Lambda^{(1)}_{\mu,ff3}(p_2,p_1), \\ &\Lambda^{(1)}_{\mu,ww3c} = \Lambda^{(1)}_{\mu,ff3c}.\end{aligned} \tag{3.40}$$

From (3.39) and (2.5) we extract the third sort of the one-loop partial corrections originating from $S^{(1)}_w(g_0, m_{e0})$ to the coupling constant g_{w0} to be

$$g^{(1)}_{ww3}(p_2, p_1) = g_0 \frac{\overline{v}_{\mathbf{p}_2 s_2} \Lambda^{(1)}_{\nu,ww3c}(p_2,p_1) \gamma_\nu v_{\mathbf{p}_1 s_1} e^{\lambda}_{\mathbf{k}_1 \nu}}{\overline{v}_{\mathbf{p}_2 s_2} \gamma_\mu v_{\mathbf{p}_1 s_1} e^{\lambda}_{\mathbf{k}_1 \mu}} + g_0 L, \tag{3.41}$$

$$g^{(1)}_{ww3}(q_2, q_1) = g_0 L. \tag{3.42}$$

4 The second sort of one-loop corrections and the total one-loop corrections

4.1 The second sort of one-loop corrections

The second sort of correction is such correction to $g^{(0)}_f$ and m_{ef0} originating from $S_w(g_0, m_{e0})$ and such correction to $g^{(0)}_w$ and m_{ew0} originating from $S_f(g_0, m_{e0})$. The characters of the second sort of corrections are as follows.

1. The momenta at the vertexes of the first sort of corrections are arbitrary. In contrast with the first sort of correction, from (2.8)-(2.11) we see that the momenta at the vertexes of the second sort of corrections must be equal to q_2, q_1 and q'.

2. From (2.8)-(2.11) and (2.3)-(2.6) we see that the second sort of corrections is easily evaluated by the first sort of corrections. For example, from (3.6) and (3.26), (2.9) and (2.11), we have

$$m^{(1)}_{efw}(q) = -m^{(1)}_{eww}(q) = -A = m^{(1)}_{ewf}(q) = -m^{(1)}_{eff}(q), \tag{4.1}$$

from (2.8), (2.10), (3.18), (3.22), (3.38) and (3.42), we can derive

$$g^{(1)}_{fw2}(q_2,q_1) = -g^{(1)}_{ww2}(q_2,q_1) = -\frac{1}{2}g_0 C = g^{(1)}_{wf2}(q_2,q_1) = -g^{(1)}_{ff2}(q_2,q_1), \tag{4.2}$$

$$g^{(1)}_{fw3}(q_2,q_1) = -g^{(1)}_{ww3}(q_2,q_1) = -g_0 L = g^{(1)}_{wf3}(q_2,q_1) = -g^{(1)}_{ff3}(q_2,q_1). \tag{4.3}$$

3. The second sort of corrections directly corrects the coupling constants and the masses, hence it is equivalent to correction to a vertex. We represent it by a circle. From [2] – (3.2), [2] – (3.5), [2] – (3.18), [2] – (3.21), (2.3)-(2.6) and (2.8)-(2.11), we can derive the Feynman rules for a circle as follows.

The second supplementary Feynman rule

A. A circle is equivalent to a vertex for the part outside the circle.

B. The momenta of the external lines of the Feynman diagram inside the circle are the momenta q_2, q_1 and q' at the subtraction point.

C. a. The dotted- line circle with two speckles denotes the coefficient

$$A'^{-1}_{mw}(\mid \underline{a}_{q_1s_1}\rangle \rightarrow \mid \underline{a}_{q_2s_2}\rangle) = \langle \underline{a}_{q_2s_2} \mid -i\int d^4x : \underline{\overline{\psi}'}\underline{\psi'} : \mid \underline{a}_{q_1s_1}\rangle^{-1}, \tag{4.4}$$

the transition amplitude inside this dotted- line circle is

$$\langle \underline{a}_{q_2s_2} \mid S^{(1)}_w(g_0, m_{e0}) \mid \underline{a}_{q_1s_1}\rangle. \tag{4.5}$$

From (4.4) and (4.5) we derive the factor $m^{(1)}_{efw}(q)$ corresponding to the dotted-line in the figures $1-B$, 3, $6-B$ and $7-B$ to be $-A$ (see (4.1)).

b. The real- line circle with two speckles denotes the coefficient

$$A'^{-1}_{mf}(\mid a_{q_1s_1}\rangle \rightarrow \mid a_{q_2s_2}\rangle) = \langle a_{q_2s_2} \mid -i\int d^4x : \overline{\psi}'\psi' : \mid a_{q_1s_1}\rangle^{-1}, \tag{4.6}$$

the transition amplitude inside this real- line circle is

$$\langle a_{q_2s_2} \mid S^{(1)}_f(g_0, m_{e0}) \mid a_{q_1s_1}\rangle. \tag{4.7}$$

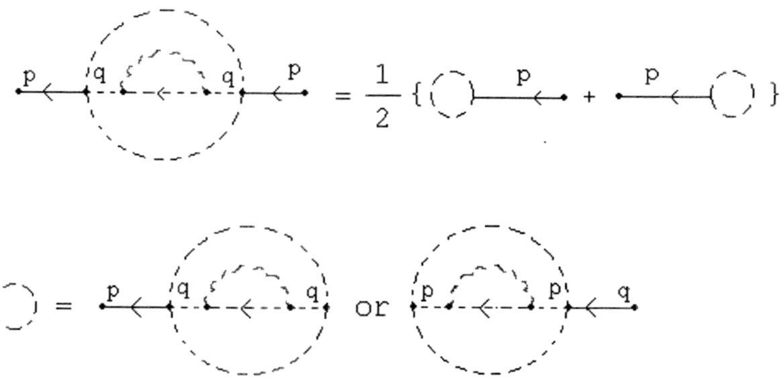

Figure 3: The contribution of $m_{efw}^{(1)}(q)$ originating from S_w for the two vertices joining $S_{Ff}(p)$.

From (4.6) and (4.7) we derive the factor $m_{ewf}^{(1)}(q)$ corresponding to the real-line circle in figures $4-B$, $6-D$ and $7-D$ to be $-A$ (see (4.1)).

c. The dotted- line circle with three speckles denotes the coefficient

$$A_{gw}^{\prime -1}\left(\mid \underline{a}_{q_1 s_1}\underline{c}_{q'\lambda}\rangle \rightarrow \mid \underline{a}_{q_2 s_2}\rangle\right)$$
$$= \{\langle \underline{a}_{q_2 s_2} \mid \int d^4x : \underline{\overline{\psi}'}\gamma_\mu \underline{A'}_\mu \underline{\psi'} : \mid \underline{a}_{q_1 s_1}\underline{c}_{q'\lambda}\rangle\}^{-1}, \tag{4.8}$$

the transition amplitude inside this dotted- line circle is

$$\langle \underline{a}_{q_2 s_2} \mid S_w^{(1)}(g_0, m_{e0}) \mid \underline{a}_{q_1 s_1}\underline{c}_{q'\lambda}\rangle. \tag{4.9}$$

From (4.8) and (4.9) we derive the factor $g_{fw2}^{(1)}(q_2, q_1)$ corresponding to the dotted-line in the figure $8-B$ and the figure $5-B$ to be $-\frac{1}{2}g_0 C$ (see (4.2)), and the factor $g_{fw3}^{(1)}(q_2, q_1)$ corresponding to the dotted-line in figure $9-B$ to be $-g_0 L$ (see (4.3)). From (4.8)-(4.9), (3.23), (3.30) and (4.6)-(4.7) (or (4.1) and (3.6)), we obtain a part of second sort of corrections to a F-vertex $g_{fw1}^{(1)}(q_2, q_1)$ corresponding to the figure 6-C-D to be $-\frac{1}{2}g_0 B$.

d. The real- line circle with three speckles denotes the coefficient

$$A_{gf}^{\prime -1}\left(\mid a_{q_1 s_1}c_{q'\lambda}\rangle \rightarrow \mid a_{q_2 s_2}\rangle\right)$$
$$= \{\langle a_{q_2 s_2} \mid \int d^4x : -\overline{\psi}'\gamma_\mu A'_\mu \psi' : \mid a_{q_1 s_1}c_{q'\lambda}\rangle\}^{-1}, \tag{4.10}$$

the transition amplitude inside this real- line circle is

$$\langle a_{q_2 s_2} \mid S_f^{(1)}(g_0, m_{e0}) \mid a_{q_1 s_1}c_{q'\lambda}\rangle. \tag{4.11}$$

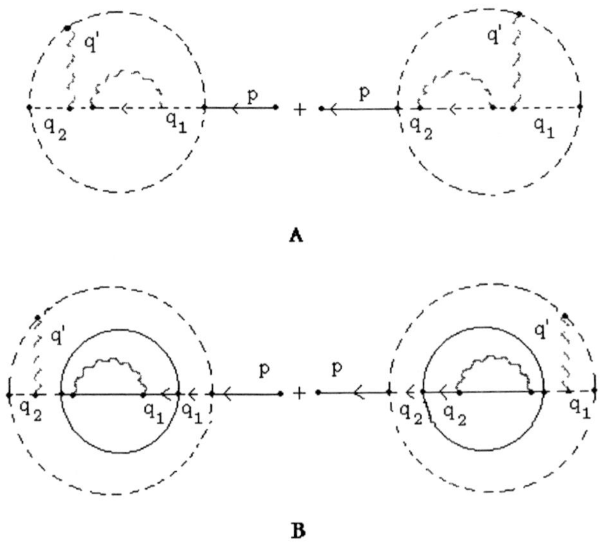

Figure 4: Fig. 4 is not a WFD1L. Fig. 4-A originates from S_w. The dotted- line circle in Fig. 4-A represents $A'^{-1}_{gw}\left(\mid \underline{a}_{q_1 s_1} \underline{c}_{q'\lambda}\rangle \to\mid \underline{a}_{q_2 s_2}\rangle\right)$ .Fig. 4-B originates from $S_w$and S_f. The real- line circle in Fig. 4-B represents $A'^{-1}_{mf}\left(\mid a_{q_1 s_1}\rangle \to\mid a_{q_2 s_2}\rangle\right)$.

Analogously to $g^{(1)}_{fw2}(q_2,q_1)$, $g^{(1)}_{fw3}(q_2,q_1)$ and $g^{(1)}_{fw1}(q_2,q_1)$, from (4.10) and (4.11) we derive the factors to be $(see(4.2))$

$$g^{(1)}_{wf2}(q_2,q_1) = -\frac{1}{2}g_0 C, \quad g^{(1)}_{wf3}(q_2,q_1) = -g_0 L, \quad g^{(1)}_{wf1}(q_2,q_1) = -\frac{1}{2}g_0 B.$$

4. Because the two sorts of corrections must simultaneously exist, both must simultaneously be considered and should be corrected to the same loop-number. For the reason, we define 'whole Feynman diagram group with n-loop'.

Definition 1 *If one group of Feynman diagrams with n-loop corresponding to the same initial state and final state is composed of complete diagrams with n-loop coming from both* $S^{(1)}_w(g_0, m_{e0})$ *and* $S^{(1)}_f(g_0, m_{e0})$*, the group of Feynman diagrams is called 'whole Feynman diagram group with n-loop'(WFDGNnL).*

For example, figures 1, 6, 7, 8, 9 and 5 are respectively a WFDG1L. Figures 2 and 3 do not form a WFDG1L, but the figures 2-4 form a WFDG1L.

Taking figure 6 as an example, we explain the construction of a WFDG1L. Because there is the correction $g^{(1)}_{ff1}$ corresponding to the figure $6-A$ and $g^{(1)}_{ff1}$ originates from

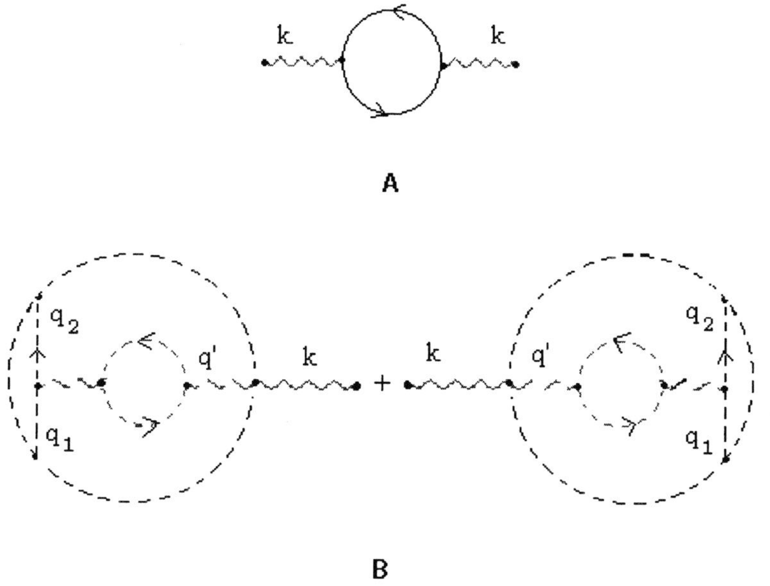

Figure 5: Fig. 5 is A WFDG1L representing the one-loop correction to D_{Ff}. Fig. 5A comes from S_f and can also be regarded as the sum of the corrections to the two vertices joining to it as Fig. 2 (is not drawn). Fig. 5B comes from S_w which is corresponds to Fig. 8A.

S_f, there must be the correction $g^{(1)}_{fw1}$ corresponding to the figure $6-C$ originating from S_w to the vertex. Because the contribution $g^{(1)}_{ff1}$ originates from $m^{(1)}_{eff}$ determined by S_f, there must be the correction $m^{(1)}_{efw}$ originating from S_w which is shown in the figure $6-B$. Correspondingly to the figure $6-B$, there must be the contribution originating from the figure $6-D$. By such method we easily construct a WFDG1L. Figure 6 contains the complete 1-loop corrections to a F-vertex derived from figure $6-A$, hence figure 6 forms a WFDG1L. Similarly, we obtain the WFDG1L's as shown by figures 1, 2-4, 5, 7, 8 and 9. Thus, because both $S_w(g_0, m_{e0})$ and $S_f(g_0, m_{e0})$ determine corrections to a F- or W-amplitude, we should use a WFDGNL to replace a Feynman diagram in conventional QFT, then go to evaluate n-loop correction to the scattering amplitude by the WFDGNL. As a result we obtain the following Feynman rule.

The third supplementary Feynman rule For an arbitrary scattering amplitude, we should firstly determine a WFDGNL corresponding to the amplitude, then sum up the integrands of the WFDGNL, last carry out the integral.

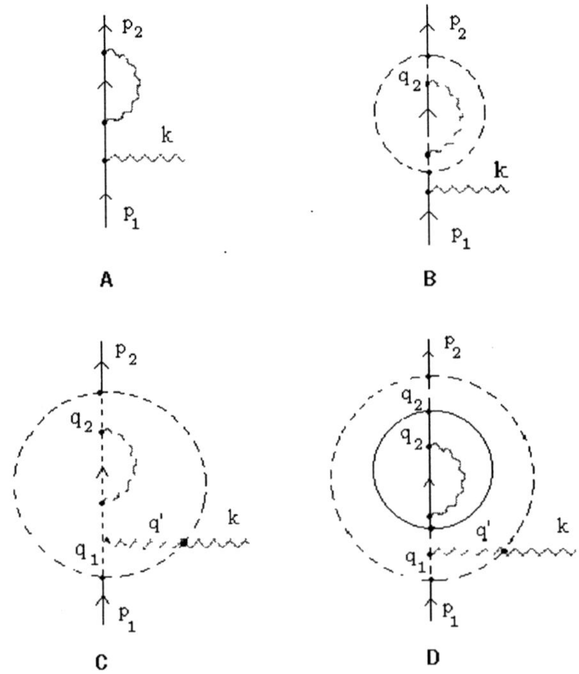

Figure 6: Fig. 6-9 are the total one-loop corrections to the scattering amplitude $A_g\left(\mid a_{\mathbf{p}_1 s_1} c_{\mathbf{k}\lambda}\rangle \rightarrow \mid a_{\mathbf{p}_2 s_2}\rangle\right)$. Fig. 6 is a WFDG1L representing a partial correction to a vertex. Fig. 6B-D are derived from Fig. 6A by S_f and S_w.

The Feynman rules in [2] and the three supplementary Feynman rules above fully determine the method evaluating a scattering amplitude by S_w and S_f.

The properties of a WFDGNL are as follows:

1. The integrands causing divergence in a WFDGNL must cancel each other out, thereby the Feynman integral of the WFDGNL must be convergent. For example, the correction to m_{ef0} coming from the WFDG1L composed of figure 1 is equal to zero (see [1] – (1.1)). From the Feynman rules, (3.17) and (4.2) we obtain the second sort of correction $g_{f2}^{(1)}$ to $g_f^{(0)}$ coming from the WFDG1L Fig. 8 to be

$$\begin{aligned} g_{f2}^{(1)} &= g_{ff2}^{(1)}(p_2, p_1) + g_{fw2}^{(1)}(q_2, q_1) \\ &= \frac{1}{2} g_0 \left[C + \Pi_{wc}^{(1)}(k)\, D_{Fw}^{-1}(k) \right] - \frac{1}{2} g_0 C \\ &= \frac{1}{2} g_0 \Pi_{wc}^{(1)}(k)\, D_{Fw}^{-1}(k), \qquad k = p_2 - p_1. \end{aligned} \tag{4.12}$$

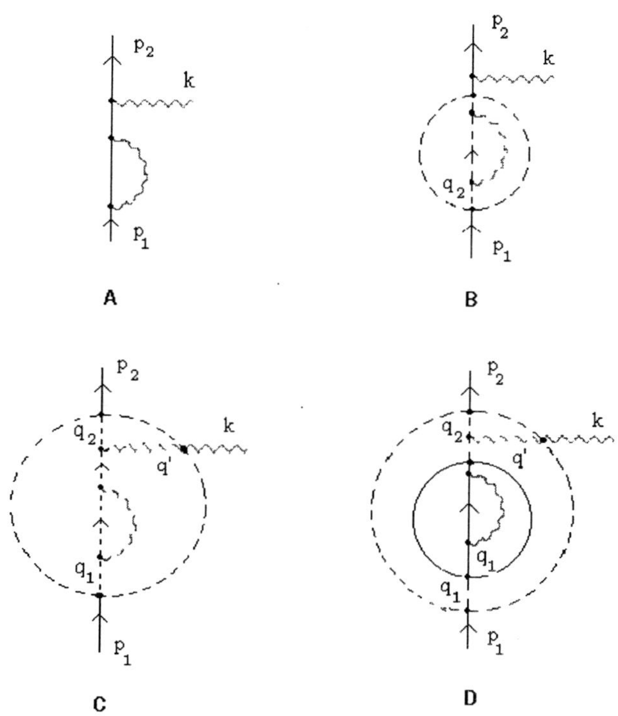

Figure 7: Fig. 7 is a WFDG1L representing a partial correction to a vertex. Fig. 7B-D are derived from Fig. 7A by S_f and S_w.

From (3.21) and (4.3) we obtain the third sort of correction $g_{f3}^{(1)}$ to $g_f^{(0)}$ coming from the WFDG1L figure 9 is

$$
\begin{aligned}
g_{f3}^{(1)}(p_2, p_1) &= g_{ff3}^{(1)}(p_2, p_1) + g_{fw3}^{(1)}(q_2, q_1) \\
&= g_0 \frac{\overline{u}_{\mathbf{p}_2 s_2} \Lambda_{\nu, ff3c}^{(1)}(p_2, p_1)\, \gamma_\nu u_{\mathbf{p}_1 s_1} e_{\mathbf{k}_1 \nu}^{\lambda}}{\overline{u}_{\mathbf{p}_2 s_2} \gamma_\mu u_{\mathbf{p}_1 s_1} e_{\mathbf{k}_1 \mu}^{\lambda}} + g_0 L - g_0 L \\
&= g_0 \frac{\overline{u}_{\mathbf{p}_2 s_2} \Lambda_{\nu, ff3c}^{(1)}(p_2, p_1)\, \gamma_\nu u_{\mathbf{p}_1 s_1} e_{\mathbf{k}_1 \nu}^{\lambda}}{\overline{u}_{\mathbf{p}_2 s_2} \gamma_\mu u_{\mathbf{p}_1 s_1} e_{\mathbf{k}_1 \mu}^{\lambda}}.
\end{aligned}
\tag{4.13}
$$

Analogously to $[1]-(1.1)$, we should firstly sum up the integrands in a WFDGNL, then complete the integral. But for shortness' sake, we directly give the results above.

2. A WFDGNL always as a whole appears in a more complicated diagram or exists by

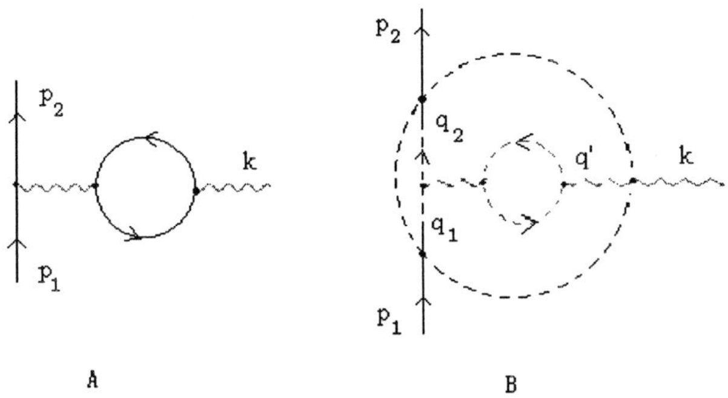

Figure 8: Fig. 8 is a WFDG1L representing a partial correction to a vertex. Fig. 8A is the first sort of corrections originating from S_f, Fig. 8B is the second sort of corrections originating from S_w.

itself. For example, the WFDG1L composed of figure 1 is a part of the WFDG1L composed of figure 6. It is possible a WFDGNL appearing in a more complicated diagram is no longer a WFDGNL. For example, when the WFDG1L figure 1 appears in figure 6, it is no longer a WFDG1L, but it is necessary that there is a new WFDGNL which contains the original group of diagrams, e.g., the WFDG1L composed of figure 6 contains figure 1.

4.2 The total one-loop corrections to g_{f0}

According to Feynman rules we easily get the corrections to g_{f0}. From (4.1) and (3.2) we obtain the sum of the two amplitudes $A^{(1)}_{gfAB}$ corresponding to figure 6 A and B

$$\begin{aligned}
A^{(1)}_{gfAB} &= (2\pi)^4\,\delta^4\,(p_2 - p_1 - k)\,\frac{1}{V}\overline{u}_{\mathbf{p}_2 s_2}\cdot\{\frac{1}{2}\Sigma^{(1)}_f\,(p_2)\,S_{Ff}\,(p_2)\,(-g_0)\gamma_\nu \\
&+ \frac{1}{2}[-i\,(2\pi)^4\,m^{(1)}_{efw} S_{Ff}\,(p_2)\,(-g_0)\gamma_\nu]\}u_{\mathbf{p}_1 s_1}\frac{1}{\sqrt{2\omega_{\mathbf{k}}V}}e^\lambda_{\mathbf{k}\mu} \\
&- (2\pi)^4\,\delta^4\,(p_2 - p_1 - k)\,\frac{1}{V}\overline{u}_{\mathbf{p}_2 s_2} \\
&\cdot\frac{1}{2}\{B + S^{-1}_{Ff}\,(p_2)\,\Sigma^{(1)}_{fc}\,(p_2)\}(-g_0)\gamma_\nu u_{\mathbf{p}_1 s_1}\frac{1}{\sqrt{2\omega_{\mathbf{k}}V}}e^\lambda_{\mathbf{k}\mu}.
\end{aligned} \tag{4.14}$$

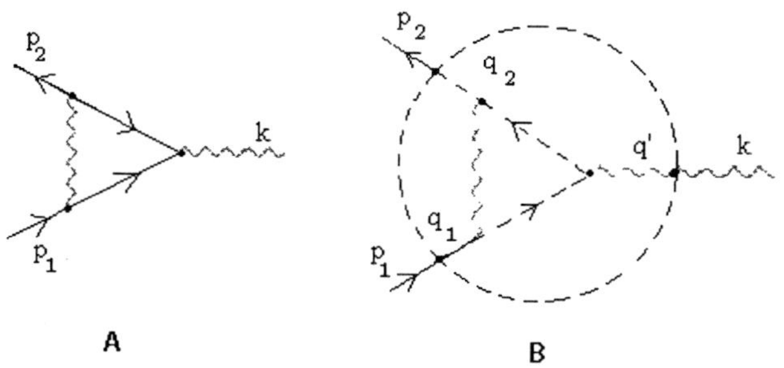

Figure 9: Fig. 9 is a WFDG1L representing a partial correction to a vertex. Fig. 9A is the first sort of corrections originating from S_f, Fig. 9B is the second sort of corrections originating from S_w.

From (4.1), (3.31) and (4.6)-(4.9), we obtain the sum of the two amplitudes $A^{(1)}_{gfCD}$ corresponding to figure $6-C-D$ is

$$\begin{aligned} A^{(1)}_{gfCD} &= \langle a_{\mathbf{p}_2 s_2} \mid -g^{(1)}_{fw1}(q_2, q_1) \int d^4x : \overline{\psi}' \gamma_\nu A'_\nu \psi' :\mid a_{\mathbf{p}_1 s_1} c_{\mathbf{k}\lambda} \rangle \\ &= (2\pi)^4 \, \delta^4 \left(p_2 - p_1 - k \right) \frac{1}{V} \overline{u}_{\mathbf{p}_2 s_2} \frac{1}{2} B g_0 \gamma_\nu u_{\mathbf{p}_1 s_1} \frac{1}{\sqrt{2\omega_{\mathbf{k}} V}} e^\lambda_{\mathbf{k}\mu} \end{aligned} \tag{4.15}$$

where

$$\begin{aligned} g^{(1)}_{fw1}(q_2, q_1) &= -\{ \langle \underline{a}_{\mathbf{q}_2 s_2} \mid [S^{(1)}_{w1} \left(g_0, m_{e0} \right) \\ &+ \int d^4x : \underline{\overline{\psi}'} m^{(1)}_{ewf}(q_2) S_{Fw}(q_2) \gamma_\nu g_0 \underline{A'_\nu} \underline{\psi'} :] \mid \underline{a}_{\mathbf{q}_1 s_1} \underline{c}_{\mathbf{q}\lambda} \rangle \} \\ &\cdot \{ \langle \underline{a}_{\mathbf{q}_2 s_2} \mid \int d^4x : \underline{\overline{\psi}'} \gamma_\mu \underline{A'_\mu} \underline{\psi'} :\mid \underline{a}_{\mathbf{q}_1 s_1} \underline{c}_{\mathbf{q}\lambda} \rangle \}^{-1} \\ &= -\frac{1}{2} B g_0. \end{aligned} \tag{4.16}$$

From (4.14) and (4.15) we obtain the transition amplitude $A^{(1)}_{g1R}$ corresponding to the WFDG1L figure $6-A-D$ to be

$$\begin{aligned} A^{(1)}_{g1R} &= A^{(1)}_{gf1AB} + A^{(1)}_{gf1CD} \\ &= \frac{1}{2} \left(2\pi \right)^4 \delta^4 \left(p_2 - p_1 - k \right) \frac{1}{V} \overline{u}_{\mathbf{p}_2 s_2} S^{-1}_{Ff} \left(p_2 \right) \Sigma^{(1)}_{fc} \left(p_2 \right) g_0 \gamma_\nu u_{\mathbf{p}_1 s_1} \frac{1}{\sqrt{2\omega_{\mathbf{k}} V}} e^\lambda_{\mathbf{k}\nu}. \end{aligned} \tag{4.17}$$

$A_{g1R}^{(1)}$ is convergent. Similarly, for the WFDG1L composed of figure 7 we have

$$\begin{aligned} A_{g1L}^{(1)} &= A_{gf2AB}^{(1)} + A_{gf2CD}^{(1)} \\ &= \frac{1}{2}(2\pi)^4 \delta^4(p_2 - p_1 - k)\frac{1}{V}\overline{u}_{\mathbf{p}_2 s_2} g_0 \gamma_\nu \Sigma_{fc}^{(1)}(p_1) S_{Ff}^{-1}(p_1) u_{\mathbf{p}_1 s_1} \frac{1}{\sqrt{2\omega_{\mathbf{k}} V}} e_{\mathbf{k}\nu}^{\lambda}, \end{aligned} \tag{4.18}$$

which is also convergent. From (4.17)-(4.18) we obtain the first sort of partial corrections $g_{f1}^{(1)}(p_2, p_1)$ to $g_{f0}(q_2, q_1)$ to be

$$\begin{aligned} g_{f1}^{(1)}(p_2, p_1) &= \frac{A_{g1R}^{(1)} + A_{g1L}^{(1)}}{\langle a_{\mathbf{p}_2 s_2} \mid -\int d^4x : \overline{\psi}'\gamma_\mu A'_\mu \psi' :\mid a_{\mathbf{p}_1 s_1} c_{\mathbf{k}_1 \lambda}\rangle} \\ &= \frac{g_0}{2}\overline{u}_{\mathbf{p}_2 s_2}\{\gamma_\nu \Sigma_{fc}^{(1)}(p_1) S_{Ff}^{-1}(p_1) + S_{Ff}^{-1}(p_2)\Sigma_{fc}^{(1)}(p_2)\gamma_\nu\} u_{\mathbf{p}_1 s_1} e_{\mathbf{k}\nu}^{\lambda} \\ &\cdot (\overline{u}_{\mathbf{p}_2 s_2}\gamma_\nu u_{\mathbf{p}_1 s_1} e_{\mathbf{k}\nu}^{\lambda})^{-1}. \end{aligned} \tag{4.19}$$

It is obvious that $g_{f1}^{(1)}(p_2, p_1)$ is convergent and $g_{f1}^{(1)}(q_2, q_1) = 0$. Feynman diagrams corresponding to any process must be composed of some WFDGNLs. Sum of WFDGNLs must be convergent. The sum of WFDGNLs 6 – 9 is the total one-loop correction $g_f^{(1)}(p_2, p_1)$ to g_{f0},

$$g_f^{(1)}(p_2, p_1) = g_{f1}^{(1)}(p_2, p_1) + g_{f2}^{(1)}(p_2, p_1) + g_{f3}^{(1)}(p_2, p_1). \tag{4.20}$$

From (4.4.12), (4.4.13) and (4.4.19) we see

$$g_f^{(1)}(p_2, p_1) \ \ is \ \ finite, \qquad g_f^{(1)}(q_2, q_1) = 0. \tag{4.21}$$

Substituting (4.20) into (2.1), we have

$$g_f^{(1-loop)}(p_2, p_1) = g_0 + g_f^{(1)}(p_2, p_1), \quad g_f^{(1-loop)}(q_2, q_1) = g_0. \tag{4.22}$$

Analogously (4.22), we can prove

$$\begin{aligned} &g_w^{(1-loop)}(p_2, p_1) = g_0 + g_w^{(1)}(p_2, p_1) = g_f^{(1-loop)}(p_2, p_1) \equiv g^{(1-loop)}(p_2, p_1), \\ &g_w^{(1-loop)}(q_2, q_1) = g_0. \end{aligned} \tag{4.23}$$

From (4.1) and (2.1) we obtain the total 1-loop correction to m_{e0} to be

$$m_{ef}^{(1)}(q) = m_{eff}^{(1)}(q) + m_{efw}^{(1)}(q) = m_{eww}^{(1)}(q) + m_{ewf}^{(1)}(q) = m_{ew}^{(1)}(q) \equiv m_e^{(1)}(q) = 0, \tag{4.24}$$

$$m_{ef}^{(1-loop)}(q) = m_{e0} + m_{ef}^{(1)}(q) = m_{e0} + m_{ew}^{(1)}(q) = m_{ew}^{(1-loop)}(q) = 0. \tag{4.25}$$

Replacing g_0 by $g^{(1-loop)}(p_2,p_1)$ and m_{e0} by $m_e^{(1-loop)}(q)$ in $S_f(g_0,m_{e0})$ and $S_w(g_0,m_{e0})$, we obtain

$$S_f^{(1-loop)} \equiv S_f\left(g_f^{(1-loop)}(p_2,p_1), m^{(1-loop)}(q)\right), \tag{4.26}$$

$$S_w^{(1-loop)} \equiv S_w\left(g_f^{(1-loop)}(p_2,p_1), m^{(1-loop)}(q)\right). \tag{4.27}$$

Because only when $p = q$, i.e. for a free F- or W-electron, the definitions of the masses $[2]-(3.17)$ and $[2]-(3.20)$ are meaningful, we take $p = q$ in $m^{(1-loop)}$. We can prove

$$m_e^{(n-loop)} = m_e^{(n-loop)}(q) = 0,$$

and when $p \neq q$, $m_e(p)$ must be attributed to correction of one or two vertex. Thus, according to the present theory, there is no correction to any external line and any propagator, and corrections to the mass of a free particle must be zero, hence there is only one sort of corrections, i.e., the sort of correction to a vertex.

All scattering amplitudes corrected to 1-loop diagrams evaluated by (4.26) or (4.27) are finite. From the deductive process above we see that in contrast with the conventional QED, there is only one sort of parameters (mass and charge at the subtraction point) which are finite and measurable, there are the two sorts of corrections originating S_f and S_w, all Feynman integrals are convergent and it is unnecessary to introduce regularization and counter-terms in the present theory. It is easily seen that the one-loop corrections derived by the present theory are the same as those derived by the given QED.

5 $n-$loop corrections for the coupling constants and the masses

The method derives

$$S_f^{(1-loop)} \equiv S_f\left(g_f^{(1-loop)}, m^{(1-loop)}\right), S_w^{(1-loop)} \equiv S_w\left(g_f^{(1-loop)}, m^{(1-loop)}\right)$$

from $S_f(g_0,m_{e0})$ and $S_w(g_0,m_{e0})$ can be generalized to derive $S_f^{((n+1)-loop)}$ and $S_w^{((n+1)-loop)}$ from $S_f^{(n-loop)}$ and $S_w^{(n-loop)}$. The recursion method is as follows:

Assume $S_f\left(g^{(n-loop)}, m_e^{(n-loop)}\right)$ and $S_w\left(g^{(n-loop)}, m_e^{(n-loop)}\right)$ to be given and

$$g_f^{(n-loop)}(p_2,p_1) = g_w^{(n-loop)}(p_2,p_1) = g^{(n-loop)}(p_2,p_1) = g_0 + \sum_{i=1}^{n} g^{(i)}(p_2,p_1),$$

$$g_f^{(i)}(p_2,p_1) = g_w^{(i)}(p_2,p_1) = g^{(i)}(p_2,p_1), \qquad g^{(n-loop)}(q_2,q_1) = g_0,$$

$$m_{ef}^{(n-loop)} = m_{ew}^{(n-loop)} = m_e^{(n-loop)}(q) = \sum_{i=1}^{n} m_e^{(i)}(q) = 0,$$

We can evaluate $m_{eff}^{(n+1)}(p)$ and $m_{ewf}^{(n+1)} = -m_{eff}^{(n+1)}(q)$ by virtue of $S_f^{(n-loop)}$, and $m_{eww}^{(n+1)}(p)$ and $m_{efw}^{(n+1)} = -m_{eww}^{(n+1)}(q)$ by virtue of $S_w^{(n-loop)}$. It can be proven

$$m_{ewf}^{(n+1)} \equiv m_{efw}^{(n+1)}, \quad m_{eff}^{(n+1)}(q) + m_{efw}^{(n+1)} \equiv m_{eww}^{(n+1)}(q) + m_{ewf}^{(n+1)} \equiv m_e^{(n+1)}(q) \equiv 0, \tag{5.1}$$

$$m_{ef}^{(n+1-loop)}(q) \equiv m_{ew}^{(n+1-loop)}(q) \equiv m_e^{(n+1-loop)}(q) \equiv m_e^{(n-loop)}(q) + m_e^{(n+1)}(q) \equiv 0, \tag{5.2}$$

For example, the 2-loop correction to the mass of a free electron is equal zero. The corresponding WFDG2L is the figure 10.

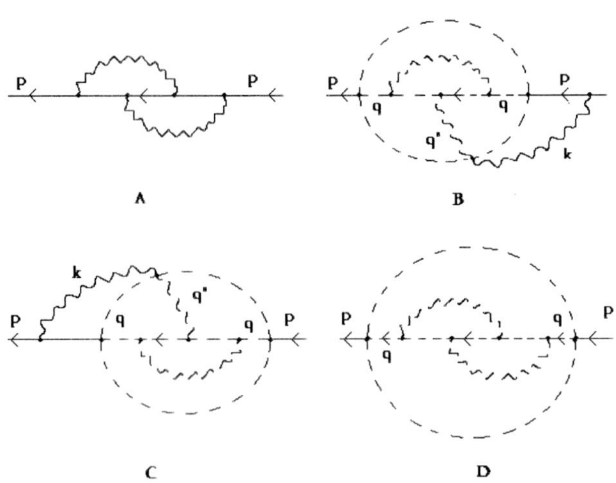

Figure 10: A WFDG2L determining the 2-loop correction to the mass of a free electron.

Replacing $m_e^{(n-loop)}$ in $S_f^{(n-loop)}$ and $S_w^{(n-loop)}$ by $m_e^{(n+1-loop)}$, we obtain

$$S_f^{\prime(n+1-loop)} \equiv S_f\left(g^{(n-loop)}(p_2, p_1), m_e^{(n+1-loop)}(q)\right), \tag{5.3}$$

$$S_w^{\prime(n+1-loop)} \equiv S_w\left(g^{(n-loop)}(p_2, p_1), m_e^{(n+1-loop)}(q)\right), \tag{5.4}$$

We can evaluate $g_{ff}^{(n+1)}(p_2,p_1)$ and $g_{wf}^{(n+1)} \equiv -g_{ff}^{(n+1)}(q_2, q_1)$ by $S_f^{\prime(n+1-loop)}$, and $g_{ww}^{(n+1)}(p_2,p_1)$ and $g_{fw}^{(n+1)} \equiv -g_{ww}^{(n+1)}(q_2, q_1)$ by $S_w^{\prime(n+1-loop)}$. It can be proven

$$g_{wf}^{(n+1)} = g_{fw}^{(n+1)}, g_{ww}^{(n+1)}(p_2,p_1) + g_{wf}^{(n+1)} = g_{ff}^{(n+1)}(p_2,p_1) + g_{fw}^{(n+1)} \equiv g^{(n+1)}(p_2,p_1), \tag{5.5}$$

$$g_f^{(n+1-loop)}(p_2,p_1)$$
$$= g_w^{(n+1-loop)}(p_2,p_1) = g^{(n+1-loop)}(p_2,p_1) \equiv g^{(n-loop)}(p_2,p_1) + g^{(n+1)}(p_2,p_1), \tag{5.6}$$

$$g^{(n+1)}(q_2,q_1) = 0, \quad g^{(n+1-loop)}(q_2,q_1) \equiv g_0. \tag{5.7}$$

Replacing $g^{(n-loop)}$ and $m_e^{(n-loop)}$ in $S_f^{(n-loop)}$ and $S_w^{(n-loop)}$ by $g^{(n+1-loop)}$ and $m_e^{(n+1-loop)}$, we obtain

$$S_f^{(n+1-loop)} \equiv S_f\left(g^{(n+1-loop)}, m_e^{(n+1-loop)}\right), \tag{5.8}$$

$$S_w^{(n+1-loop)} \equiv S_w\left(g^{(n+1-loop)}, m_e^{(n+1-loop)}\right). \tag{5.9}$$

$g^{(n+1)}(p_2,p_1)$ is finite. It must be noted that all $m_{fw}^{(n+1)}$, $m_{wf}^{(n+1)}$, $g_{wf}^{(n+1)}$, $g_{fw}^{(n+1)}$ are independent of momenta p_2, p_1 and k, since they are defined at the subtraction point. All scattering amplitudes approximate to $(n+1) - loop$ diagrams evaluated by virtue of $S_f^{((n+1)-loop)}$ and $S_w^{((n+1)-loop)}$ are finite. Detailed discussion will be given in another paper.

6 Generalize to the $SU(2) \times U(1)$ electroweak unified model and interaction between W-matter and F-matter

6.1 Generalize to the $SU(2) \times U(1)$ electroweak unified model

On the basis of the idea we can construct a left-right symmetric electroweak unified model. Taking the lepton part of the G-W-S model for example, the corresponding Lagrangian density will become

$$\mathcal{L} = \mathcal{L}_F + \mathcal{L}_W - V_F - V_W, \tag{6.1}$$

$$\begin{aligned}\mathcal{L}_F = &-\overline{\psi}_L\gamma_\mu(\partial_\mu - i\cdot G_F\cdot\frac{\tau^j}{2}A_\mu^j + \frac{i}{2}\cdot G'_F\cdot B_\mu)\cdot\psi_L\\ &-\frac{1}{4}F_{\mu\nu}^j\cdot F_{\mu\nu}^j - \frac{1}{4}F_{\mu\nu}\cdot F_{\mu\nu}\\ &-(\partial_\mu\phi^+ + i\phi^+\cdot G_F\cdot\frac{\tau^j}{2}A_\mu^j + \frac{i}{2}\phi^+\cdot G'_F\cdot B_\mu)\\ &\cdot(\partial_\mu - i\cdot G_F\cdot\frac{\tau^j}{2}A_\mu^j - \frac{i}{2}\cdot G'_F\cdot B_\mu)\phi\\ &-(\overline{e}_R\cdot M_F^+\cdot\phi^+\psi_L + \overline{\psi}_L\phi\cdot M_F\cdot e_R),\end{aligned} \tag{6.2}$$

$$V_F = -\phi^+\cdot\Omega_F\cdot\phi + \frac{1}{4}\phi^+\phi\cdot\Lambda_F\cdot\phi^+\phi, \tag{6.3}$$

$$\begin{aligned}\mathcal{L}_W = &\underline{\overline{\psi}}_R\gamma_\mu(\partial_\mu + i\cdot G_W\cdot\frac{\tau^j}{2}\underline{A}_\mu^j - \frac{i}{2}\cdot G'_W\cdot\underline{B}_\mu)\cdot\underline{\psi}_R\\ &-\frac{1}{4}\underline{F}_{\mu\nu}^j\cdot\underline{F}_{\mu\nu}^j - \frac{1}{4}\underline{F}_{\mu\nu}\cdot\underline{F}_{\mu\nu}\\ &-(\partial_\mu\underline{\phi}^+ + i\underline{\phi}^+\cdot G_W\cdot\frac{\tau^j}{2}\underline{A}_\mu^j + \frac{i}{2}\underline{\phi}^+\cdot G'_W\cdot\underline{B}_\mu)\\ &\cdot(\partial_\mu - i\cdot G_W\cdot\frac{\tau^j}{2}\underline{A}_\mu^j - \frac{i}{2}\cdot G'_W\cdot\underline{B}_\mu)\underline{\phi}\\ &+(\underline{\overline{e}}_L\cdot M_W^+\cdot\underline{\phi}^+\underline{\psi}_R + \underline{\overline{\psi}}_R\underline{\phi}\cdot M_W\cdot\underline{e}_L),\end{aligned} \tag{6.4}$$

$$V_W = -\underline{\phi}^+\cdot\Omega_W\cdot\underline{\phi} + \frac{1}{4}\underline{\phi}^+\underline{\phi}\cdot\Lambda_W\cdot\underline{\phi}^+\underline{\phi} \tag{6.5}$$

where G_F, G'_F, M_F, Ω_F, Λ_F, G_W, G'_W, M_W, Ω_W and Λ_W are all operators,

$$\psi_L = \begin{pmatrix} \upsilon_e \\ e \end{pmatrix}_L, \quad e_R, \qquad \phi = \begin{pmatrix} \varphi^+ \\ \varphi^0 \end{pmatrix}, \tag{6.6}$$

$$F_{\mu\nu}^i = \partial_\mu A_\nu^i - \partial_\nu A_\mu^i + \varepsilon_{ijk}\cdot G_F\cdot A_\mu^j A_\nu^k, \tag{6.7}$$

$$F_{\mu\nu} = \partial_\mu B_\nu - \partial_\nu B_\mu, \tag{6.8}$$

$$\underline{\psi}_R = \begin{pmatrix} \underline{\nu}_e \\ \underline{e} \end{pmatrix}_R, \quad \underline{e}_L, \qquad \underline{\phi} = \begin{pmatrix} \underline{\varphi}^+ \\ \underline{\varphi}^0 \end{pmatrix}, \tag{6.9}$$

$$\underline{F}_{\mu\nu}^i = \partial_\mu\underline{A}_\nu^j - \partial_\nu\underline{A}_\mu^j + \varepsilon_{ijk}\cdot G_W\cdot\underline{A}_\nu^j\underline{A}_\mu^k, \tag{6.10}$$

$$\underline{F}_{\mu\nu} = \partial_\mu \underline{B}_\nu - \partial_\nu \underline{B}_\mu. \tag{6.11}$$

$$\langle \underline{\phi} \rangle_0 = \begin{pmatrix} 0 \\ v \end{pmatrix}, \qquad \langle \phi \rangle_0 = \begin{pmatrix} 0 \\ v \end{pmatrix}. \tag{6.12}$$

Analogously to the new QED, we can prove for the electroweak unified model that all Feynman integrals are convergent, it is not necessary to introduce counter-terms and regularization, there is only one sort of parameters which are all finite and measurable (at the subtraction point), there is no such parameters as a bare mass and a bare charge, and there is no triangle anomaly. The energy of the ground state of all fields except the Higgs fields is still equal to zero. As the standard electroweak unified model, that the expectation values of the Higgs fields are not equal to zero. In this case we can determine the sum of the cosmological constant λ and the contribution of Higgs fields according to astronomical observation values. In contrast with the other left-right electroweak unified models, there is no unknown massive particles in the present model. From the model we see that the world is left-right symmetrical on principle since $\mathcal{L}_f + \mathcal{L}_w$ is symmetric, but because either $\mathcal{L}_f$ and $\mathcal{L}_w$ are asymmetric, the world in which we exist is left-right asymmetrical in fact.

6.2 Interaction between W-matter and F-matter

There is no interaction between W-particles and F-particles by a given quantizable field, hence only possibility is that there is repulsion or gravitation of the two sorts of particles. If the new interaction is gravitation, it is possible that W-matter is the candidate for dark matter.

Because there are the two sorts of particles corresponding to $\mathcal{L}_f$ and $\mathcal{L}_w$, the energy-momentum tensor $T_{\mu\nu}$ should be written as

$$T_{\mu\nu} = T_{F\mu\nu} + T_{W\mu\nu}. \tag{6.13}$$

If the energy expectation valve of the Higgs fields is equal to zero, we have $\langle 0 \mid H \mid 0 \rangle = 0$. The Einstein's equation should also be written as

$$R_{\mu\nu} - \frac{1}{2} g_{\mu\nu} R + \lambda g_{\mu\nu} = -8\pi G \left(T_{F\mu\nu} + T_{W\mu\nu} \right). \tag{6.1}$$

Because there is no other interaction between the F-particles and the W-particles except the gravitation, we existing in F-world cannot detect the W-particles by other methods except the graviton. Thus, W-matter must be the dark matter for the F-world, and vice versa. Because the F-world and the W-world are symmetric, it is possible that the W-matter is 50 per cent of all matter in the cosmos. Other components of dark matter for the F-world may possibly be other undetected F-matter. The F-world is left-hand world, then the W-world is the right-hand world. Detailed discussion is given in [4].

It is also possible that the new interaction is repulsion or there is new and more important relationship between W-particles and F-particles. We will discuss the problem in another paper in detail.

7 Conclusions and prospects

We have evaluated the one-loop corrections which are the same as those derived by the conventional QED, and have supplemented three new Feynman rules and one concept of WFDGNL. Feynman diagrams corresponding to any process must be composed of some WFDGNLs. The integrands causing divergence in a WFDGNL will cancel each other out, hence correction coming from a WFDGNL must be convergent and it is unnecessary to introduce regularization and counter-terms.

On the same basis as the new QED, we obtain naturally a new generalized $SU(2)\times U(1)$ electroweak unified model whose $\mathcal{L} = \mathcal{L}_f + \mathcal{L}_w$, here $\mathcal{L}$ is left-right symmetric. Thus the world is left-right symmetric in principle, but the part in which we exist is asymmetric because both $\mathcal{L}_w$ and $\mathcal{L}_f$ are asymmetric. This model does not contain any unknown particle with a massive mass.

A conjecture that there is gravitation between the W-matter and the F-matter is presented and the W-matter is identified as 'dark matter'. It is possible that the new interaction is the origin of some cosmic phenomena.

It is seen that the concepts of the new QED can also be generalized to QCD.

Acknowledgement

I am very grateful to Professor Zhan-yao Zhao for his best support and Professor Zhao-yan Wu for helpful discussions.

References

[1] Shi-Hao Chen, *Quantum Field Theory Without Divergence: Quantization for Free Fields*.

[2] Shi-Hao Chen, *Quantum Field Theory Without Divergence: Quantization for Interacting Fields*.

[3] Liao-Fu Luo, *Quantum Field Theory, Jiangsu science and technology publishing house* , (1990). Hong-yuan Zhu, *Quantum Field Theory*, Science publishing house (1960).

[4] Shi-Hao Chen, *A Possible Candidate for Dark Matter*, hep-th/0103234.

In: Quantum Field Theory: New Research
Editor: O. Kovras, pp. 171-192

ISBN 1-59454-509-X

Chapter 6

EINSTEIN-PODOLSKY-ROSEN AND BELL'S PARADOXES IN QUANTUM FIELD THEORIES

Daniele Tommasini*
Departamento de F´sica Aplicada, Área de F´sica Teórica,
Universidad de Vigo 32004 Ourense, Spain

Abstract

The so-called Einstein-Podolsky-Rosen (EPR) and Bell's theorems are often supposed to prove that the local causality of Quantum Field Theory (QFT) is spoiled by the measurement process. This would imply an instantaneous, unphysical influence between distant measurements which would be hardly compatible with Special Relativity. Recently, actual experiments inspired in a proposal by Popper have been argued to disprove such 'nonlocal collapse' of the state vector. As a consequence, the 'orthodox' interpretation of the quantum theory, in which the state vector is used to describe the single events, has to be abandoned. It is then necessary to search a way out of the apparent contradiction between locality versus EPR and Bell's theorems. QFT may help, since it prevents the production of entangled states with a definite number of particles, that are postulated by EPR. A 'minimal statistical interpretation' can then allow for a full reconciliation with locality, although it renounces to understand the single event.

1 Introduction

In 1935 Einstein, Podolsky and Rosen (EPR) provided one of the most severe criticism to the quantum theory with a paper entitled "Can Quantum-Mechanical Description of Physical Reality Be Considered Complete?", which has eventually become one of the most cited paper in the history of physics. In the abstract, they summarize their argument as follows:

*E-mail: daniele@uvigo.es

"In a complete theory there is an element corresponding to each element of reality. A sufficient condition for the reality of a physical quantity is the possibility of predicting it with certainty, without disturbing the system. In quantum mechanics in the case of two physical quantities described by non-commuting operators, the knowledge of one precludes the knowledge of the other. Then either (1) the description of reality given by the wave function in quantum mechanics is not complete or (2) these two quantities cannot have simultaneous reality. Consideration of the problem of making predictions concerning a system on the basis of measurements made on another system that had previously interacted with it leads to the result that if (1) is false then (2) is also false. One is thus led to conclude that the description of reality as given by a wave function is not complete" [1].

For Einstein and collaborators "the basic motivation was not to invent paradoxes; it was to build a strong logical reasoning which, starting from well-defined assumptions (roughly speaking: locality and some form of realism), would lead ineluctably to a clear conclusion (quantum mechanics is incomplete, and even: physics is deterministic)" [2]. In fact, the EPR argument has been one of the main motivations for seeking a "complete" deterministic theory underlying quantum mechanics. In their (thought) "EPR experiment", the measurement of a physical quantity on a system A did influence instantaneously, and in a *deterministic* way, the result of a corresponding measurement performed on another spatially separated system B that had been interacting with A in the past. This fact was considered to be a hint for a more complete theory, underlying the probabilistic quantum theory, involving additional "hidden variables" and allowing for the recovery of determinism and locality.

However, in the mid sixties Bell proved that deterministic hidden variable theories were actually viable, but they could not reproduce all the results of the quantum theory [3], unless they implied an instantaneous action at a distance [4], as Bohm's theory [5]. He proposed a set of "Bell's inequalities" for the spin correlations in a realization of the EPR-Bohm experiment, that were violated by QM and respected by any local deterministic hidden variable theory. Since the actual experiments [6, 7] confirmed the predictions of the quantum theory, local determinism was ruled out. *This result will be called hereafter the "Bell's theorem"*.

Therefore, it was deduced that the wave function (or state vector) description was a complete description of the single event, and EPR theorem forced to conclude that it had to be a "nonlocal" theory. Hereafter, I will call this argument the "EPR+Bell" proof of nonlocality, since it is based on both EPR and Bell's theorem. As a result, "quantum nonlocality" has been considered an experimental evidence, and it was really believed that the two distant measurements in the EPR experiments do actually influence each other instantaneously. The "speed of quantum information" has even been "measured" to be greater than $1.5 \times 10^4 c$ [8].

Such a "spooky action at a distance", as Einstein called it, would make the quantum theory incompatible with special relativity [1] although it is recognized that the EPR correlations do not allow for superluminal signaling, e.g. they cannot be used to synchronize clocks (see

[1] As Ballentine and Jarrett remarked, "such a contradiction, if indeed one exists, between two fundamental and exceedingly well verified theories would constitute a major crisis in theoretical physics. One may wonder why so few physicists are apparently concerned (or even aware of) such a crisis" [9].

ref. [2] for a review). However, any kind of "nonlocality" or instantaneous "distant influence" would be unacceptable in a relativistic world: due to the relativity of the simultaneity, suitable observers would describe this influence (whatever it is) as an effect of the future on the past [9].

On the other hand, the last half of the past century has seen the triumph of Quantum Field Theory (QFT). This has been argued to be the unique reasonable realization of a Relativistic Quantum Mechanics [10], and it can be thought to be the "low energy" limit of any possible Theory of Everything. In fact, an extremely successful description of Particle Physics, valid at least up to energies $\sim$ 100 GeV, has been obtained with the Weinberg - Salam Standard Model [11], which is based on the hypothesis that all the known interactions (except gravity) can be derived from a *local* symmetry SU(3)$\times$SU(2)$\times$SU(1). The field equations define a perfectly Lorentz-invariant, causal and local theory [10, 11]. Of course, these characteristics are most welcome in a relativistic world. However, they are usually thought to be broken by the process of measurement [2, 7, 8, 12, 13], which would imply the nonlocal collapse of the state vector of the system onto an "out" state, an eigenstate of the observed quantities (e.g. the momenta and helicities of the observed particles). This collapse postulate works to obtain correct theoretical predictions, however it implies that the measurement process itself is a sort of discontinuous process that cannot be described with the smooth, linear evolution that applies to all known interactions (this is the so-called "measurement problem", see refs. [2, 14] for reviews showing different points of view).

In our opinion, it is necessary to avoid the collapse and the measurement problem, and describe the measurement process with the same local QFT laws that describe particle interactions. Here, after reviewing EPR and Bell's theorems, we will discuss a recent argument by Unnikrishnan [15], based on a new experimental result, that may be used to disprove once and for all the nonlocal collapse of the orthodox interpretation. We will then discuss the remaining possibilities for an interpretation of the quantum theory, taking into account the greater indeterminism of the Weinberg-Salam Standard Model (SM) [10, 11, 16, 17], predicting that the number of particles that can be produced in any process involving an interaction is always uncertain [16, 17]. As a consequence, a measurement on A in an EPR experiment does not imply a certain prediction for the distant particle B, as required by the EPR argument, and EPR theorem can be somewhat relaxed. Finally, we will focus on the Minimal Statistical Interpretation of QFT, and we will present our conclusions.

2 The EPR-Bohm thought-experiment and the EPR theorem

Although all the present discussion can be easily generalized to EPR experiments involving any kind of particles, hereafter I will consider the so-called "EPR-Bohm" thought-experiment [18]. Two particles A and B are emitted by a source; far apart, some conserved observable, such as a component of angular momentum (spin, helicity or polarization), is measured on particle A. According to the usual quantum-mechanical treatment, the measurement carried out on A reduces its state into an eigenstate of the measured observable, whose conservation immediately forces the second particle (B) to "collapse" into a corresponding eigenstate of this observable as well. For instance, let A and B be two spin 1/2 particles, produced with zero total angular momentum in a singlet spin state, described by the "entangled" spin vector

$$|\psi\rangle = \frac{1}{\sqrt{2}} \left(|+\rangle_A |-\rangle_B - |-\rangle_A |+\rangle_B \right), \tag{1}$$

where $|\pm\rangle_A$ are the usual eigenstates of the spin component $S_z(A)$ of particle A with eigenvalues $\pm\hbar/2$ respectively (this example is usually called the "EPR-Bohm" experiment).

Assuming the state of Eq. (1), it is easy to see that the measurement of the spin component S_z performed independently on any of the two particles can give both values $\pm\hbar/2$, each with probability 1/2. On the other hand, if in a given single event $S_z(A)$ is measured on A and found equal to, say, $+\hbar/2$, it will then be possible to *predict with certainty* the result of the measurement of $S_z(B)$ on the distant particle B, that will give $-\hbar/2$. The quantity S_z observed on A would then instantaneously acquire "an element of physical reality" also on B, according to the original definition: *"If, without in any way disturbing a system we can predict with certainty (i.e. with probability equal to unity) the value of a physical quantity, then there is an element of physical reality corresponding to this physical quantity"* [1] (the italics and the parenthesis also belong to the original paper). Moreover, the element of physical reality on B depends on the actual measurement that is done on A: for instance, if instead of measuring the component $S_z(A)$ of the angular momentum we decided to measure an observable incompatible with it, such as the component $S_x(A)$, then the state of the distant particle B after such a distant measurement would become an eigenstate of $S_x(B)$, rather than one of $S_z(B)$. Therefore, assuming that the two systems are no longer interacting, EPR deduced that two quantum-mechanically incompatible quantities ($S_z(B)$ and $S_x(B)$ in the example above) could be given a simultaneous reality. They then concluded that "the wave function does not provide a complete description of the physical reality"; otherwise, the definite values of $S_z(B)$ and $S_x(B)$ would have to "enter into the complete description, according to the condition of completeness" that they had defined as follows: *"every element of the physical reality must have a counterpart in the physical theory"* [1].

The EPR argument (later called paradox, see e.g. Ref. [19]) is so rigorous, that it has been reformulated as a theorem (see e.g. refs. [2, 14, 20]): *"If the predictions of quantum mechanics are correct (even for systems made of remote correlated particles) and if physical reality can be described in a local (or separable) way, then quantum mechanics is necessarily incomplete: some 'elements of reality' exist in Nature that are ignored by this theory"* [2]. Or, as formulated by Einstein himself in 1949 [19]:

"The paradox forces us to relinquish one of the following two assertions:"

1. the description by means of the wave function is *complete*,

2. the physical realities of spatially separated objects are independent of each other.

Since "Einstein's locality" assertion 2) was considered unquestionable by EPR, they deduced that the wave function did not provide a complete description of the state of a system. This was a very powerful argument in favor of deterministic (and local) hidden variable theories. In such theories, all the observables have a definite value in the single system that is under consideration. The dispersion of the probability distributions observed in the repetition of the experiment on an ensemble of identically prepared systems is merely a "statistical mechanics" effect. Such a "cryptodeterminism" (see page 155 of ref. [20]) would explain the fact that the measurement of a component of the spin of A apparently has a deterministic effect on the distant measurement of the same component of the spin of B: both results would actually be the deterministic consequence of the common production of the two particles.

The importance of this argument, based on their objective definition of physical reality, is that it holds almost independently of the interpretation of the theory, with the exception of deterministic interpretations introducing hidden variables [2]. It is then impossible to find an "EPR-paradox-free" interpretation of the probabilistic quantum mechanics based on Eq. (1).

3 Bell's theorem

In 1964, John Bell proved that no local deterministic theory could reproduce all the predictions of the quantum theory. In particular, he found a difference for the predicted spin correlations in a EPR-Bohm-like experiment: the quantum correlations are greater than those that can be achieved in a hidden variable theory.

Let us reproduce Bell's argument in a way that will make manifest its underlying assumptions. Suppose that we have a statistical set of EPR-Bohm pairs, described by the spin-singlet vector (1), that are detected in coincidence in opposite directions away from the production point. If we measure the component $\vec{S}(A)\cdot\vec{a} \equiv \frac{\hbar}{2}\sigma_{\vec{a}}(A)$ of the spin of particle A along the unit vector $\vec{a}$, and the $\vec{S}(B)\cdot\vec{b} \equiv \frac{\hbar}{2}\sigma_{\vec{b}}(B)$ of the spin of particle B along the unit vector $\vec{b}$, the spin-spin correlation function is predicted by Quantum Mechanics to be

$$\langle\sigma_{\vec{a}}(A)\sigma_{\vec{b}}(B)\rangle = -\vec{a}\cdot\vec{b} = -\cos\theta, \tag{2}$$

where θ is the angle between the directions $\vec{a}$ and $\vec{b}$.

Let us consider now a local hidden variables theory, in which all the components of the spins of each particle A_n and B_n, of each single n-esimal copy of the statistical set, have a definite value of the spin before measurement, as required by EPR argument. In this case, measurement just reveals that preexisting value. Even though we cannot know them, we can therefore assume definite values of the spin components $\sigma_{\vec{a}}(A_n)$ and $\sigma_{\vec{a}'}(A_n)$ of particle A_n along two *different* directions $\vec{a}$ and $\vec{a}'$, and similarly for the spin components of particle B_n along two directions $\vec{b}$ and $\vec{b}'$. We can therefore consider the quantity

$$C_n \equiv \left[\sigma_{\vec{a}}(A)\sigma_{\vec{b}}(B) - \sigma_{\vec{a}'}(A)\sigma_{\vec{b}}(B) - \sigma_{\vec{a}}(A)\sigma_{\vec{b}'}(B) - \sigma_{\vec{a}'}(A)\sigma_{\vec{b}'}(B)\right]_n. \tag{3}$$

Taking into account that each component of $\vec{\sigma}$ only can take the values ± 1, it is easy to see that the quantity (3) can only take the values $-2, +2$, or 0. Therefore, $-2 \leq C_n \leq +2$. If we now compute the mean value $C \equiv \frac{1}{N}\sum_{n=1}^{N} C_n$ over all the pairs in our statistical set, we find the inequality $-2 \leq \langle C\rangle = \frac{1}{N}\sum_{n=1}^{N} C_n \leq +2$, which is also valid in the $N \to \infty$ limit. Using the distributive property of the sum, we finally find the famous Bell's inequality:

$$|\langle\sigma_{\vec{a}}(A)\sigma_{\vec{b}}(B)\rangle - \langle\sigma_{\vec{a}'}(A)\sigma_{\vec{b}}(B)\rangle - \langle\sigma_{\vec{a}}(A)\sigma_{\vec{b}'}(B)\rangle - \langle\sigma_{\vec{a}'}(A)\sigma_{\vec{b}'}(B)\rangle| \leq 2. \quad (4)$$

Our derivation shows that this inequality depends on the crucial assumption that in the single event any component of the spin of the particles A and B has a definite value, which can only take the values $\pm\hbar/2$. This assumption seems to be forced by EPR argument.

The inequality (4) provides a limitation for any deterministic local hidden variable theory. Its importance relies in the fact that it is violated by the quantum theory. In fact, using the quantum correlation eq. (2), and choosing e.g. three coplanar directions $\vec{a} = (1,0,0)$, $\vec{b} = (1,0,0)$, $\vec{a}' = (-1/2, \sqrt{3}/2, 0)$, $\vec{b}' = (-1/2, -\sqrt{3}/2, 0)$ (forming angles of 120 degrees) equation (2) gives $|\langle C\rangle| = \frac{5}{2} > 2$, thus violating Bell's inequality (4). This implies that in the quantum theory it is not possible to assume that in a single event all the spin components are simultaneously defined; therefore, there can be no reasonable local deterministic theory underlying the quantum theory. On the other hand, it has been argued that "in any reasonable hidden variables model all quantum observables must commute simultaneously" [21], and both Bell's theorem and the original no-go theorem by Von Neumann's [22] actually show the impossibility of such a completely commuting description [21].

In any case, Bell's theorem provides a quantitive test for local hidden variables (or for local determinism, or for commutativity) versus the quantum theory. Now, the existing experiments show that Bell-like inequalities are violated, under the so-called fair-sampling assumption: only the events in which A and B particles are detected in coincidence are selected, which is a small subset of all the events in the case of the actual experiments using entangled photons. Such an assumption seems to be natural, since Bell's argument, as discussed above, applies precisely to this statistical subset.

4 An experiment against quantum collapse

Taken together with the experimental results, EPR and Bell's arguments have been thought to provide a rigorous proof of the existence of an instantaneous influence between distant measurements, while the quantum description of the single event using the wave function (or the state vector) was considered to be complete. It is then believed that the wave function not only describes the statistical ensemble, but also the single events. This hypothesis explicitly shows the nonlocality of the theory. Let us consider e.g. a process in which a wave function describing the state of a particle propagates according with Schrödinger equation on a wide wave front. When the particle is detected, the wave function collapses instantaneously to zero in all the space but in the detector. As we have mentioned above, this interpretation is hardly compatible with Special Relativity and causality; moreover, it attributes a magical role to the measuring process, as we shall see later. Here, we would like to mention an argument due to Unnikrishnan [15] that may provide a definitive disapproval of the quantum collapse hypothesis.

Unnikrishnan considered an actual realization of an experiment proposed by Popper [23]. It is an EPR-like experiment in which A and B are produced with zero total momentum (e.g. as arising from a decay of a system at rest). According with the orthodox collapse interpretation, when particle A is detected at the position of experimenter Alice (say), at a distance D from the production point, particle B disentangles from particle A, and its wave function collapses in a the opposite direction, with a position uncertainty comparable to the precision of the space localization of the first particle, essentially given by the size of Alice's detector. Let Δx be that uncertainty in a direction x orthogonal to the line between the production point and Alice. After the collapse induced by the measurement on A, the intermination on the momentum component p_x of particle B is then $\Delta p_x \geq \frac{\hbar}{2\Delta x}$, where we are using the Heisemberg principle for the single events as required in the orthodox collapse interpretation. Therefore, after the detection on A, the wave packet describing particle B would spread with an angular uncertainty $\Delta\theta \sim \frac{\Delta p_x}{p} \sim \frac{\hbar}{p\Delta x}$ from the point where it is supposed to have collapsed. However, the actual experiments show that particle B is actually detected in the direction opposite to B even though the detection of B is made at larger distances. More precisely, by measuring on a statistical ensemble the angle at which particle B appears, the Heisemberg uncertainty relation for the x components of position and momentum of B in the instant in which A is detected appears to be badly violated, $\Delta p_x \Delta x << \hbar/2$ [24, 15]. This shows that the wave function collapse does not apply to the single event of the statistical ensemble. This invalidates the orthodox interpretation.

Another natural conclusion would be that $\Delta p_x \Delta x$ could be arbitrarily small in the single event: in other words, Unnikrishnan argument would be a further proof, complementary to EPR's theorem, of the fact that all observables have to be simultaneously defined in the single event, as in a hidden variables theory. For this reason, Unnikrishnan's paper presents the above argument against the nonlocal collapse together with a hidden variable model that apparently violates Bell's theorem, without realizing that his prescription for the computation of probabilities is nonlocal. Perhaps due to this mistake, Unnikrishan's paper did not receive the attention it deserved. In fact, even though he does not provide a viable solution to the problem, Unnikrishnan proved that the actual realization of Popper's experiment [24] leads to a violation of the predictions of the nonlocal collapse postulate [2]. I think that this is a very important result, since it disproves the orthodox interpretation of the quantum theory, that is accepted by a large part of the literature. As far as I know, no counterargument has been presented against this part of his work.

[2]Another possible reason for the general misunderstanding of Unnikrishnan's paper might be the fact that, in the original proposal, Popper's thought-experiment was pretended to show that the quantum collapse postulate lead to superluminal *signalling*, which was shown to be an incorrect argument [25, 26]. However, Unnikrishnan does not need this assumption at all.

Strictly speaking, Unnikrishnan's argument only disproves the collapse of the wave function depending on the space coordinates. It is natural to conclude that no collapse is produced in the spin part of the state vector neither[3].

As we have noted, if $\Delta p_x \Delta x$ could be arbitrarily small in the single event, then it would be natural to conclude that all the observables have sharp values in the single event. The particles would have definite trajectories and deterministic movement. Since local hidden variables explanations are ruled out by Bell's theorem, the only way of reconciling EPR, Bell's and Unnikrishnan's arguments seems to be a *nonlocal* hidden variables theory, such as Bohm's (or Unnikrishnan's) models. As far as I know, however, there is no satisfactory relativistic generalization of such theories. It may be possible that such a generalization is not possible, precisely due to the nonlocality of Bohm's theory. Since I will only be interested in interpretations of the quantum theory that can also apply to the QFT description of Particle Physics, nonlocal hidden variables theories will be not considered in the following discussion.

5 The uncertainty about the number of photons

The EPR argument, as described above, depends on the assumption of a state with a definite number of particles (two in our example), which is incorrect in Relativistic Quantum Mechanics, as shown in Refs. [16, 17]. In fact, *the modern QFT description of Particle Physics predicts that it is impossible to prepare a state with a definite number of particles as the result of a given physical process, since additional real particles can always be created in the production process itself.* Which additional species can appear depends on the available energy. Since massless particles can have arbitrarily low energy, the possible presence of real photons should always be taken into account in the theoretical treatment. This corresponds to a basic characteristic of the QFT description of Particle Physics [10, 11]: *it predicts a non-vanishing and finite probability for any process that does not violate the fundamental symmetries.* In fact, in Particle Physics experiments, it is so rare to find an "accidental cancellation" for the rate of an allowed process that such a case would be considered a hint for some new symmetry forbidding that channel. In other words, all the new particles that can be created without violating the universal conservation laws can actually be produced, and any definite process involving the creation of a particular set of particles has its corresponding amplitude of probability, which can eventually be computed approximately by drawing the relevant Feynman diagrams (when perturbation theory is applicable). In particular, since photons have zero rest mass, their energy can be arbitrarily low. Since they also have zero charge and colour, we can conclude that *an arbitrary number of additional photons, with total energy compatible with energy conservation, can always be created in coincidence with any physical process.* In the EPR-Bohm case, in which the considered

[3]Note however that the violation of Bell's inequalities concerns precisely the spin variables. In principle, one might consider a mixed possibility, in which position and momentum are simultaneously defined in the single event, while the spin part does suffer a nonlocal collapse as a consequence of measurement. Of course, such a possibility would be hardly compatible with special relativity.

EPR pair are spin-1/2 particles, additional photons can always be radiated at least by the external legs of the Feynman diagram that describes the process. A similar correction also applies when the EPR-Bohm particles have no total electric charge. For instance, neutral kaons are made out of charged quarks, whose lines can radiate additional photons, as in the case of charged fermions. In the case of an EPR pair of photons, two additional photons can also be radiated by the external legs of the relevant production Feynman diagram through loop diagrams involving charged fermions. At low energies, the rate for such a loop diagram is small, since it is suppressed by four powers of the fine structure constant and by the electron propagators in the loop (which are larger than the available energy, unless one considers ideal EPR experiments with very energetic photons, at or above the MeV range), although it is nonvanishing; more importantly, even in this case there is a larger rate for the emission of additional photons due to the charged particles that are necessarily involved in the relevant production vertex. For a neutrino (or a Higgs boson), it is easy to construct loop diagrams involving virtual W bosons and charged fermions to which a photon line can be attached. In the case of composite particles, such as the neutral K or B mesons, the production process involves the constituent quarks, charged particles to which external photon lines can be attached [4].

The uncertainty about photons radiation can also be related to a symmetry principle. In fact, it is based on two points: the existence of massless neutral particles, the photons; and of the fermion-photon vertex, that allows for the radiation of photons by any external line of the relevant Feynman diagrams. But it is well known that both the electromagnetic vertex and the masslessness of the photon are the direct consequences of the local, unbroken (electromagnetic) gauge symmetry.

As an explicit example, let us consider the decay of the neutral pion π^0. This is a good elementary way to obtain a pair of entangled photons having vanishing total angular momentum, since $\pi^0 \to \gamma\gamma$ is by far the most probable decay channel of the pion. Moreover, this example has the advantage that we can know the numerical amount of the uncertainty in the number of particles by using the existing data for the branching ratios of the decay channels of the pion. Heuristically, we can say that the state that is produced as a result of the decay of an ensemble of π^0 is

$$|\Psi\rangle \simeq 0.9940|\Psi_{\gamma\gamma}\rangle + 0.1095|\Psi_{\gamma e^+e^-}\rangle + 0.0056|\Psi_{e^+e^-e^+e^-}\rangle + 0.00027|\Psi_{e^+e^-}\rangle + \cdots, \quad (5)$$

where each component respectively describes a normalized state involving two photons, or a photon and an electron-positron pair, etc., and the coefficients are the square root of the rates for the corresponding channels, as given in the Review of Particle Physics [27]. The previous simple description can be used for the present purposes, leading to the same results that can be obtained by a more correct treatment in terms of density matrices or QFT Green functions. In this particular case, the branching ratio for the production of (two) additional photons is exceptionally small, being of the order of α^4. The main effect of the

[4] In all such cases, additional photons can also be radiated by the lines of all the possible charged particles (besides the EPR pair) that are involved in the relevant "blob" production process.

uncertainty in the number of particles is then due to the component $|\Psi_{\gamma e^+e^-}\rangle$. In fact, if Alice detects a photon A and measures one of its polarization components, then there is a probability $0.9940^2 = 0.988$ that Bob will also receive a photon B showing the maximal quantum correlation with Alice's. In the rest of the cases, no certain prediction can be made on B from the measurement on A.

In general, the total probability for the creation of additional particles is expected to be of order α (or α^2 in the presence of selection rules when the electric dipole approximation can be applied, as in the case of the photons that are emitted in the cascade decay of an excited atomic state) with respect to the process involving only particles A and B, although the precise suppression factor depends on the particular case that is considered. The rates for the production of a given number of additional photons should be compared to the rate for the process in which only particles A and B are emitted, corresponding to the bare diagram without any additional photons attached (that would imply the same correlations as the old quantum-mechanical approach) [5]. In any case, such rates are suppressed by increasing powers of the fine structure constant $\alpha \simeq 1/137$, depending on the considered number of additional photons. Since particle A is detected when a measure (for instance of some angular momentum) is made on it, its energy E_A can also be measured. Therefore the upper limit for the total energy of the additional photons is $\Lambda = E - E_A - m_B c^2$ (where E is the total energy liberated in the basic production process). This limit reduces the phase space available for the diagrams involving an increasing number of additional photons. For our purposes, it is sufficient to note that there is a non-vanishing probability for additional particles (at least photons) to be created, and that they contribute to energy, momentum and angular momentum conservation.

6 The uncertainty on EPR theorem

According to the previous discussion, the state vector arising from the interaction is *never* an eigenstate of the operator counting the number of photons: *the number of photons cannot be determined (it never gets a physical reality)* [16, 17]. This implies that *it is never correct to use a state with a fixed number of particles, such as that of Eq. (1), as emerging from a given interaction.* Of course, this can be a very good approximation. However, EPR argument requires *certain* predictions.

Now, in a given Feynman diagram, the conservation laws hold for the set including particles A and B together with all the additional photons that appear in that diagram. Therefore, *after the measurement on A in any given single event, the energy, momentum and angular momentum conservation laws do not hold for the two particle (sub)system, A and B*. The detection of particle A does not necessarily correspond to particle B appearing in the opposite direction. Moreover, *the measurement on A does not allow for a certain prediction of the value of the considered conserved quantity* (be it energy, momentum or angular momentum) on B (B is not put in an eigenstate of the observable that has been measured on

[5]The "Infrared Divergencies" related to the integration over arbitrarily small photons momenta can be handled as shown in Chapter 13 of Ref. [10], and they eventually cancel.

A). For instance, in the EPR-Bohm experiment, S_z *will not be given a "physical reality" on B after it is measured on the distant particle A.* According to our previous discussion, this may save the theory from the EPR theorem. Note that this result holds even for a small probability of additional photons radiation.

Note that we can know that particle B appears in the given region, and that it is in a given eigenstate of the considered observable, only *after* detecting the particle B and measuring the considered observable on it. Therefore, the physical reality is given to the observables on B only after the measurement on its own location is performed. *In this sense, QFT respects EPR local realism: the elements of EPRphysical reality of the theory can be obtained only after local measurements.* According to this definition, we could even say that QFT is locally realistic, although such a definition is usually reserved to hidden variables theories. This is due to the fact that QFT has *less* elements of EPR physical reality, and is more uncertain, than nonrelativistic quantum mechanics. In fact, the only predictions that it allows are on probabilities and average values. This greater uncertainty protects QFT from the EPR theorem. It seems that the latter implies the choice between between two opposite possibilities: determinism (hidden variables), or complete lack of determinism for the single event (QFT). We also see that the SM fulfills the EPR criterion of completeness that was cited above: for instance, in QFT the Fock space state vector after the measurement of a conserved charge on a massive particle is an eigenvector of that one-particle charge operator. The element of physical reality that appears after the measurement then has a counterpart in the theory, being the corresponding eigenvalue (i.e. the definite value) of this one-particle observable.

Ultimately, the recovery of this (limited) local realism can be attributed to the local gauge symmetry that implies the uncertainty about the photons as we have seen. I think that this result is not surprising, since the local gauge symmetry implies local interactions. Note also that the possibility of radiating arbitrarily soft photons corresponds to the "infrared" behavior of the theory, i.e. to its long distance properties, which are precisely those that are expected to be relevant for the discussion of distant measurements. On the other hand, the importance of the infrared effects for guaranteeing the causality of QFT has also be stressed in Refs. [28, 29].

Incidentally, since it is impossible to *prepare* a state with a definite number of photons, and since such an uncertainty for any given process cannot be made arbitrarily small, we may even argue that it is not possible to give a physical reality (not even locally) to any observable, except to the charges and masses (that are the invariants of the theory). [6]

Therefore, we no longer have to decide between statements 1) and 2) in EPR theorem: QFT remains an EPR-complete theory and yet it does not satisfy condition 1), that implicitly assumed the entangled two particle state vector. Therefore QFT can satisfy 2) in EPR theorem. In particular, *the EPR+Bell proof of nonlocality is removed.*

---

[6]In QFT, the usual assumption that the state of a system can be *prepared* by measuring a Complete Set of Commuting Observables is also incorrect, e.g. it is impossible to determine the occupation numbers of the photon states arising from a given process. Of course, the usual Fock space basis of QFT, diagonalizing all the occupation numbers, can still be used as a mathematical tool.

This result relies on only well-established physics and it does not depend on any particular interpretation of the theory. However, it is clear that a decision about the locality of QFT can be made only after examining the description of the measurement process. If (and only if) this can be done in a local way, without postulating any global collapse of the state vector, then QFT will be automatically a causal and local theory. We will now look for an interpretation that executes this program.

7 The interpretation of QFT

If we do not introduce any hidden variables or new physics beyond QFT, we are left with two possibilities for an interpretation [17]:

I. The state vector applies to the single system. Now, since the state vector of a free system evolves deterministically in Quantum Mechanics and in QFT, the joint state of the measuring apparatus (including all the "environment" which interacts with it) and the object system after the measurement has to be determined by that before the measurement. In particular, the position of the pointer, i.e. the result of the measurement, has to be the deterministic consequence of the initial conditions, and the only possible source of indeterminism is the unavoidable statistical ignorance of the state of the environmental variables. Since the QFT laws are local, the world would be intrinsically deterministic and local. This possibility is logically consistent, but it seems to be unable to provide a satisfactory solution to the "measurement problem" (see below).

   The "orthodox" interpretations [2, 20] introduce the collapse postulate in order to reconcile the assumption that the state vector applies to the single system with the fact that the measurement gives sharp results. The measurement process is then considered a magical process, different from the physical interactions that are well described by QFT. I think that this ad hoc assumption is very unnatural in QFT; it also contradicts the experience in particle physics detectors, that shows that the measurement process is determined by the same strong and electroweak interactions that are described by QFT. Moreover, the collapse of the state vector has to simultaneously involve all the space and explicitly violates locality and Lorentz symmetry. This is unacceptable in a relativistic world, as discussed above. In spite of all these contradictions and absurdities, orthodox interpretations are currently a common choice, due to the pressure of both EPR and Bell's theorems taken together.

   In non-relativistic Quantum Mechanics, a more reasonable framework to assign a state vector to the single system is based on a stochastic modification of Schrödinger's equation [30]. Here, I will not discuss these kinds of interpretations since for the moment they have not been implemented to take into account Special Relativity in a completely consistent way. Moreover, they go somewhat beyond the purposes of the present paper since they suppose the introduction of new physics beyond QFT.

II. The remaining possibility for interpreting QFT without introducing new physics is to assume that the state vector does not describe the single system (which I will also call event), but only describes an ensemble of identically prepared copies of the system (more precisely, statistical operators should be used, since photons uncertainty prevents the preparation of a pure state as discussed below). This minimal statistical interpretation is clearly more economical than orthodox ones that use the unnecessary assumption that the state vector also describes the single systems. Moreover, it is very natural in QFT: for instance, if we consider a single particle that can decay, the theory is not able to say when it will actually decay, which direction the particles that are produced in the decay process will take, and which of the possible decay channels will be chosen.[7] Similarly, in a Young double slit experiment, we are not able to predict anything about the single particle that will hit the screen in a random position.

As a matter of fact, the photons uncertainty itself implies that *QFT does not make any prediction on the single event* (i.e. on the single copy of the system), with the exception of the charges and masses of the particles that will possibly appear. However, *QFT predicts probability rates and cross sections that can be compared with the frequencies of the results for the repetition of an experiment on a statistical ensemble of equally-prepared copies of the considered system.* Therefore, it is natural (or at least conservative) to assume that the state vector only describes the ensemble, and not the single copy of the system (that we do not describe at all).

Of course, very convincing arguments for a statistical interpretations of the quantum theory have already been provided in literature, see e.g. refs. [14, 31, 32] and references therein. The most important is the fact that it naturally removes the measurement problem. Let me briefly summarize how this actually occurs.

For simplicity's sake, I will consider the measurement of an observable $\mathcal{A}$ in a two dimensional space of states. Let α_1 and α_2 be the (different) eigenvalues of $\mathcal{A}$, and let $|\alpha_1\rangle$, $|\alpha_2\rangle$ the corresponding eigenstates. If the (normalized) state of the object system is $|\psi\rangle = c_1|\alpha_1\rangle + c_2|\alpha_2\rangle$, then the measurement of $\mathcal{A}$ will give either the result α_1 with probability $|c_1|^2$ or the result α_2 with probability $|c_2|^2$. After the measurement, the usual collapse postulate implies that the state is reduced to one of the eigenvectors of $\mathcal{A}$, depending on the result of the measurement: for instance, if the result is α_1, the state after the measurement is reduced to $|\alpha_1\rangle$. The problem is that this postulate is incompatible with the Schrödinger equation (or the field equations) that imply a smooth and lineal evolution. In fact, let $|\Phi\rangle$ be the intimal state of the measuring apparatus (that belongs to a different Hilbert space than that of the object system), and let Φ_i be its states when the results α_i are obtained, for $i = 1, 2$ respectively (let these vectors also describe the so-called "environment"). This means that if the initial state of the object system was one of the eigenvectors of $\mathcal{A}$, say $|\alpha_1\rangle$, then

[7] Note that the result summarized in the previous section imply that there are *always* an infinite number of possible decay channels, involving an arbitrary number of additional photons; of course, usually there are also different channels involving other particles, such as neutrinos or different charged particles (for sufficient mass of the decaying particle).

the corresponding initial state for the composite system made of our object + measurement device would be the tensor product $|\alpha_1\rangle|\Phi\rangle$, and the state after the measurement would be the tensor product $|\alpha_1\rangle|\Phi_1\rangle$. Similarly, $|\alpha_2\rangle|\Phi\rangle \rightarrow |\alpha_2\rangle|\Phi_2\rangle$ as a consequence of the measurement. If the measurement process could be described by the same linear evolution that applies to any physical process (the Schrödinger equation or the field equations), when the object system is not in an eigenstate of $\mathcal{A}$ the previous equations necessarily imply the following result for the measurement

$$(c_1|\alpha_1\rangle + c_2|\alpha_2\rangle)|\Phi\rangle \rightarrow c_1|\alpha_1\rangle|\Phi_1\rangle + c_2|\alpha_2\rangle|\Phi_2\rangle\,. \tag{6}$$

Now, if we assign a state to the individual system, as done in the usual "orthodox" interpretation of QM, we get a wrong result, since after measurement the system will be put in one of the two eigenvectors, not in the linear combination of eq. (6) (a measurement gives a definite result, not a superposition). This is the so-called *measurement problem.* The usual "orthodox" interpretation introduces the collapse of the state vector by hand, and therefore requires a nonlinear evolution law for the measurement process, which is different from the linear evolution that describes any other process (in other words, within this interpretation the measurement process cannot be described by the quantum theory itself). In my opinion, any interpretation that does not give a better answer to the measurement problem should simply be discarded, for several good reasons: we know from half a century of detector building that the particles are detected due to the usual electroweak and strong interactions, that are described by the linear equations of the Standard Model. Moreover, the collapse postulate is ultimately responsible for the paradoxes (that we might better call inconsistencies) of the quantum theory. In particular, it introduces a privileged reference frame, the Laboratory; the global description of the collapse is responsible for the supposed, paradoxical nonlocality of the theory, thus violating Special Relativity.

How does the statistical interpretation avoid the "measurement problem"? It assumes that the state vector only describes a statistical *ensemble* $\mathcal{E}$ of identical copies of the considered system, and it does not describe the single copy. The state after the measurement *is* the linear superposition of eq. (6). In fact, this state correctly describes the probabilities $|c_1|^2$ and $|c_2|^2$ for having obtained α_1 or α_2. Moreover, the single event *has* a definite result, although the theory does not predict it. The events that have given the result α_1 form a subensemble $\mathcal{E}_1$ of $\mathcal{E}$, while those that gave α_2 correspond to a different subensemble $\mathcal{E}_2$ (with $\mathcal{E} = \mathcal{E}_1 U \mathcal{E}_2$). After the measurement, the experimenter (or the measuring device) selects only the events that have given a particular result, say α_1, and this corresponds to reducing the statistical ensemble to $\mathcal{E}_1$. After this selection of the events, the state vector is the one that describes the new ensemble $\mathcal{E}_1$, which is $|\alpha_1\rangle|\Phi_1\rangle$, as in the usual collapse postulate (but here we have no paradox since we are not associating such a state to the individual system and we did not need a nonlinear evolution during the measurement process).

I recommend the excellent reviews [14, 31, 32] for a more complete discussion in terms of mixed states (which may be more fundamental than the pure states). Note that in ref. [14] the EPR theorem led to the conclusion that the quantum theory had to be completed: the single system had to have precise values of anticommuting observables like momenta and positions, which played the role of hidden variables. As I have commented in the introduction, this was precisely the kind of solution that Einstein tended to favor, however (at least in its radical version) it is ruled out by Bell's theorem. Here, after removing EPR theorem, we do not need to introduce hidden variables. Ironically, we have come to a similar conclusion as EPR (the state vector does not describe the single system), although now we do not need to provide a more complete description! This fact may have important philosophical consequences. Although I prefer to use the term "statistical", this is essentially the "correlation interpretation" described in ref. [2] (see also ref. [33]), to which we are adding the relaxation of EPR theorem.

Incidentally, within this interpretation the world (i.e. the single event) *has* an objective consistency, independently of the possible measurements (no need to rely on any mysterious "quantum consciousness"). We merely cannot *describe* it but statistically.

As a result, the measurement process can be considered a physical process involving quantum systems, that can be described by the quantum theory itself. On the other hand, the viability of such a description has been confirmed explicitly by recent studies, relying for the moment on the nonrelativistic QM (see e.g. [34] and references therein). Here, I will generalize this conclusion by assuming that the measurement process may be described precisely by the Standard Model itself, in agreement with the actual experience of Particle Physicists. This implies that QFT with this statistical interpretation is a fully local theory. In fact, causality and locality are satisfied by the Green functions of the theory (and then by the scattering matrix) [10, 11]. In other words, *there is no possible source of nonlocality in the theory.* You get back what you put in: if you put the nonlocal collapse, you get nonlocality. When we only use the local QFT interactions even to describe the measuring process for the statistical ensemble, we get a fully local theory.

It has been claimed that in statistical interpretations which do not introduce hidden variables "all the systems that have the same wave function are identical, since nothing differentiates them" [35]. Such a criticism would be correct if we did attribute the wave function to the single system. In a purely probabilistic theory, the only conclusion that could be reached with this kind of consideration would be that the minimal statistical interpretation does not explain *why* the measurements give sharp, different values, although it allows for this. On the other hand, the unique known kind of interpretations that would give a real "explanation" would be those based on hidden variables, which have problems with Bell's theorem (an exception is Bohm's theory, which I will not consider here since it is non-relativistic from the beginning and it has not been implemented to an interpretation of QFT). May be that we will never solve this mystery, which might reach the limits of science, that seems to be unable to figure out a consistent description of the single events. For the moment, QFT with its statistical interpretation is not an *explanation,* but at least it is a consistent (and local) *description* of the ensemble.

8 The EPR correlations in QFT

Although we have already seen that QFT with the statistical interpretation is a local theory, it is interesting to discuss how this fact is shown in the EPR correlations that it predicts [17].

Let us assume for simplicity that in an EPR-Bohm experiment the data analysis only records the "coincident events" with a particle A appearing in Alice's detector O_A and a (say different) particle B appearing in Bob's detector O_B (but all the following discussion can be easily generalized to the case of also considering the coincident events when B is caught by O_A and A is caught by O_B, and to the case of A and B being identical, indistinguishable particles). I will call $\mathcal{E}$ the statistical ensemble of such coincident events, that have to be selected by two local measurements on both particles A and B. Suppose that O_A measures the component $\vec{S}(A)\cdot\vec{a}$ of the spin of A, and O_B measures the component $\vec{S}(B)\cdot\vec{b}$ of the spin of B. Let $s_a = \pm\hbar/2$ and $s_b = \pm\hbar/2$ indicate the corresponding eigenvalues (i.e. the possible results of a measurement) of these spin projections. [8]

Now, the statistics over the ensemble $\mathcal{E}$ allows for the experimental evaluation of the spin correlations $\langle\vec{S}(A)\cdot\vec{a}\,\vec{S}(B)\cdot\vec{b}\rangle$. In QFT, such a correlation function has to be computed from the rate $\Gamma(s_a, s_b)$ for those coincident events where particle A and B are found with definite values s_a and s_b of their spin components. To give an example, I will assume that A and B are created in the decay process of a particle X (e.g. we may consider the decay of the possible Higgs boson into an electron-positron pair, that can be calculated in a straightforward way in the Standard Model), but the whole discussion which follows can be easily generalized e.g. to the case when A and B arise from a scattering process. I will compute the correlation at the lowest order, neglecting the rates for the creation of additional photons in coincidence with A and B. In fact, although the effect of these additional photons was important for removing the EPR argument, the contribution of the diagrams involving additional photons to the spin correlations is small [16], due to the fact that their rates are suppressed by powers of the fine structure constant and by a phase space factor depending on the small solid angles Ω_A and Ω_B intercepted by the detectors as seen from the production point (as far as we consider only the ensemble $\mathcal{E}$). A good approximation for the relevant QFT rate will be

$$\Gamma(s_a, s_b) \simeq \frac{c^2}{2(2\pi)^2\hbar M_X}\int_{\Omega_A}\frac{d^3\vec{p}_A}{2E_A}\int_{\Omega_B}\frac{d^3\vec{p}_B}{2E_B}|\mathcal{M}(\vec{p}_A, s_a, \vec{p}_B, s_b)|^2\delta^4(p_A + p_B - p_X) \tag{7}$$

where the variables of integration $p_A = (E_A/c, \vec{p}_A)$, $p_B = (E_B/c, \vec{p}_B)$ correspond to the four momenta of the two particles A and B, and M_X is the mass of the decaying particle that produces them (see e.g. eq. (A.57) of ref. [36]). On the other hand, $\mathcal{M}(\vec{p}_A, s_a, \vec{p}_B, s_b)$ is the Feynman amplitude for the process. Assuming that the two detectors are placed in exactly opposite directions and intercept similar solid angles, we can perform the integrals and get

$$\Gamma(s_a, s_b) \simeq \frac{\Omega_A}{4\pi}\frac{|\vec{p}_A|}{8\pi\hbar c M_X^2}|\mathcal{M}(\vec{p}_A, s_a, -\vec{p}_A, s_b)|^2\,, \tag{8}$$

[8] More precisely, we understand that a basis of Dirac spinors has to be used.

where now

$$|\vec{p}_A| = cM_X^{-1}\sqrt{M_X^4 + M_A^4 + M_B^4 - 2M_X^2M_A^2 - 2M_X^2M_B^2 - 2M_A^2M_B^2}$$

is the modulus of the momentum, as given by energy conservation (here we have chosen the rest frame of the decaying particle).

Restricting ourselves to the statistical ensemble $\mathcal{E}$, we can define the probability of obtaining s_a and s_b by dividing the rate in eq. (8) by the total rate corresponding to this statistical ensemble, i.e.

$$\begin{aligned}\mathcal{P}(s_a, s_b) &\equiv \frac{\Gamma(s_a, s_b)}{\sum_{s'_a=\pm\hbar/2}\sum_{s'_b=\pm\hbar/2}\Gamma(s'_a, s'_b)} \\ &\simeq \frac{|\mathcal{M}(\vec{p}_A, s_a, -\vec{p}_A, s_b)|^2}{\sum_{s'_a=\pm\hbar/2}\sum_{s'_b=\pm\hbar/2}|\mathcal{M}(\vec{p}_A, s'_a, -\vec{p}_A, s'_b)|^2}\,.\end{aligned} \tag{9}$$

Now, in QFT the Feynman amplitude $\mathcal{M}$ is invariant under the full Lorentz group (transforming the momenta and spin/helicities as shown in ref. [10]). In particular, it is invariant under rotations, thus it conserves angular momentum. In the usual EPR-Bohm experiment we assume that the decaying system M_X has zero angular momentum, thus A and B are created in a spin-singlet state (remember that we are neglecting any possible additional particles in this computation). Therefore, independently of the explicit form of the amplitude $\mathcal{M}$, that depends on the particular process under consideration, we get

$$\mathcal{P}(+_a, +_b) = \mathcal{P}(-_a, -_b) \simeq \frac{1}{2}\sin^2\left(\frac{\theta}{2}\right), \qquad \mathcal{P}(+_a, -_b) = \mathcal{P}(-_a, +_b) \simeq \frac{1}{2}\cos^2\left(\frac{\theta}{2}\right), \tag{10}$$

where θ is the angle between the orientations $\vec{a}$ and $\vec{b}$ of the spin-measuring devices, and I have indicated $\pm\hbar/2$ with the sign $\pm$. We can now evaluate the spin-spin correlation (for the ensemble $\mathcal{E}$) as

$$\langle s_a s_b\rangle = \sum_{s_a=\pm\hbar/2}\sum_{s_b=\pm\hbar/2}\mathcal{P}(s_a, s_b)s_a s_b \simeq -\frac{\hbar^2}{4}\cos\theta\,. \tag{11}$$

This is the same result obtained in the usual QM treatment [32, 2]. There are however two important differences. Firstly, now we know that it needs two local measurements on both A and B, and that it is merely an approximation. Secondly, we see that this result arises from eq. (9), which only depends on the invariant Feynman amplitude $\mathcal{M}$. Now, in the computation of the Feynman amplitudes all the conservation laws have a local origin [10, 11], and in particular the global angular momentum conservation is a consequence of the local conservation, as we expected from the discussion of the previous section.

This is also reflected by the fact that the correlation does not depend on the distance: it is the same for large and small distances. It is true that one can then change the axis $\vec{a}$ and $\vec{b}$ of the distant detectors, but the correlation that is computed with the new axis could also be computed for small distances. The correlation has then to be created in the production process; although it depends nontrivially on the experimental arrangement in O_A and O_B, it does not corresponded to any influence at a distance.

In fact, eq. (10) satisfies the only real locality conditions that are imposed by Special Relativity, according to Ballentine and Jarrett [9]:

$$\sum_{s_b} \mathcal{P}(s_a, s_b) = \frac{1}{2}, \quad \text{for} \quad s_a = \pm\frac{\hbar}{2}; \qquad \sum_{s_a} \mathcal{P}(s_a, s_b) = \frac{1}{2}, \quad \text{for} \quad s_b = \pm\frac{\hbar}{2}, \tag{12}$$

valid for whatever choice of orientations $\vec{a}$ and $\vec{b}$ of the detectors. In particular, detector O_A observes the same distribution of probability independently of the settings of the distant detector O_B. This is also sufficient to prevent the possibility of any superluminal communication. On the other hand, eq. (11) coincides with the usual QM result, that agrees with the actual experiments and violates Bell's inequalities. As Ballentine and Jarrett have argued, this means that it is not possible to find a set of parameters λ, carrying the information on the state and the initial conditions, so that the probability can be factorized as

$$\mathcal{P}(s_a, s_b, \lambda) = \sum_{s'_b} \mathcal{P}(s_a, s'_b, \lambda) \sum_{s'_a} \mathcal{P}(s'_a, s_b, \lambda), \tag{13}$$

where the dependence on λ in the probabilities corresponds to partitioning the ensemble of the events in subensembles that have equal conditions λ. The impossibility of finding such a decomposition implies that the measurement on A gives additional information about the measurement on B, with respect to the information that can be contained in the state preparation. This only proves that the quantum theory is less predictive than it would be using the state vector to describe the single system. This reduction of predictivity is unavoidable as far as we limit the description only to the statistics on the ensemble of copies of the system.

A complete discussion can be found in ref. [9]. Here, I will merely point out that the measurement on A unavoidably gives an information for the measurement on B, and this information depends on the orientation $\vec{a}$ of the apparatus O_A. In fact, let me call $\mathcal{E}(s_a, s_b)$ the partition of the total ensemble $\mathcal{E}$ of the coincident events, where for instance $\mathcal{E}(+_a, +_b)$ is the ensemble of the events that have given the results $s_a = +\hbar/2$, $s_b = +\hbar/2$ after the measurement. This partition depends on the choice of the orientations $\vec{a}$ and $\vec{b}$ of the apparatuses, and changes if we modify one of these orientations. Since the results of the single measurements are not predicted by the theory, a partition can be obtained only *after* actually performing the measurements. The probabilities $\mathcal{P}(s_a, s_b)$ can be computed by counting the number of events that belong to the different subensembles $\mathcal{E}(s_a, s_b)$ of the partition of $\mathcal{E}$ and dividing by the total number of events in $\mathcal{E}$ (of course, this computation would give the correct probabilities only in the limit where $\mathcal{E}$ counts infinite events). It is clear that these probabilities depend on the partition that is chosen, in other words they depend nontrivially (and in a "nonseparable" way) on the orientations of the two apparatuses and on the results of the single measurements, without implying any nonlocality. [9] On the other hand, although it cannot be generalized to prove nonlocality, Bell's Theorem may remain an important argument against local determinism [9].

[9] In Ballentine and Jarrett's paper [9], the final considerations on the EPR incompleteness argument should

9 Conclusions

The EPR and Bell's arguments have been reviewed, emphasizing their assumptions. EPR theorem states that the quantum theory has to be embedded in a hidden variables theory, eventually allowing for the recovery of determinism, otherwise it would imply a "spooky action at a distance". Bell's theorem and experiments rule out the local hidden variables solution, so that it has been thought that quantum theory and Nature are intrinsically nonlocal. The orthodox nonlocal collapse postulate, however, leads to several inconsistencies, such as the measurement problem in its most severe form; moreover, it makes the theory incompatible with Special Relativity. On the other hand, an argument by Unnikrishnan, interpreting a recent experimental result, can be used to disprove the orthodox nonlocal collapse. We have then shown that the Standard Model of Particle Physics prevents the production of states having a definite number of particles, contradicting a basic assumption of the EPR argument. This result is particularly important since it does not depend on the interpretation of the theory, and it removes one of the most disturbing paradoxes of the quantum theory, the violation of locality in the "objective reality", due to the fact that an undetermined number of photons can appear in coincidence with the observed particles in an EPR experiment. This has been used to remove one of the supposed proofs of nonlocality as well, that based on the EPR argument and on the original Bell's Theorem. The great uncertainty of QFT also provides a hint for a (minimal) statistical interpretation that renounces describing the single events. Such an interpretation does not assume any global collapse of the state vector and removes the "measurement problem" in a natural way, since it allows for describing the measurement as a physical quantum process, in agreement with recent results and with the experience of particle physicists. This also allows for a recovery of locality *without introducing hidden variables.* We have then shown how the EPR correlations should be computed in QFT using Lorentz invariant Feynman amplitudes. Bell's theorem may still be used in its original formulation to rule out local determinism, but it cannot prevent the probabilistic QFT to be a local theory. We have no guarantee that a better understanding of the quantum correlations will ever be found, although it could be hoped that this will eventually be achieved in a possible ultimate Theory of Everything. In any case, I think that locality and Lorentz symmetry will not be so badly violated as to allow for whatever instantaneous effect between very distant objects, since QFT will presumably remain a good approximation in the "low energy" regime (corresponding precisely to the long distance behavior). On the other hand, these results can be expected to be maintained or even strengthened in a possible quantum gravity, since General Relativity has been argued to require a local interpretation of the correlations [37]. For the moment, science is not able to offer a consistent picture of the single event, although its description of the statistics can be consistent.

---

be updated. Now, QFT satisfies the EPR criterion of completeness, although it allows for *less* reality than a classically complete theory. On the other hand, QFT does not predict anything on the single event, and it is "predictively incomplete" [9].

Acknowledgements

I thank F. Benatti, G.C. Ghirardi and H. Michinel for useful discussions.

References

[1] A. Einstein, B. Podolsky and N. Rosen, Can quantum mechanical description of physical reality be considered complete?, *Phys. Rev.* **47** (1935) 777.

[2] F. Laloë, Do we really understand quantum mechanics? Strange correlations, paradoxes, and theorems, *Am. J. Phys.* **69** (2001) 655.

[3] J. Bell, *On the Einstein-Podolsky-Rosen paradox*, Physics **1** (1964) 195.

[4] J. Bell, On the problem of hidden variables in quantum mechanics, *Rev. Mod. Phys.* **38** (1966) 447.

[5] D. Bohm, A suggested interpretation of the quantum theory in terms of hidden variables 1, *Phys. Rev.* **85** (1952) 166.

[6] A. Aspect, J. Dalibard and G. Roger, Experimental test of Bell's inequalities using time varying analyzers, *Phys. Rev. Lett.* **49** (1982) 1804.

[7] A. Zeilinger, Experiment and the foundations of quantum physics, *Rev. Mod. Phys.* **71** (1999) S288.

[8] V. Scarani, W. Tittel, H. Zbinden and N. Gisin, The speed of quantum information and the preferred frame: analysis of experimental data, *Phys. Lett.* **A276** (2000) 1.

[9] L.E. Ballentine and J.P. Jarrett, Bell's theorem: does quantum mechanics contradict relativity?, *Am. J. Phys.* **55** (1987) 696.

[10] S. Weinberg, *The Quantum Theory of Fields*, vol. I (Cambridge University Press, 1995).

[11] S. Weinberg, *The Quantum Theory of Fields*, vol. II (Cambridge University Press, 1996).

[12] Y. Aharonov and D.Z. Albert, Can we make sense out of the measurement process in relativistic quantum mechanics?, *Phys. Rev.* **D24** (1981) 359;
Y. Aharonov, D.Z. Albert and L. Vaidman, Measurement process in relativistic quantum theory, *Phys. Rev.* **D34** (1986) 1805.

[13] H.P. Stapp, Nonlocal character of quantum theory, *Am. J. Phys.* **65** (1997) 300.

[14] L.E. Ballentine, The statistical interpretation of quantum mechanics, *Rev. Mod. Phys.* **42** (1970) 358.

[15] C.N. Unnikrishnan, Einstein was right: proof of absence of spooky state reduction in quantum mechanics, *Found. Phys. Lett.* **15** (2002) 1.

[16] D. Tommasini, Photons uncertainty solves Einstein-Podolsky-Rosen paradox, *Opt. Spectrosc.* **94** (2003) 741.

[17] D. Tommasini, Reality, measurement and locality in Quantum field Theory, *J. High Energy Physics (JHEP)* **07** (2002) 039.

[18] D. Bohm, *Quantum Theory*, (Prentice-Hall, 1951).

[19] A. Einstein, in *Albert Einstein, philosopher-scientist*, P.A. Schilpp ed., Library of Living Philosophers, Evanston, 1949.

[20] A. Peres, *Quantum theory: concepts and methods*, Kluwer Academic Publishers, 1995.

[21] J.D. Malley, In a hidden variables model all quantum observables must commute simultaneously, quant-ph/0402126, to appear in *Phys. Rev. A*.

[22] J. von Neumann, *Mathematical foundations of Quantum Mechanics*, Princeton University Press, 1955.

[23] K. Popper, *Die Naturwissenschaften* **22** (1934) 807.

[24] Y. H. Kim and Y. Shih, Experimental realization of Popper's experiment: violation of the uncertainty principle?, *Found. Phys.* **29** (1999) 1849.

[25] G.C. Ghirardi, A. Rimini and T. Weber, General argument against superluminal transmission through the quantum-mechanical measurement process, *Lett. Nuovo Cimento* **27** (1980) 293.

[26] G.C. Ghirardi, *Un'occhiata alle carte di Dio*, Il Saggiatore, Milano 2001.

[27] Particle data Group (K. Hagiwara et al.), Review of Particle Physics, *Phys. Rev.* **D66** (2002) 010001.

[28] G. Compagno, R. Passante, and F. Persico, Virtual photons, causality and atomic dynamics in spontaneous emission, *J. Mod. Opt.* **37** (1990) 1377.

[29] G. Compagno, G. Palma, R. Passante and F. Persico, Relativistic causality and quantum-mechanical states in the fermi problem, *Chem. Phys.* **198** (1995) 19.

[30] G.C. Ghirardi, A. Rimini and T. Weber, A unified dynamics for micro and macro systems, *Phys. Rev.* **D34**1986470.

[31] F.J. Belinfante, *Measurements and time reversal in objective quantum theory*, Pergamon, 1975.

[32] B.H. Bransden and C.J. Joachain, *Quantum mechanics*, 2nd edition Prentice Hall, 2000.

[33] C.A. Fuchs and A. Peres, Quantum theory needs no 'interpretation', *Physics Today* **53** (2000) 70.

[34] C. Presilla, R. Onofrio and U. Tambini, Measurement quantum mechanics and experiments on quantum zeno effect, *Ann. Phys.* **248** (1996) 95.

[35] B. d'Espagnat, *Veiled reality* Addison-Wesley, 1995.

[36] M.E. Peskin and D.V. Schroeder, *An introduction to quantum field theory* Perseus Books, 1995.

[37] H. von Borzeszkowski and M.B. Mensky, EPR effect in gravitational field: nature of nonlocality, *Phys. Lett.* **A269** (2000) 204.

In: Quantum Field Theory: New Research
Editor: O. Kovras, pp. 193-224

ISBN 1-59454-509-X

Chapter 7

RENORMALIZATION GROUP METHODS IN HAMILTONIAN FORMULATION OF FIELD THEORIES

***Amir H. Rezaeian** and Niels R. Walet*†**
Department of Physics, UMIST, PO Box 88,
Manchester, M60 1QD, UK

Abstract

An effective Hamiltonian field theory for a (given scale) can be obtained by systematically decoupling irrelevant degrees of freedom (e.g., high-energy modes and many-body states) from relevant ones using a consistent renormalization scheme. Such a procedure is usually rather complicated and is plagued by the so-called Tamm-Dancoff renormalization problem. Here we present a succinct discussion of recent studies of such problems. Our method is based on many-body techniques and the Wilsonian exact renormalization group. In one sense, it resembles similarity renormalization group. However, neither perturbation theory nor unitarity of the similarity transformation are essential for this method. The non-unitarity of the approach is related to the fact that we have a biorthogonal representation of the given many-body problem. This, in fact, simplifies the diagonalization of the Hamiltonian matrix. We discuss its (non-)perturbative implementation. As illustrative examples we obtain results for the one-loop renormalized extended Lee model and the two-loop renormalized ϕ^4 theory.

1 Introduction

The main goal of traditional renormalization theory is to determine when and how the cancellation of divergences originating from the locality of quantum field theory may occur.

*E-mail: Rezaeian@Theory.phy.umist.ac.uk
†E-mail: Niels.Walet@umist.ac.uk

This is essential if one wants to have meaningful quantitative results. However, it is by no means obvious how quantum fluctuations associated with short distance scales can be incorporated and controlled through the choice of a few parameters only, typically bare masses and coupling constants or by the counterterms in renormalized perturbation theory.

The development of Wilson's renormalization group (RG) formalism [1] allowed physicists to produce a logically reasonable picture of renormalization in which perturbation theory at arbitrary high energy scale can be matched with perturbation expansion at another scale, without invoking the details of intermediate scales. In the Wilsonian approach, all of the parameters of a renormalizable field theory can be thought of as scale-dependent objects and their flows is governed by the so-called RG differential equations.

Motivated by Wilson's picture, effective field theory approaches have been introduced to replace complicated fundamental theories with simpler theories based only on the relevant degrees of freedom at the physical scale of interest [2]. The basis of the EFT concept is the recognition of the importance of different typical energy scales in nature, where each scale has its own characteristic degrees of freedom. In strong interactions the transition from the fundamental to the effective level is induced by a phase transition that takes place around $\Lambda_{\rm QCD} \simeq 1$GeV via the spontaneous breaking of chiral symmetry, which generates pseudoscalar Goldstone bosons. This coincides, of course, with the emergence of nuclei and nuclear mather, as opposed to the quark-gluon plasma and quark matter expected to occur at high temperature and high density. Therefore, at low energies ($E < \Lambda_{\rm QCD}$), the relevant degrees of freedom are not quarks and gluons, but pseudoscalar mesons and other hadrons. The resulting description is a chiral EFT, which has much in common with traditional potential models. In particular, there might be an intermediate regime where a non-relativistic model is inadequate but where relatively few hadronic degrees of freedom can be used to faithfully describe both nuclear structure and response. If this is the case, one should be able to describe strongly interacting hadronic systems in this effective model.

The power of Hamiltonian methods is well known from the study of non-relativistic many-body systems and from strongly-interacting few particle systems, even though a Lagrangian approach is usually chosen for relativistic theories. One might prefer to obtain the effective interaction using the covariant Lagrangian formalism and then consider the ground state and collectively excited states in the non-covariant Hamiltonian formalism by exploiting many-body techniques. For the description of physical states and in particular bound states, the Hamiltonian formalism is preferable over Lagrangian one. This is due to the fact that these problems are not naturally defined covariantly. For a bound state the interaction time scale is infinite, and thus a time-independent approach is better suited. However, the Lagrangian can not generally be converted to a Hamiltonian if the effective Lagrangian contains higher-order time-derivatives since no Legendre transformation exits for such a case. Therefore one may wish to obtain the effective interaction in a unified self-consistent way within the Hamiltonian formalism. The renormalization group transformation is used to derive the physical Hamiltonian that can describe experiment. To implement a RG calculation, one should define a space of Hamiltonians and find a certain RG transformation which maps this space into itself. Then one should study the topology of the Hamiltonian space, by searching for the fixed points and studying the trajectories of the Hamiltonian with respect to these fixed points. At the fixed points we have a scale-invariant quantum field theory. Near the fixed point, the irrelevant operators in the original Hamiltonian have small coefficients, and we are only left with the relevant and marginal operators. The coefficients of these operators correspond to the parameters of the renormalized field theory. In this way, in a renormalizable field theory, we disregard information about the evolution of irrelevant terms. The fact that irrelevant terms can be dropped near the fixed point does not necessarily imply that they are unimportant at low-energy scales of experimental interest. This depends on how sensitive the physical observables are to physics near the scale of the cutoff. Therefore, it is of interest to develop a RG method in which the irrelevant variables are treated on an equal footing with the relevant and marginal variables (the schemes are presented here have this advantage).

Hamiltonian methods for strongly-interacting systems are intrinsically non-perturbative and usually contain a Tamm-Dancoff type approximation, in the sense that one expands the bound state in states containing a small number of particles. This truncation of the Fock space gives rise to a new class of non-perturbative divergences, since the truncation does not allow us to take into account all diagrams for any given order in perturbation theory. Therefore renormalization issues have to be considered carefully. Two very different remedies for this issue are the use of light-front Tamm-Dancoff field theory (LFFT) [3] and the application of the coupled cluster method (CCM) [4, 5]. However, both methods are too complicated to attack the issue in a self-consistent way. In the last decade extensive attempts have been made to give a workable prescription for renormalization within the Hamiltonian formalism [6, 7, 8, 9]. Commonly unitary transformations are used to decouple the high- and low-energy modes aiming at the partial diagonalization of the Hamiltonian. One of the most elegant approaches in this context is the similarity renormalization group (SRG) proposed by Glazek and Wilson [6] (and by Wegner [7] independently). The SRG [6, 7] is designed to be free of small energy denominators and to eliminate interactions which change the energies of the unperturbed states by a large amount. However, there are several problems with this approach: it is hard to incorporate loop expansions within the method, the SRG can not systematically remove interactions which change the number of particles (i.e, when the Hamiltonian is not diagonal in particle number space), and most importantly, the computations are complex and there is no efficient non-perturbative calculation scheme.

In this chapter we introduce a new method [9] for obtaining the low-energy effective operators in the framework of a CCM approach. The transformation constructed avoids the small denominators that plague old-fashioned perturbation theory. Neither perturbation theory nor unitarity of the transformation are essential for this method. The method is non-perturbative, since there is no expansion in the coupling constant; nonetheless, the CCM can be conceived as a topological expansion in the number of correlated excitations. We show that introducing a double similarity transformation using linked-cluster amplitudes will simplify the partial diagonalization underlying renormalization in Hamiltonian approaches. However, a price must be paid: due to the truncation the similarity transformations are not unitary, and accordingly the hermiticity of the resultant effective Hamiltonian is not manifest. This is related to the fact that we have a biorthogonal representation of the given many-body problem. There is a long tradition of such approaches. The first we are aware of are Dyson-type bosonization schemes [10]. [Here one chooses to map the generators of a Lie algebra, such that the raising generators have a particularly simple representation.] The space of states is mapped onto a larger space where the physically realizable states are obtained by constrained dynamics. This is closely related to CCM formalism, where the extended phase space is a complex manifold, the physical subspace constraint function is of second class and the physical shell itself is a Kähler manifold [11]. The second is the Suzuki-Lee method in the nuclear many-body (NMT) problem [12, 13], which reduces the full many-body problem to a problem in a small configuration space and introduces a related effective interaction. The effective interaction is naturally understood as the result of certain transformations which decouple a model space from its complement. As is well know in the theory of effective interactions, unitarity of the transformation used for decoupling or diagonalization is not necessary. Actually, the advantage of a non-unitarity approach is that it can give a very simple description for both diagonalization and ground state. This has been discussed by many authors [14] and, although it might lead to a non-hermitian effective Hamiltonian, it has been shown that hermiticity can be recovered [11, 15]. Notice that defining a good model space can in principle control the accuracy of CCM [16, 17].

To solve the relativistic bound state problem one needs to systematically and simultaneously decouple 1) the high-energy from low-energy modes and 2) the many- from the few-particle states. We emphasize in this paper that CCM can in principle be an adequate method to attack both these requirements. Our hope is to fully utilize Wilsonian Exact renormalization group [1] within the CCM formalism. Here the high energy modes will be integrated out leading to a modified low-energy Hamiltonian in an effective many-body space. Notice that our formulation does not depend on the form of dynamics and can be used for any quantization scheme, e.g., equal time or light-cone.

2 Traditional approaches and their problems

The Tamm-Dancoff approximation [18] was developed in the 1950's to describe a relativistic bound state in terms of a small number of particles. It was soon revealed that the Tamm-Dancoff truncation gives rise to a new class of non-perturbative divergences, since the truncation does not allow us to take into account all diagrams at a given order in perturbation theory. On the other hand, any naive renormalization violates Poincaré symmetry and the cluster decomposition property (the cluster decomposition means that if two subsystems at very large space-like separation cease to interact then the wave function becomes multiplicatively separable). One of the simplest example of the Tamm-Dancoff approximation is the constituent picture of QCD where one describes a QCD bound state $|\psi\rangle$ within a truncated Fock-space,

$$|\psi\rangle = \phi_1|q\bar{q}\rangle + \phi_2|q\bar{q}g\rangle + \phi_3|q\bar{q}q\bar{q}\rangle + \dots$$

we use a shorthand notation for the Fock-space where q is a quark, $\bar{q}$ an antiquark, and g stands for a gluon. Now the bound-state problem is solved via the Schrödinger equation $H^{QCD}|\psi\rangle = E|\psi\rangle$. It is well known that in the complicated equal-time vacuum forces bound states contain an infinite number of particles that are part of the physical vacuum on which hadrons are built. On the other hand, interactions in a field theory couple states with arbitrarily large difference in both free energy and numbers of particles. Thus any Fock-space expansion can hardly be justified without being supplemented with a prescription for decoupling of the high-energy from the low-energy modes and the many-body from few-particle states. This problem in the context of the Hamiltonian formulation can be expresed by asking how the Hamiltonian matrix is diagonalized in particle- and momentum-space.

In his earliest work Wilson[19] exploited a Bloch type transformation [20] to reduce the Hamiltonian matrix by lowering a cutoff which was initially imposed on the individual states. Later Wilson abandoned this formulation in favour of a Lagrangian one. The most important reason was that the Bloch transformation is ill-defined and produces unphysical divergences. These divergences emerge from denominators which contain a small energy difference between states retained and states removed by the transformation, and appear across the boundary line at λ .

Two remedies for this issue are the use of light front coordinates [3] and application of the CCM [5]. In the light-front Tamm-Dancoff field theory (LFFT) the quantization plane is chosen to coincide with the light front, therefore the divergences that plagued the original theories seem to disappear [21] since here vacuum remains trivial. Furthermore, not having to include interactions in boost operators allows a renormalizable truncation scheme [22]. One of the most important difficulties in LFFT is the complicated structure of the renormalization process [23]. In principle, ad-hoc counterterms can not be prevented if one is to preserve the underlying symmetry. In the standard form of CCM, on the other hand, the amplitudes obey a system of coupled non-linear equations which contain some ill-defined terms because of ultraviolet divergences. It has been shown [24] that the ill-defined amplitudes, which are also called critical topologies, can be systematically removed, by exploiting the linked-cluster property of the ground state. This can be done by introducing a mapping which transfers them into a finite representations without making any approximation such as a coupling expansion. Thus far this resummation method has been restricted to superrenormalizable theories due to its complexity.

Recently Wilson and Glazek [6] and indepently Wegner [7] have re-investigated this issue and introduced a new scheme, the similarity renormalization group (SRG). The SRG resembles the original Wilsonian renormalization group formulation [19], since a transformation that explicitly runs the cutoff is developed. However, here one runs a cutoff on energy differences rather than of individual states. In the SRG framework one has to calculate narrow matrix instead of small matrix, and the cutoff can be conceived as a band width. Therefore by construction the perturbation expansion for transformed Hamiltonians contains no small-energy denominators. Here we review the general formulation of the SRG introduced in the original papers by Glazek and Wilson [6] and independently by Wegner [7].

2.1 Glazek-Wilson formulation

We introduce a unitary transformation aiming at partially diagonalizing the Hamiltonian so that no couplings between states with energy differences larger than λ are present. The unitary transformation defines a set of Hamiltonians H_λ which interpolate between the initial Hamiltonian ($\lambda = \Delta$) and the effective Hamiltonian H_λ. This λ plays the role of a flow parameter. Assume that the Hamiltonian at scale λ can be written $H_\lambda = H_{0\lambda} + H_{I\lambda}$, where $H_{0\lambda}$ is the free Hamiltonian and $H_{I\lambda}$ contains (bare) interactions and counterterms. We introduce an auxiliary function $x_{ij\lambda} = \langle i|x_\lambda|j\rangle$ of the states with labels i and j for a given λ. If we denote the eigenvalue of $H_{0\lambda}$ with $E_{i\lambda}$, x is defined as

$$x_{ij\lambda} = \frac{|E_{i\lambda} - E_{j\lambda}|}{E_{i\lambda} + E_{j\lambda} + \lambda}. \tag{1}$$

The modulus of the function $x_{ij\lambda}$ is close to 1 when one of the energies is much larger than the other and also much larger than the cutoff λ, x approaches 0 when the energies are similar or small in comparison to the cutoff. One then introduces smooth projectors $u_{ij\lambda} = \langle i|u_\lambda|j\rangle = u(x_{ij\lambda})$ and $r_{ij\lambda} = 1 - u_{ij\lambda} = r(x_{ij\lambda})$. Now by means of u and r one can separate each matrix into two parts $M = D(M) + R(M)$, where we define $D(M)_{ij} = u_{ij\lambda}M_{ij}$ and corresponding by $R(M)_{ij} = r_{ij\lambda}M_{ij}$. The functions u and r are needed in order to ensure smoothness and differentiability, and consequently a continuous transition between different parts of the Hamiltonian matrix. The function u and r are the key elements in making the diagonalization free of small-energy denominators. These functions are implemented as a form factor in every vertex of the interaction. We construct an infinitesimal unitary transformation eliminating the part of Hamiltonian which has only non-zero elements far away from the diagonal, thus they can not produce small-energy denominators. This continuous unitary transformation satisfies,

$$\frac{dH_\lambda}{d\lambda} = [T_\lambda, H_\lambda]. \tag{2}$$

The generator T_λ is anti-Hermitian and is chosen in such a way that $H_\lambda = D(Q_\lambda) = Q_\lambda u_\lambda$, where Q is arbitrary in the far-off-diagonal region. In terms of Q, the matrix elements of Eq. (2) satisfy

$$\frac{du_{ij\lambda}}{d\lambda}Q_{ij\lambda} + u_{ij\lambda}\frac{dQ_{ij\lambda}}{d\lambda} = T_{ij\lambda}(E_{j\lambda} - E_{i\lambda}) + [T_\lambda, H_{I\lambda}]_{ij}. \tag{3}$$

In the above equation we have two unknowns, Q_λ and T_λ. As additional input we use the fact that, for a given λ, the Hamiltonian H_λ can be additionally unitary transformed without violating the relation $D(Q_\lambda) = H_\lambda$. We regroup the above equation in the form,

$$u_{ij\lambda}\frac{dQ_{ij\lambda}}{d\lambda} - T_{ij\lambda}(E_{j\lambda} - E_{i\lambda}) = [T_\lambda, H_{I\lambda}]_{ij} - \frac{du_{ij\lambda}}{d\lambda}Q_{ij\lambda} = G_{ij\lambda}. \tag{4}$$

The unknowns on the left hand-side are determined by first solving Eq. (4) neglecting the commutator on the right-hand side; the result is then substituted into the right-hand side, and solved iteratively until convergence is reached. The D and R parts of the operator G can be defined,

$$\begin{aligned} u_{ij\lambda}\frac{dQ_{ij\lambda}}{d\lambda} &= D(G_\lambda)_{ij}, \\ T_{ij\lambda}(E_{j\lambda}-E_{i\lambda}) &= -R(G_\lambda)_{ij}. \end{aligned} \tag{5}$$

¿From Eqs. (4, 5) one can immediately obtain the generator T and the Hamiltonian flow equation

$$T_{ij\lambda} = \frac{r_{ij\lambda}}{E_{i\lambda}-E_{j\lambda}}\left([T_\lambda, H_{I\lambda}]_{ij} - \frac{d\ln u_{ij\lambda}}{d\lambda}H_{ij\lambda}\right), \tag{6}$$

$$\frac{dH_{ij\lambda}}{d\lambda} = u_{ij\lambda}[T_\lambda, H_{I\lambda}]_{ij} + r_{ij\lambda}\frac{d\ln u_{ij\lambda}}{d\lambda}H_{ij\lambda}. \tag{7}$$

It is obvious from above equations that no small-energy denominators $E_{i\lambda}-E_{j\lambda}$ arises out side of the band, and within the band zone, we have $T=0$. The equations (6,7) can be solved iteratively.

2.2 Wegner Formulation

Wegner's formulation of the SRG is defined in very elegant way aiming at diagonalization of Hamiltonian in a block-diagonal form with the number of particles conserved in each block. Again a unitary transformation is used with flow parameter s that range from 0 to ∞,

$$\frac{dH(s)}{ds} = [T(s), H(s)]. \tag{8}$$

We separate the Hamiltonian in diagonal H_d and the rest part H_r. We use that tr H^2 is invariant under the unitary transformation, therefore we have $\text{tr } H_d^2 + \text{tr } H_r^2 = \text{tr } H^2 =$ const. This means that $\text{tr } H_r^2$ falls monotonously if $\text{tr } H_d^2$ increases. One can use Eq. (8) to obtain

$$\frac{d\text{tr } H_d^2}{ds} = \frac{d}{ds}\sum_i H_{ii}^2 = 2\sum_i H_{ii}\sum_j (T_{ij}H_{ji} - H_{ij}T_{ji}) = -2\sum_{ij} T_{ji}H_{ji}(H_{jj}-H_{ii}). \tag{9}$$

The right hand side must be negative. Therefore the simplest choice for the generator is $T_{ji} = H_{ji}(H_{jj}-H_{ii})$ or

$$T(s) = [H_d(s), H_r(s)]. \tag{10}$$

One can show by making use of this definition that,

$$\begin{aligned} \frac{dH_{ij}(s)}{ds} &= \sum_j (H_{ii}(s) + H_{jj}(s) - 2H_{kk}(s))\, H_{ik}(s)H_{kj}(s), \\ \frac{d}{ds}\sum_{i\neq j} H_{ij}^2 &= -2\sum_{ij} T_{ij}^2. \end{aligned} \tag{11}$$

Therefore $\sum_{i\neq j} H_{ij}^2$ indeed falls monotonously. When $s \to \infty$ the derivative vanishes and we have $T_s \to 0$, at this limit the procedure of block-diagonalization is completed. At this point, the unitary transformation Eqs (8,10) is completely defined. The only freedom is in the choice of separation of the Hamiltonian into a "diagonal" and a "rest" part. Of course this depends on the given physical problem. As a illustration of the method, we show how perturbation theory can be applied in this formalism. For a given values of s we have,

$$\begin{aligned} H(s) &= H_d^{(0)} + H_r^{(1)} + H_r^{(2)} + ..., \quad (12)\\ T(s) &= [H_d(s), H_r(s)] = [H_d^{(0)}, H_r^{(1)}] + [H_d^{(0)}, H_r^{(2)}] + ... \\ &= T^{(1)} + T^{(2)} + ..., \quad (13) \end{aligned}$$

where the superscript denotes the order in the bare coupling constant. The part $H_d^{(0)}$ is the free Hamiltonian. The index r denotes the rest of the Hamiltonian. Note that generally the diagonal part in the flow equation is the full particle number conserving part of the effective Hamiltonian. The choice of only $H_d^{(0)}$ as the diagonal part leads to the simplest band-diagonal structure where the particle number is conserved. We use the basis of the eigenfunctions of the free Hamiltonian $H_d^{(0)}|i\rangle = E_i|i\rangle$ to obtain the matrix elements of Eqs (8,10),

$$\begin{aligned} \frac{dH_{ij}}{ds} &= -(E_i - E_j)^2 H_{rij}^{(1)} + [T^{(1)}, H_{rij}^{(1)}] - (E_i - E_j)^2 H_{rij}^{(2)} + ..., \quad (14)\\ T_{ij} &= (E_i - E_j) H_{rij}^{(1)} + (E_i - E_j) H_{rij}^{(2)} + ..., \quad (15) \end{aligned}$$

where the energy differences are given by

$$E_i - E_j = \sum_{k=1}^{n_1} E_{ik} - \sum_{k=1}^{n_2} E_{jk}, \quad (16)$$

and E_{ik} and E_{jk} are the energies of the creation and annihilation particles, respectively. To leading order in perturbation theory, one finds

$$\begin{aligned} \frac{dH_{rij}^{(1)}}{ds} &= -(E_i - E_j)^2 H_{rij}^{(1)}, \\ H_{rij}^{(1)}(s) &= H_{rij}^{(1)}(s=0) u_{ij}(s), \\ u_{ij}(s) &= e^{-(E_i - E_j)^2 s}. \quad (17) \end{aligned}$$

The flow-parameter s has dimension $1/(\text{energy})^2$ and related to the similarity width λ (ultraviolet cutoff) by $s = 1/\lambda^2$. This implies that the matrix elements of the interaction which change the number of particles are strongly suppressed, since we have $|E_i - E_j| > \lambda$. The similarity generator in Wegner's formulation corresponds to the choice of a gaussian similarity function with uniform width. In the next leading order, one has to deal separately with the diagonal and rest parts. In analogy to the Glazek-Wilson method we introduce $H_r^{(2)} = u(s)\bar{H}_r^{(2)}(s)$, and the solution reads,

$$\begin{aligned}
\bar{H}_{rij}^{(2)}(s) &= \bar{H}_{rij}^{(2)}(s=0) + \int_0^s ds' u(s')[T^{(1)}, H^{(1)}]_{rij}(s'), \\
H_{dij}^{(2)}(s) &= H_{dij}^{(2)}(s=0) + \int_0^s ds'[T^{(1)}, H^{(1)}]_{dij}(s').
\end{aligned} \tag{18}$$

It is obvious that for the non-diagonal term a smooth form factor appears in natural way to suppress the off-diagonal interaction. In other words, the particle number changing interactions are eliminated while a new terms are produced. The procedure can be extended to arbitrarily high orders. The counterterms can be determined order-by-order using the idea of coupling coherence, namely that under similarity transformation Hamiltonian remains form invariant (see section IV).

3 A General formulation of the Similarity renormalization group

In this section we pave the way for an introduction of the coupled-cluster RG, and consider the similarity renormalization group in a more general framework without requiring the unitarity. The discussion in this section is partially based on the work of Suzuki and Okamoto [13]. Let us consider a system described by a Hamiltonian $H(\Lambda)$ which has, at the very beginning, a large cut-off Λ. We assume that the renormalized Hamiltonian $H^{\text{eff}}(\Lambda)$ up to scale Λ can be written as the sum of the canonical Hamiltonian and a "counterterm" $H_C(\Lambda)$,

$$H^{\text{eff}}(\Lambda) = H(\Lambda) + H_C(\Lambda)\,. \tag{19}$$

Our aim is to construct the renormalized Hamiltonian by obtaining this counterterm. Now imagine that we restrict the Hamiltonian to a lower energy scale (μ), where we want to find an effective Hamiltonian $H^{\text{eff}}(\mu)$ which has the same energy spectrum as the original Hamiltonian in the smaller space. The cut-off μ can be conceived as a flow parameter. The value of $\mu = \Lambda$ corresponds to the initial bare regulated Hamiltonian. Formally, we wish to transform the Hamiltonian to a new basis, where the medium-energy modes $\mu < k < \Lambda$, decouple from the low-energy ones, while the low-energy spectrum remains unchanged. We split the Hilbert space by means of flow-parameter μ into two subspaces, the intermediate-energy space Q containing modes with $\mu < k < \Lambda$ and a low-energy space P with $\mu \leq k$. Our renormalization approach is based on decoupling of the complement space Q from the model space P. Thereby the decoupling transformation generates a new effective interaction $\delta H(\mu, \Lambda)$ containing the effects of physics between the scales Λ and μ. One can then determine the counterterm by requiring coupling coherence [8, 25, 26], namely that the transformed Hamiltonian has the same form as the original one but with Λ replaced by μ everywhere. (This is in contrast to the popular Effective Field Theory approach, where one includes all permissible couplings of a given order and fixes them by requiring observable computed be both cutoff-independent and Lorentz covariant.)

We define two projector operators, also called P and Q, which project a state onto the model space and its complement, satisfy $P^2 = P$, $Q^2 = Q$, $PQ = 0$ and $P + Q = 1$. We introduce an isometry operator G which maps states in the P- onto the Q- space,

$$|q\rangle = G|p\rangle \qquad (|q\rangle \in Q, |p\rangle \in P)\,. \tag{20}$$

The operator G is the basic ingredient in a family of "integrating-out operators", and passes information about the correlations of the high energy modes to the low-energy space. The operator G obeys $G = QGP$, $GQ = 0$, $PG = 0$ and $G^n = 0$ for $n \geqslant 2$. The counterintuitive choice that G maps from model to complement space is due to the definition Eq. (23) below (c.f. the relation between the active and passive view of rotations). In order to give a general form of the effective low-energy Hamiltonian, we define another operator $X(n, \mu, \Lambda)$,

$$X(n, \mu, \Lambda) = (1 + G)(1 + G^\dagger G + GG^\dagger)^n\,. \tag{21}$$

(n is a real number.) The inverse of $X(n, \mu, \Lambda)$ can be obtained explicitly,

$$X^{-1}(n, \mu, \Lambda) = (1 + G^\dagger G + GG^\dagger)^{-n}(1 - G)\,. \tag{22}$$

The special case $n = 0$ is equivalent to the transformation introduced in ref. [27] to relate the hermitian and non-hermitian effective operators in the energy-independent Suzuki-Lee approach. We now consider the transformation of $H(\Lambda)$ defined as

$$\overline{H}(n, \mu, \Lambda) = X^{-1}(n, \mu, \Lambda)H(\Lambda)X(n, \mu, \Lambda)\,, \tag{23}$$

where we have

$$H(\Lambda) \to \overline{H}(n, \mu, \Lambda) \equiv H(\mu) + \delta H(\mu, \Lambda)\,. \tag{24}$$

One can prove that if $\overline{H}(n, \mu, \Lambda)$ satisfies the desirable decoupling property,

$$Q\overline{H}(n, \mu, \Lambda)P = 0\,, \tag{25}$$

or more explicitly, by substituting the definition of $X(n, \mu, \Lambda)$ and $X^{-1}(n, \mu, \Lambda)$ from Eqs. (21)–(22),

$$QH(\Lambda)P + QH(\Lambda)QG - GPH(\Lambda)P - GPH(\Lambda)QG = 0\,, \tag{26}$$

that $H^{\text{eff}}(\mu) \equiv \mathcal{H}(n, \mu) = P\overline{H}(n, \mu, \Lambda)P$ is an effective Hamiltonian for the low energy degrees of freedom. In other words, it should have the same low-energy eigenvalues as the original Hamiltonian. The proof is as follows:

Consider an eigenvalue equation in the P space for a state $|\phi(k)\rangle \in P$,

$$P\overline{H}(n, \mu, \Lambda)P|\phi(k)\rangle = E_k P X^{-1}(n, \mu, \Lambda)X(n, \mu, \Lambda)P|\phi(k)\rangle\,. \tag{27}$$

By multiplying both sides by $X(n,\mu,\Lambda)$ and making use of the decoupling property Eq. (25), we obtain

$$H(\Lambda)X(n,\mu,\Lambda)P|\phi(k)\rangle = E_k X(n,\mu,\Lambda)P|\phi(k)\rangle\,. \tag{28}$$

This equation means that E_k in Eq. (27) agrees with one of the eigenvalue of $H(\Lambda)$ and $X(n,\mu,\Lambda)P|\phi(k)\rangle$ is the corresponding eigenstate. Now we demand that

$$H^{\text{eff}}(\mu) \equiv H(\mu) + H_C(\mu)\,. \tag{29}$$

This requirement uniquely determines the counterterm H_C.

In the same way we can also obtain the Q-space effective Hamiltonian, from the definition of $\overline{H}(n,\mu,\Lambda)$. It can be seen that if G satisfies the requirement in Eq. (26), then we have additional decoupling condition

$$P\overline{H}(n,\mu,\Lambda)Q = 0\,. \tag{30}$$

We will argue later that *both* of the decoupling conditions Eqs. (25) and (30) are necessary in order to have a sector-independent renormalization scheme. The word "sector" here means the given truncated Fock space. Let us now clarify the meaning of this concept. To maintain the generality of the previous discussion, we use here the well known Bloch-Feshbach formalism [20, 28, 29]. The Bloch-Feshbach method exploits projection operators in the Hilbert space in order to determine effective operators in some restricted model space. This technique seems to be more universal than Wilson's renormalization formulated in a Lagrangian framework. This is due to the fact that in the Bloch-Feshbach formalism, other irrelevant degrees of freedom (such as high angular momentum, spin degrees of freedom, number of particles, etc.) can be systematically eliminated in the same fashion.

Assume that the full space Schrödinger equation is $H(\Lambda)|\psi\rangle = E|\psi\rangle$ and for simplicity $|\psi\rangle$ has been normalized to one. We explicitly construct the energy dependent effective Hamiltonian in this formalism,

$$H^{\text{eff}} = P\overline{H}P + P\overline{H}Q\frac{1}{E - Q\overline{H}Q}Q\overline{H}P\,, \tag{31}$$

where $\overline{H}$ can be a similarity transformed Hamiltonian. This equation resembles the one for Brueckner's reaction matrix (or "G"-matrix) equation in nuclear many-body theory (NMT). In the same way for arbitrary operator O (after a potential similarity transformation), we construct the effective operator

$$\begin{aligned} O^{\text{eff}} \;&=\; P\overline{O}P + P\overline{H}Q\frac{1}{E - Q\overline{H}Q}Q\overline{O}P + P\overline{O}Q\frac{1}{E - Q\overline{H}Q}Q\overline{H}P + \\ &+ P\overline{H}Q\frac{1}{E - Q\overline{H}Q}Q\overline{O}Q\frac{1}{E - Q\overline{H}Q}Q\overline{H}P\,. \end{aligned} \tag{32}$$

The E-dependence in Eqs. (31) and (32) emerges from the fact that the effective interaction in the reduced space is not assumed to be decoupled from the excluded space. However, by using the decoupling conditions introduced in Eqs. (25) and (30), we observe that energy dependence can be removed, and the effective operators become

$$\begin{aligned} H^{\rm eff} &= P\overline{H}P = \mathcal{H}(n,\mu)\,, \\ O^{\rm eff} &= P\overline{O}P = \mathcal{O}(n,\mu)\,. \end{aligned} \tag{33}$$

The decoupling property makes the operators in one sector independent of the other sector. The effects of the excluded sector is taken into account by imposing the decoupling conditions. This is closely related to the folded diagram method in NMT for removing energy-dependence [30]. (It is well-known in NMT that E-dependence in the G-matrix emerges from non-folded diagrams which can be systematically eliminated using the effective interaction approach). The above argument was given without assuming an explicit form for X and thus the decoupling conditions are more fundamental than the prescription used to derive these conditions. We will show later that one can choose a transformation X, together with the model space and its complement, which avoids the occurrence of "small energy denominators". We now show that Lorentz covariance in a given sector does not hinge on a special form of similarity transformation. Assume the existence of ten Poincaré generators L_i satisfying

$$[L_i, L_j] = \sum a_{ij}^k L_k\,, \tag{34}$$

where a_{ij}^k are the structure coefficients. One can show that if the operators L_i satisfy the decoupling conditions $Q\bar{L}_iP = 0$ and $P\bar{L}_iQ = 0$ then it follows that

$$[L_i^{\rm eff}, L_j^{\rm eff}] = \sum a_{ij}^k L_k^{\rm eff}\,. \tag{35}$$

This leads to a relativistic description even after simultaneously integrating out the high-frequency modes and reducing the number of particles. Indeed we conjecture that requiring the decoupling conditions makes the effective Hamiltonian free of Lorentz-noninvariant operators for a given truncated sector regardless of the regularization scheme. However, one may still be faced with an effective Hamiltonian which violates gauge invariance (for e.g., when sharp cutoff is employed).

Note that the solution to Eq. (26) is independent of the number n. One can make use of Eq. (26) and its complex conjugate to show that for any real number n, the following relation for the effective low-energy Hamiltonian

$$\mathcal{H}(n,\mu) = \mathcal{H}^\dagger(-n-1,\mu)\,. \tag{36}$$

The case $n = -1/2$ is special since the effective Hamiltonian is hermitian,

$$\mathcal{H}(-1/2,\mu) = (P + G^\dagger G)^{1/2} H(\Lambda)(P+G)(P+G^\dagger G)^{-1/2}\,. \tag{37}$$

Hermiticity can be verified from the relation [31]

$$e^T P = (1+G)(P+G^\dagger G)^{-1/2}\,, \tag{38}$$

where,

$$T = \arctan(G - G^\dagger) = \sum_{n=0}^{\infty} \frac{(-1)^n}{2n+1}\left(G(G^\dagger G)^n - \text{h.c.}\right). \tag{39}$$

Since the operator T is anti-hermitian, e^T is a unitary operator. From the above expression Eq. (37) can be written in the explicitly hermitian form

$$\mathcal{H}\left(-\frac{1}{2}, \mu\right) = Pe^{-T}H(\Lambda)e^{T}P. \tag{40}$$

As was already emphasized, renormalization based on unitary transformations is more complicated and non-economical. Thus we will explore a non-unitary approach. An interesting non-hermitian effective low-energy Hamiltonian can be obtained for $n = 0$,

$$\mathcal{H}(0, \mu, \Lambda) = PH(\Lambda)(P + QG). \tag{41}$$

This form resembles the Bloch and Horowitz type of effective Hamiltonian as used in NMT [28], and was the one used by Wilson in his original work on quantum field theory [20](see section II). In the context of the CCM, this form leads to the folded diagram expansion well known in many-body theory [32]. It is of interest that various effective low-energy Hamiltonians can be constructed according to Eq. (33) by the use of the mapping operator G which all obey the decoupling property Eq. (25) and Eq. (30). Neither perturbation theory nor hermiticity is essential for this large class of effective Hamiltonians.

4 The coupled-cluster Renormalization group

The CCM approach is, of course, just one of the ways of describing the relevant spectrum by means of non-unitary transformations. According to our prescription the model space is P : $\{|L\rangle \otimes |0, b\rangle_h, L \leq \mu\}$, where $|0, b\rangle_h$ is a bare high energy vacuum (the ground state of high-momentum of free-Hamiltonian) which is annihilated by all the high frequency annihilation operators $\{C_I\}$ (for a given quantization scheme, e.g., equal time or light-cone) , the set of indices $\{I\}$ therefore defines a subsystem, or cluster, within the full system of a given configuration. The actual choice depends upon the particular system under consideration. In general, the operators $\{C_I\}$ will be products (or sums of products) of suitable single-particle operators. We assume that the annihilation and its corresponding creation $\{C_I^\dagger\}$ subalgebras and the state $|0, b\rangle_h$ are cyclic, so that the linear combination of state $\{C_I^\dagger|0, b\rangle_h\}$ and $\{\,_h\langle b, 0|C_I\}$ span the decoupled Hilbert space of the high-momentum modes, $\{|H\rangle\}$, where $\mu < H < \Lambda$. It is also convenient, but not necessary, to impose the orthogonality condition, $\langle 0|C_I C_J^\dagger|0\rangle = \delta(I, J)$, where $\delta(I, J)$ is a Kronecker delta symbol. The complement space is Q : $\{|L\rangle \otimes (|H\rangle - |0, b\rangle_h)\}$. Our main goal is to decouple the P-space from the Q-space. This gives sense to the partial diagonalization of the high-energy part of the Hamiltonian. The states in full Hilbert space are constructed by adding correlated clusters of high-energy modes onto the P-space, or equivalently integrating out the high-energy modes from the Hamiltonian,

$$|f\rangle = X(\mu,\Lambda)|p\rangle = e^{\hat{S}}e^{-\hat{S}'}|0,b\rangle_h \otimes |L\rangle = e^{\hat{S}}|0,b\rangle_h \otimes |L\rangle\,, \tag{42}$$

$$\langle\widetilde{f}| = \langle L|\otimes\, _h\langle b,0|X^{-1}(\mu,\Lambda) = \langle L|\otimes\, _h\langle 0|e^{\hat{S}'}e^{-\hat{S}}\,, \tag{43}$$

where the operators $X(\mu,\Lambda)$ and $X^{-1}(\mu,\Lambda)$ have been expanded in terms of independent coupled cluster excitations I,

$$\hat{S} = \sum_{m=0}\hat{S}_m\left(\frac{\mu}{\Lambda}\right)^m, \qquad \hat{S}_m = \sum_I{}' \hat{s}_I C_I^{\dagger}\,,$$
$$\hat{S}' = \sum_{m=0}\hat{S}'_m\left(\frac{\mu}{\Lambda}\right)^m, \qquad \hat{S}'_m = \sum_I{}' \hat{s}'_I C_I\,. \tag{44}$$

Here the primed sum means that at least one fast particle is created or destroyed $(I \neq 0)$, and momentum conservation in $P \oplus Q$ is included in $\hat{s}_I$ and $\hat{s}'_I$. $\hat{S}_m(\hat{S}'_m)$ are not generally commutable in the low-energy Fock space, whereas they are by construction commutable in the high-energy Fock space. It is immediately clear that states in the interacting Hilbert space are normalized, $\langle\widetilde{f}|f\rangle = {}_h\langle b,0|0,b\rangle_h = 1$. We have two types of parameters in this procedure: One is the coupling constant of the theory (λ), and the other is the ratio of cutoffs (μ/Λ). The explicit power counting makes the degree of divergence of each order smaller than the previous one. According to our logic, Eq. (41) can be written as

$$\mathcal{H}(\mu) = {}_h\langle b,0|X^{-1}(\mu,\Lambda)H(\Lambda)X(\mu,\Lambda)|0,b\rangle_h\,, \tag{45}$$

with $X(\mu,\Lambda)$ and $X^{-1}(\mu,\Lambda)$ defined in Eq. (42) and Eq. (43). We require that effective Hamiltonian $\mathcal{H}(\mu)$ obtained in this way remains form invariant or coherent [8, 25, 26]. This requirement satisfies on an infinitely long renormalization group trajectory and thus does constitutes a renormalized Hamiltonian. Thereby one can readily identify the counter terms produced from expansion of Eq. (45).

It is well-know in many-body applications that the exponential Ansatz Eqs. (42) and (43) guarantees automatically proper size-exclusivity and conformity with the Goldstone linked-cluster theorem to all level of truncation. This parametrization does not manifestly preserve hermitian conjugacy. However, it is compatible with the Hellmann-Feynman theorem (HFT), in other words, demanding hermiticity will violate this theorem at any level of truncation. On the other hand, with this parametrization the phase space $\{\hat{s}_I, \hat{s}'_I\}$ for a given m is a symplectic differentiable manifold. Thereby all the geometrical properties of the configuration space can be precisely defined. (In a more ordinary language, the canonical equations of motion with respect to phase space define a set of trajectories, which fill the whole dynamically allowed region of the phase space.) There is a deep connection between these three properties and we can not give up one without losing something else as well [33]. The individual amplitudes for a given m, $\{\hat{s}^m_I, \hat{s}'^m_I\} \equiv \{\hat{s}_I, \hat{s}'_I\}_m$, can generally be functionals of the low- and high-energy field operators and have to be fixed by the dynamics of quantum system. This is a complicated set of requirements. However, we require less than that. Suppose that after a similar transformation of Hamiltonian, $\overline{H}$, we obtain an effective Hamiltonian of the form

$$\overline{H} = H(\text{low}) + H_{\text{free}}(\text{high}) + C_I^{\dagger} V_{IJ} C_J \,, \tag{46}$$

where V_{IJ} is an arbitrary operator in the low frequency space. The I and J indices should be chosen such that the last term in Eq. (46) contains at least one creation- operator and one annihilation-operator of high frequency. By using Rayleigh-Schrödinger perturbation theory, it can be shown that the free high-energy vacuum state of $H_{\text{free}}(\text{high})$ is annihilated by Eq. (46) and remains without correction at any order of perturbation theory. Having said that, we will now consider how to find the individual amplitudes $\{\hat{s}_I, \hat{s}'_I\}_m$ that transfer the Hamiltonian into the form Eq. (46). We split the Hamiltonian in five parts:

$$H = H_1 + H_2^{\text{free}}(\text{high}) + V_C(C_I^{\dagger}) + V_A(C_I) + V_B \,, \tag{47}$$

where H_1 contains only the low frequency modes with $k \leq \mu$, H_2 is the free Hamiltonian for all modes with $\mu < k < \Lambda$, V_C contains low frequency operators and products of the high frequency creation operators $C_I^{\dagger}$ and V_A is the hermitian conjugate of V_C. The remaining terms are contained in V_B, these terms contain at least one annihilation and creation operators of the high energy modes. Our goal is to eliminate V_C and V_A since V_B annihilates the vacuum. The ket-state coefficients $\{\hat{s}_I\}_m$ are worked out via the ket-state Schrödinger equation $H(\Lambda)|f\rangle = E|f\rangle$ written in the form

$$\langle 0|C_I e^{-\hat{S}} H e^{\hat{S}}|0\rangle = 0 \,, \qquad \forall I \neq 0 \,. \tag{48}$$

The bra-state coefficients $\{\hat{s}_I, \hat{s}'_I\}_m$ are obtained by making use of the Schrödinger equation defined for the bra-state, $\langle \widetilde{f}|H(\Lambda) = \langle \widetilde{f}|E$. First we project both sides on $C_I^{\dagger}|0\rangle$, then we eliminate E by making use of the ket-state equation projection with the state $\langle 0|e^{\hat{S}'} C_I^{\dagger}$ to yield the equations

$$\langle 0|e^{\hat{S}'} e^{-\hat{S}} [H, C_I^{\dagger}] e^{\hat{S}} e^{-\hat{S}'}|0\rangle = 0 \,, \qquad \forall I \neq 0 \,. \tag{49}$$

Alternatively one can in a unified way apply $e^{\hat{S}} e^{-\hat{S}'} C_I^{\dagger}|0\rangle$ on the Schrödinger equation for the bra-state and obtain

$$\langle 0|e^{\hat{S}'} e^{-\hat{S}} H e^{\hat{S}} e^{-\hat{S}'} C_I^{\dagger}|0\rangle = 0 \,, \qquad \forall I \neq 0 \,. \tag{50}$$

Equation (48) and Eqs. (49) or (50) provide two sets of formally exact, microscopic, operatorial coupled non-linear equations for the ket and bra. One can solve the coupled equations in Eq. (48) to work out $\{\hat{s}_I\}_m$ and then use them as an input in Eqs. (49) or (50).

It is important to notice that Eqs. (48) and (49) can be also derived by requiring that the effective low-energy Hamiltonian defined in Eq. (45), be stationary (i.e. $\delta\mathcal{H}(\mu) = 0$) with respect to all variations in each of the independent functional $\{\hat{s}_I, \hat{s}'_I\}_m$. One can easily verify that the requirements $\delta\mathcal{H}(\mu)/\delta\hat{s}_I = 0$ and $\delta\mathcal{H}(\mu)/\delta\hat{s}'_I = 0$ yield Eqs. (49)

and (48). The combination of Eqs. (48) and (49) does not manifestly satisfy the decoupling property as set out in Eqs. (25) and (30). On the other hand Eqs. (48) and (50) satisfy these conditions. Equations (48) and (50) imply that all interactions including creation and annihilation of fast particles ("I") are eliminated from the transformed Hamiltonian $\mathcal{H}(\mu)$ in Eq. (45). In other words, these are decoupling conditions leading to the elimination of V_C and V_A from Eq. (47), which is, in essence, a block-diagonalization. Therefore it makes sense for our purpose to use Eqs. (48) and (50) for obtaining the unknown coefficients, losing some of the elegance of the CCM elsewhere.

So far everything has been introduced rigorously without invoking any approximation. In practice one needs to truncate both sets of coefficients $\{\hat{s}_I, \hat{s}'_I\}_m$ at a given order of m. A consistent truncation scheme is the so-called SUB(n, m) scheme, where the n-body partition of the operator $\{\hat{S}, \hat{S}'\}$ is truncated so that one sets the higher partition with $I > n$ to zero at a given accuracy m. Notice that, Eqs. (49) and (50) provide two equivalent sets of equations in the exact form, however after the truncation they can in principle be different. Eqs. (48) and (50) are compatible with the decoupling property at any level of the truncation, whereas Eqs. (48) combined with (49) are fully consistent with HFT at any level of truncation. Thus the low-energy effective form of an arbitrary operator can be computed according to Eq. (33) in the same truncation scheme used for the renormalization of the Hamiltonian. In particular, we will show that only in the lowest order ($m = 0$), equations (49) and (50) are equivalent, independent of the physical system and the truncation scheme.

Although our method is non-perturbative, perturbation theory can be recovered from it. In this way, its simple structure for loop expansion will be obvious and we will observe that at lower order hermiticity is preserved. Now we illustrate how this is realizable in our approach. Assume that V_C and V_A are of order λ, we will diagonalize the Hamiltonian, at leading order in λ up to the desired accuracy in μ/Λ. We use the commutator-expansion

$$e^{-S} H e^{S} = H + [H, S] + \frac{1}{2!}[[H, S], S] + \cdots . \tag{51}$$

Eq. (48) can be organized perturbatively in order of m, aiming at elimination of the high momenta degree of freedom up to the first order in the coupling constant, thus yields

$$\begin{aligned}
m = 0: &\quad \langle 0|C_I(V_C + [H_2, \hat{S}_0])|0\rangle = 0\,, \\
m = 1: &\quad \langle 0|C_I([H_1, \hat{S}_0] + [H_2, \hat{S}_1] + [V_A, \hat{S}_1] + [V_C, \hat{S}_1])|0\rangle = 0\,, \\
&\quad \vdots \\
m = n: &\quad \langle 0|C_I([H_1, \hat{S}_{n-1}] + [H_2, \hat{S}_n] + [V_A, \hat{S}_n] + [V_C, \hat{S}_n])|0\rangle = 0\,,
\end{aligned} \tag{52}$$

where $I \neq 0$. Notice that $\hat{S}_0$ is chosen to cancel V_C in the effective Hamiltonian, hence it is at least of order of λ, consequently it generates a new term $[H_1, \hat{S}_0]$ which is of higher order in μ/Λ and can be canceled out on the next orders by $\hat{S}_1$. The logic for obtaining the equations above is based on the fact that $\hat{S}_n$ should be smaller than $\hat{S}_{n-1}$ (for sake of convergence) and that the equations should be consistent with each other. Since $H_2, V_A, V_C \approx \Lambda$

and $H_1 \approx \mu$, from Eq. (52) we have the desired relation $\hat{S}_n \approx \frac{\mu}{\Lambda}\hat{S}_{n-1}$. The same procedure can be applied for Eq. (50) which leads to the introduction of a new series of equations in order of m,

$$\begin{aligned}
m=0: &\quad \langle 0|(V_A - [H_2, \hat{S}'_0])C_I^\dagger|0\rangle = 0\,,\\
m=1: &\quad \langle 0|([H_1, \hat{S}'_0] + [H_2, \hat{S}'_1] + [V_C, \hat{S}'_1] + [V_A, \hat{S}'_1] - [V_A, \hat{S}_1])C_I^\dagger|0\rangle = 0\,,\\
&\quad \vdots\\
m=n: &\quad \langle 0|([H_1, \hat{S}'_{n-1}] + [H_2, \hat{S}'_n] + [V_C, \hat{S}'_n] + [V_A, \hat{S}'_n] - [V_A, \hat{S}_n])C_I^\dagger|0\rangle = 0\,. \qquad (53)
\end{aligned}$$

Alternatively, we can use Eq. (49) to yield the equations

$$\begin{aligned}
m=0: &\quad \langle 0|\big([V_A, C_I^\dagger] - [[H_2, C_I^\dagger], \hat{S}'_0]\big)|0\rangle = 0\,,\\
m=1: &\quad \langle 0|\big([[V_A, C_I^\dagger], \hat{S}_1] - [[H_2, C_I^\dagger], \hat{S}'_1] - [[V_A, C_I^\dagger], \hat{S}'_1]\big)|0\rangle = 0\,,\\
&\quad \vdots\\
m=n: &\quad \langle 0|\big([V_A, C_I^\dagger], \hat{S}_n] - [[H_2, C_I^\dagger], \hat{S}'_n] - [[V_A, C_I^\dagger], \hat{S}'_n]\big)|0\rangle = 0\,. \qquad (54)
\end{aligned}$$

It is obvious that at order $m = 0$, Eqs. (53) and (54) are the same and $\hat{S}'_0 = \hat{S}_0^\dagger$, which indicates that the similarity transformation at this level remains unitary. It should be noted that diagonalization at first order in the coupling constant introduces a low-energy effective Hamiltonian in Eq. (45) which is valid up to the order λ^3. In the same way, diagonalization at second order in λ modifies the Hamiltonian at order λ^4 and leads generally to a non-unitarity transformation. In this way one can proceed to diagonalize the Hamiltonian at a given order in λ with desired accuracy in μ/Λ . Finally, the renormalization process is completed by introducing the correct $Z(\Lambda)$ factors which redefine the divergences emerging from Eq. (45).

5 Coupling Coherence condition

One of the most severe problems for the traditional light-front RG is that an infinite number of relevant and marginal operators are required [34]. This is due to the fact that light-front cutoff violate the underlying symmetry, e.g., Lorentz covariant and gauge symmetries, since these are continuous symmetries, their violation in principle leads to an introduction of infinite number of symmetry violating counterterms (with new couplings), in order to maintain the symmetry of the effective Hamiltonian. In terms of the effective field theory approach, in general some sort of fine tuning is required to fix the strength of the new couplings so that the underlying symmetry is restored. One should note that in order to reduce the number of momentum degrees of freedom, one must introduce a real cutoff, such as a momentum cutoff or a lattice cutoff. However, dealing with divergences do not require necessarily a decrease in degrees of freedom. In fact, one may even increase the degrees of freedom, e.g., the Pauli-Villars or the dimensional regularization methods [36].

The main idea behind the coupling coherence renormalization condition [25, 26] is that the Hamiltonian is form-invariant on the RG trajectory. This condition isolates and repairs the hidden symmetries [25, 26].

$$H(\Lambda) \equiv \mathcal{H}(\mu), \tag{55}$$

In order words, rewriting the Hamiltonian in different degrees of freedom does not change the operator itself. One may think of $\mathcal{H}(\mu)$ as QCD written in terms of constituent quarks and gluons and $H(\Lambda)$ as the same QCD Hamiltonian written in terms of canonical quarks and gluons, associated with partons and current quarks. The SRG and the coupled-cluster RG with coupling coherence allows one to construct effective theories with the same number of couplings as the underlying fundamental theory, even when the cutoff violate symmetries of the theory. This does not preclude the emergence of the new couplings, however, they depend on the original coupling and will vanish if the fundamental couplings are turned off. This boundary condition together with the RG equations determines their dependence on the fundamental coupling.

As an illustrative example [26], we consider following interaction

$$V(\phi) = \frac{\lambda_1}{4!}\phi_1^4 + \frac{\lambda_2}{4!}\phi_2^2 + \frac{\lambda_3}{4!}\phi_1^2\phi_2^2, \tag{56}$$

where ϕ_1 and ϕ_2 are scalar fields. We want to investigate that under what conditions the couplings are independent of each other. Consider the Gell-Mann-Low equations [35] up to one-loop in perturbation theory, ignoring the masses,

$$\begin{aligned}
\frac{\delta\lambda_1}{\delta t} &= 3\xi\lambda_1^2 + \frac{1}{12}\xi\lambda_3^2, \\
\frac{\delta\lambda_2}{\delta t} &= 3\xi\lambda_2^2 + \frac{1}{12}\xi\lambda_3^2, \\
\frac{\delta\lambda_3}{\delta t} &= \frac{2}{3}\xi\lambda_2^3 + \xi\lambda_3(\lambda_1 + \lambda_2),
\end{aligned} \tag{57}$$

where $t = \log(\Lambda/\mu)$ and $\xi = \hbar/(16\pi^2)$. Assume that there is only one independent variable $\bar{\lambda} = \lambda_1$, and λ_2, λ_3 are functions of $\bar{\lambda}$. Now one can simplify Eq. (57),

$$\begin{aligned}
\left(3\bar{\lambda}^2 + \frac{1}{12}\lambda_3^2\right)\frac{\delta\lambda_2}{\delta\bar{\lambda}} &= 3\lambda_2^2 + \frac{1}{12}\lambda_3^2, \\
\left(3\bar{\lambda}^2 + \frac{1}{12}\lambda_3^2\right)\frac{\delta\lambda_3}{\delta\bar{\lambda}} &= \frac{2}{3}\lambda_3^2 + \bar{\lambda}\lambda_3 + \lambda_2\lambda_3.
\end{aligned} \tag{58}$$

At the leading order, above equations have two distinct solutions, one is when $\lambda_2 = \bar{\lambda}$ and $\lambda_3 = 2\bar{\lambda}$, in this case we have

$$V(\phi) = \frac{\bar{\lambda}}{4!}\left(\phi_1^2 + \phi_2^2\right)^2. \tag{59}$$

Therefore we recover the $O(2)$ symmetric theory. The order solution is $\lambda_2 = \bar{\lambda}$ and $\lambda_3 = 6\bar{\lambda}$ which leads to two decoupled scalar fields,

$$V(\phi) = \frac{\bar{\lambda}}{2.4!}\left((\phi_1+\phi_2)^4 + (\phi_1-\phi_2)^4\right), \tag{60}$$

One can conclude that λ_2 and λ_3 do not run independently with the cutoff if and only if there is a symmetry which connect their strength to λ_1. The Condition that a limited number of couplings run with cutoff independently reveals the symmetries broken by the regulator and repair them. More interesting, it may be used as well to uncover symmetries that are broken by the vacuum. This may reconcile the trivial vacuum in light-front field theory and vacuum symmetry breaking problem.

6 Example I: Φ^4 theory

We now apply this formalism to the computation of the effective Hamiltonian for ϕ^4 theory up to two-loop order in equal-time quantization. The bare ϕ^4 theory Hamiltonian is [36]

$$H = \int d^3x \left(\frac{1}{2}\pi^2(x) + \frac{1}{2}\phi(x)\big(-\nabla^2 + m^2\big)\phi(x) + g\phi^4(x)\right). \tag{61}$$

According to our logic the ultraviolet-finite Hamiltonian is obtained by introducing counterterms, which depend on the UV cutoff Λ and some arbitrary renormalization scale. This redefines the parameters of the theory and defines the effective low-energy Hamiltonian. The renormalized Hamiltonian has the form

$$H = \int d^3x \left(\frac{Z_\pi}{2}\pi^2(x) + \frac{1}{2}\sqrt{Z_\phi}\phi(x)\big(-\nabla^2 + Z_m m^2\big)\sqrt{Z_\phi}\phi(x) + Z_g Z_\phi^2 g\phi^4(x) + ...\right). \tag{62}$$

Although the factorization in the above equation is scheme-dependent, the Λ dependence itself is not. Each of Z-factors has an expansion of the form.

$$Z = 1 + f_1(\Lambda)\lambda + f_2(\Lambda)\lambda^2 + \ldots, \tag{63}$$

where λ is a generic coupling constant of theory and has been defined at a given renormalization scale M. The functions f_n will be obtained order-by-order, by summing up contributions of the fast modes between μ and Λ, in the sense that $Z(\Lambda) \to Z(\mu)$ and $f_n(\Lambda) \to f_n(\mu)$. This means that the low-energy correlation functions are invariants of the renormalization group flow. One can therefore assume that the Z's are initially 1 and choose the corresponding f's from the condition that the cut-off dependence be cancelled out after computing the effective Hamiltonian in the desired loop order. Even though the newly generated interactions are sensitive to the regularization scheme (as is well known

[37], a sharp cutoff may lead to new non-local interaction terms), nevertheless one can ignore these if they are irrelevant in the renormalization group sense. We now split field operators into high- and low-momentum modes; $\phi(x) = \phi_L(x) + \phi_H(x)$, where $\phi_L(x)$ denotes modes of low-frequency with momentum $k \leq \mu$ and $\phi_H(x)$ denotes modes of high-frequency with momentum constrained to a shell $\mu < k \leq \Lambda$. The field $\phi_H(x)$ can be conceived as a background to which the $\phi_L(x)$-modes are coupled. Therefore, in the standard diagrammatic language, integrating out the high-frequency modes $\phi_H(x)$ implies that only high-frequency modes appear in internal lines. The field $\phi_H(x)$ is represented in Fock space as

$$\phi_H(x) = \sum_{\mu<k\leq\Lambda} \frac{1}{\sqrt{2\omega_k}}(a_k e^{ikx} + a_k^{\dagger} e^{-ikx}), \tag{64}$$

where $\omega_k = \sqrt{k^2+m^2}$ and the operators a_k and $a_k^{\dagger}$ satisfy the standard boson commutation rules.

¿From now on all summations are implicitly over the high-frequency modes $\mu < k \leq \Lambda$. The Hamiltonian in terms of high- and low-frequency modes can be written as, after normal ordering with respect to high-frequency modes,

$$H = H_1 + H_2 + V_B + V_C + V_A, \tag{65}$$

where we define,

$$\begin{aligned}
H_1 &= \int \left(\frac{1}{2}\pi_L^2(x) + \frac{1}{2}\phi_L(x)\big(-\nabla^2 + m^2\big)\phi_L(x) + g\phi_L^4(x)\right),\\
H_2 &= \sum \omega_k a_k^{\dagger} a_k,\\
V_B &= g\sum\int \frac{e^{i(p+q+r-k)x}}{\sqrt{\omega_k\omega_p\omega q\omega_r}} a_k^{\dagger} a_p a_q a_r + \frac{3e^{i(p+q-r-k)x}}{4\sqrt{\omega_k\omega_p\omega q\omega_r}} a_k^{\dagger} a_p^{\dagger} a_q a_r\\
&\quad +6\phi_L(x)\frac{e^{i(p+q-k)x}}{\sqrt{2\omega_k\omega_p\omega_q}} a_k^{\dagger} a_p a_q + 3\big(\phi_L^2(x) + \frac{1}{2\omega_r}\big)\frac{e^{i(k-p)x}}{\sqrt{\omega_k\omega_p}} a_p^{\dagger} a_k\\
&\quad +\frac{3\phi_L^2(x)}{2\omega_r} + \text{h.c.},\\
V_C &= g\sum\int V_C^4\, a_k^{\dagger} a_p^{\dagger} a_q^{\dagger} a_r^{\dagger} + V_C^3\, a_k^{\dagger} a_p^{\dagger} a_q^{\dagger} + V_C^2\, a_k^{\dagger} a_p^{\dagger} + V_C^1\, a_k^{\dagger},\\
V_A &= V_C^{\dagger},\\
V_C^1 &= \left(\frac{6\phi_L(x)}{\omega_p} + 4\phi_L^3(x)\right)\frac{e^{-ikx}}{\sqrt{2\omega_k}}, \qquad V_C^2 = 3\left(\phi_L^2(x) + \frac{1}{2\omega_r}\right)\frac{e^{-i(k+p)x}}{\sqrt{\omega_k\omega_p}},\\
V_C^3 &= 2\phi_L(x)\frac{e^{-i(k+p+q)x}}{\sqrt{2\omega_k\omega_p\omega_k}}, \qquad V_C^4 = \frac{e^{-i(k+p+q+r)x}}{4\sqrt{\omega_k\omega_p\omega_q\omega_r}}.
\end{aligned} \tag{66}$$

The high-energy configurations in the Fock space are specified by $\{C_I \rightarrow \prod_{i=1} a_{k_i}\}$ and $\{C_I^{\dagger} \rightarrow \prod_{i=1} a_{k_i}^{\dagger})\}$. Up to two-loop expansion, our renormalization scheme requires to keep $S(S')$ at least to order $n = 4$, which allows us to eliminate the pure terms V_C and V_A at a lower level of expansion. The $\hat{S}(\hat{S})$ operators consistent with a $SUB(4,m)$ truncation scheme are,

$$\begin{aligned}
\hat{S}_m &= \int \sum \left(\hat{S}^1_m \, a^\dagger_k + \hat{S}^2_m \, a^\dagger_k a^\dagger_p + \hat{S}^3_m \, a^\dagger_k a^\dagger_p a^\dagger_q + \hat{S}^4_m \, a^\dagger_k a^\dagger_p a^\dagger_q a^\dagger_r \right), \\
\hat{S}'_m &= \int \sum \left(\hat{S}'^1_m \, a_k + \hat{S}'^2_m \, a_k a_p + \hat{S}'^3_m \, a_k a_p a_q + \hat{S}^4_m \, a_k a_p a_q a_r \right). \qquad (67)
\end{aligned}$$

One can expand Eqs. (48,50) in terms of μ/Λ, leading to the introduction of a consistent hierarchy of equations in powers of m [9], which can be solved for the coefficients $\hat{S}_m(\hat{S}'_m)$ in Eq. (67). We split the diagonalization of the Hamiltonian matrix in an upper and lower triangle part, using the double similarity transformation. One may notice that the "most non-diagonal" terms in the Hamiltonian are V_C and V_A (in the light-front Hamiltonian such terms do not exist because modes with longitudinal momentum identically zero are not allowed). The potential V_B is already partially diagonalized and does not change the vacuum of the high-energy states. Therefore, here we employ a minimal scheme, aiming at removal of V_A and V_C only.

We restrict ourselves to the elimination of the high-energy degrees of freedom up to the first order in the coupling constant g and second order in the ratio of cutoffs μ/Λ. Therefore, our truncation scheme is called $SUB(4,2)$. For $m = 0$ one finds,

$$\begin{aligned}
S^1_0 &= -g\frac{V^1_C}{\omega_k}, & S^2_0 &= -g\frac{V^2_C}{\omega_k+\omega_p}, \\
S^3_0 &= -g\frac{V^3_C}{\omega_k+\omega_p+\omega_q}, & S^4_0 &= -g\frac{V^4_C}{\omega_k+\omega_p+\omega_q+\omega_r}, \qquad (68)
\end{aligned}$$

where the V_C^{1-4} are defined in Eq. (66). Here, one has $S'_0 = S^\dagger_0$ [9]. At this stage the results for the one-loop renormalization can be computed. We evaluate the effective Hamiltonian by substituting $S(S')$ from Eqs. (67) and (68) into Eq. (45). In order to achieve renormalization, one should identify the potentially divergent terms (when $\Lambda \to \infty$) in the expansion of $H^{\text{eff}}(\mu)$. Such a process generally can be done by inventing a power-counting rule, using the property $S_n \simeq \frac{\mu}{\Lambda} S_{n-1}$. Here we take $\omega_k \simeq |k|$ for $\mu \gg m$ and replace $\sum_k$ by $\int \frac{d^3k}{(2\pi)^3}$. The standard tadpole one-loop mass renormalization arises from V_B due to normal-ordering. We add this divergent term to H_1 and renormalize the bare mass

$$\begin{aligned}
\delta H^{\text{1-loop}} &= \langle 0|V_B|0\rangle = 6g\sum\int\frac{\phi^2(x)}{2\omega_k} = \frac{3g}{4\pi^2}(\Lambda^2-\mu^2)\int d^3x\phi^2(x), \\
Z_m &= 1-\frac{3g}{2\pi^2}(\Lambda^2-\mu^2). \qquad (69)
\end{aligned}$$

In this order the contribution of the terms $[V_C, S]$, $[V_A, S']$ and $[H_1, S(S')]$ are zero, after projection on to the high-energy vacuum. The only divergent contributions come from $[V_A^{2(3)}, S_0^{2(3)}]$ due to a double and third contraction of the high-frequency fields respectively.

There are two other divergent terms, $([V_C^{2(3)}, S_0^{\prime 2(3)}]$, however they are harmless and are cancelled out by the divergence of $[[H_2, S_0], S_0^{\prime 2(3)}]$. One thus obtains,

$$\begin{aligned}\delta H &= -\frac{18g^2}{(2\pi)^6}\int \frac{\phi^2(x)\phi^2(y)}{\omega_k\omega_p(\omega_k+\omega_p)}e^{i(k+p)(x-y)} \\ &- \frac{12g^2}{(2\pi)^9}\int \frac{\phi(x)\phi(y)}{\omega_k\omega_p\omega_q(\omega_k+\omega_p+\omega_q)}e^{i(k+p+q)(x-y)}. \end{aligned} \quad (70)$$

In general evaluation of integrals like Eq. (70) may produce non-localities. This is due to the fact that the total momentum in integrands of Eq. (70), namely $r_1 = p+q$ and $r_2 = k+p+q$ are in the low-momentum space. To evaluate such integrations, one can firstly reduce the potential divergent integrals by a change of variable, for example for the first integrand we use $p, q \rightarrow p, r_1$, and then expand the integrand in r_1/p. Therefore, after expansion and evaluating the momentum integrals, one may be faced with non-analytic terms in the low-momentum space. However here these are irrelevant and will thus be ignored. We find

$$\begin{aligned}\delta H^{\text{1-loop}} &= -\frac{9g^2}{2\pi^2}\ln\left(\frac{\Lambda}{\mu}\right)\int d^3x\phi^4(x) - \frac{3g^2}{2\pi^4}(2\ln 2 - 1)\Lambda^2\int d^3x\phi^2(x) \\ &+ \frac{3g^2}{16\pi^4}\ln\left(\frac{\Lambda}{\mu}\right)\int d^3x(\nabla\phi(x))^2 + \text{finite terms}. \end{aligned} \quad (71)$$

One can immediately deduce the renormalization factors Z_g and Z_ϕ from above expression

$$Z_g = 1 + \frac{9g^2}{2\pi^2}\ln\left(\frac{\Lambda}{\mu}\right), \quad (72)$$

$$Z_\phi = 1 - \frac{3g^2}{8\pi^4}\ln\left(\frac{\Lambda}{\mu}\right). \quad (73)$$

The unknown coefficients in expression S_1 is computed by making use of Eq. (68) and solving coupled equations (48), therefore one may yield,

$$\begin{aligned}
S_1^1 &= \frac{6ge^{-ikx}}{\omega_k^2\sqrt{2\omega_k}}\left(2\phi_L(x) - 2i\pi_L(x)\phi_L^2(x) - \frac{i\pi_L(x)}{\omega_p}\right) - \frac{g}{\omega_k}\textstyle\sum_{\nu=1}^{3}\frac{1}{\nu!}V_A^\nu S_1^{\nu+1}, \\
S_1^2 &= \frac{3ge^{-i(k+p)x}}{(\omega_k+\omega_p)^2\sqrt{\omega_k\omega_p}}\Big(1 - i2\pi_L(x)\phi_L(x)\Big) - \frac{g}{\omega_k+\omega_p}\left([V_C^1, S_1^1] + \textstyle\sum_{\nu=1}^{2}\frac{1}{\nu!}V_A^\nu S_1^{\nu+2}\right) \\
S_1^3 &= -\frac{2ige^{-i(k+p+q)x}}{(\omega_k+\omega_p+\omega_q)^2\sqrt{2\omega_k\omega_p\omega_q}}\pi_L(x) - \frac{g}{(\omega_k+\omega_p+\omega_q)}\left(V_A^1 S_1^4 + \textstyle\sum_{\nu=1}^{2}[V_C^\nu, S_1^{3-\nu}]\right), \\
S_1^4 &= -\frac{g}{(\omega_k+\omega_p+\omega_q+\omega_r)}\textstyle\sum_{\nu=1}^{3}[V_C^{4-\nu}, S_1^\nu].
\end{aligned} \quad (74)$$

In the above expression summation over dummy momentum indices is assumed. One can find $\hat{S}_1'$ in the same manner by exploiting Eq. (50) and using Eq. (74) as an input, which leads to

$$S_1^{\prime\nu} = (S_1^\nu)^\dagger + S_1^{\prime\nu a} \qquad \nu = 1, ..., 4, \quad (75)$$

with the notations,

$$
\begin{aligned}
S_1^{\prime 1a} &= \frac{g}{\omega_k}\Big(\sum_{\nu=1}^{3}\frac{1}{\nu!}S_1^{\prime(\nu+1)a}V_C^{\nu} - \sum_{\nu=1}^{3}\frac{1}{\nu!}V_A^{\nu+1}S_1^{\nu}\Big),\\
S_1^{\prime 2a} &= \frac{g}{\omega_k+\omega_p}\Big(\sum_{\nu=1}^{2}\frac{1}{\nu!}S_1^{\prime(\nu+2)a}V_C^{\nu}(q) - \sum_{\nu=1}^{2}\frac{1}{\nu!}V_A^{\nu+2}S_1^{\nu} + [V_A^1, S_1^{\prime 1a}]\Big),\\
S_1^{\prime 3a} &= \frac{g}{\omega_k+\omega_p+\omega_q}\Big(S_1^{\prime 4a}V_C^1 - V_A^4 S_1^1 + \sum_{\nu=1}^{2}[V_A^{\nu}, S_1^{\prime(3-\nu)a}]\Big),\\
S_1^{\prime 4a} &= \frac{g}{(\omega_k+\omega_p+\omega_q+\omega_r)}\sum_{\nu=1}^{3}[V_A^{\nu}, S_1^{\prime(4-\nu)a}].
\end{aligned} \tag{76}
$$

The only divergent contribution up to order g^2 arises from,

$$\delta H = -\langle 0|[[H_1, S_1], S_0']|0\rangle, \tag{77}$$

After the evaluation of the leading divergent part, we find that

$$\delta H = -\frac{3g^2}{16\pi^4}\ln\left(\frac{\Lambda}{\mu}\right)\int d^3x\,\pi^2(x), \tag{78}$$

which contributes to the two-loop wave-function renormalization Z_π. By comparing Eqs. (73) and (78), one may conclude that $Z_\pi = Z_\phi^{-1}$, as it should be. To finish the renormalization up to two-loop order, one should also take into account the contribution at order g^3. The divergent terms at this level originate from

$$\delta H = -\langle 0|\Big[[(V_A + 1/2V_C + V_B), S_0], S_0'\Big]|0\rangle. \tag{79}$$

After a straightforward but lengthy computation one can obtain the leading divergent parts,

$$\delta H = \frac{27g^3}{2\pi^4}\Big[\big[\ln\left(\frac{\Lambda}{\mu}\right)\big]^2 + \ln\left(\frac{\Lambda}{\mu}\right)\Big]\int d^3x\phi^4(x), \tag{80}$$

this term should be added to Eq. (70), therefore one can immediately deduce the correct total renormalization factor Z_g up to two-loop order,

$$Z_g = 1 + \frac{9g^2}{2\pi^2}\ln\left(\frac{\Lambda}{\mu}\right) + \frac{g^3}{4\pi^4}\left(81\left(\ln\left(\frac{\Lambda}{\mu}\right)\right)^2 - 51\ln\left(\frac{\Lambda}{\mu}\right)\right). \tag{81}$$

One can now immediately obtain the well-known [36] two-loop β-function and anomalous dimension by making use of Eqs. (73, 81).

It is important to point out that the diagonalization at first order in the coupling constant defines a correct low-energy effective Hamiltonian which is valid up to order g^3. Having said that, from Eq. (75) one can observe that the non-hermiticity of the $\hat{S}$ operator appears at order g^2 and in a lower order of μ/Λ. As we have shown, non-hermiticity is negligible up to two-loop order (asymmetric terms appear in irrelevant contributions). We conjecture that, for the present model, non-hermitian terms only appear in irrelevant contributions, whatever the order of truncation.

7 Example II: Extended Lee Model

As an illustrative example, we will now apply the formalism introduced in the last chapter to determine the effective Hamiltonian for ELM up to the one-loop order. We define four kinds of particles, the V-particle and N-particle as two different fermions and the θ and $\bar{\theta}$ as a scalar boson and anti-boson respectively. Here $a(k)$, $a^{\dagger}(k)$ and $b(k)$, $b^{\dagger}(k)$ are the annihilation and creation operators which satisfy boson commutator rules. The $V(p), V^{\dagger}(p)$ and $N(p)$, $N^{\dagger}(p)$ define the fermion sector and obey the usual anticommutator rules. The bare ELM Hamiltonian then reads

$$
\begin{aligned}
H &= H_0 + H_I, \\
H_0 &= \int d^3p\, \omega_V(p) V^{\dagger}(p)V(p) + \int d^3p\, \omega_N(p) N^{\dagger}(p)N(p) \\
&+ \int d^3k\, \omega_{\theta}(k) a^{\dagger}(k)a(k) + \int d^3k\, \omega_{\bar{\theta}}(k) b^{\dagger}(k)b(k), \\
H_I &= \lambda_1 (2\pi)^{-3/2} \int \frac{d^3k d^3p}{(2\omega_{\theta}(k))^{1/2}} V^{\dagger}(p)N(p-k)a(k) \\
&+ \lambda_2 (2\pi)^{-3/2} \int \frac{d^3k d^3p}{(2\omega_{\bar{\theta}}(k))^{1/2}} N^{\dagger}(p)V(p-k)b(k) + \text{h.c.}. \qquad (82)
\end{aligned}
$$

The kinetic energy generically is defined $\omega_O(k) = \sqrt{k^2 + m_O^2}$ where the indice O can be either $(V, N, \theta, \bar{\theta})$. The interaction term in H_I describes the processes;

$$V \rightleftarrows N + \theta, \qquad (83)$$

$$N \rightleftarrows V + \bar{\theta}. \qquad (84)$$

The crossing symmetry become manifest if we take $\lambda_1 = \lambda_2$ and equal masses for boson and anti-boson. For sake of generality we will ignore crossing symmetry at the moment. The Lee model [38] can be recovered if we decouple the anti-boson $\bar{\theta}$, $\lambda_2 \to 0$. In the Lee model the virtual process Eq. (84) is not included and thus the N-particle state remains unrenormalized and the model become exactly solvable.

It is believed that the Lee model is asymptotically free for space-time dimension D less than four [39]. With on-shell renormalization one can show that the Lee model for $D > 4$ (odd D) is ultraviolet stable and not asymptotically free [40]. It is well known that such a model in four dimension exhibit a ghost state as the cutoff is removed. The Hamiltonian Eq. (82) exhibits two symmetries; it is straightforward to verify that following operators commute with H

$$
\begin{aligned}
B &= \int d^3p\, V^{\dagger}(p)V(p) + \int d^3p\, N^{\dagger}(p)N(p), \\
Q &= \int d^3p\, N^{\dagger}(p)N(p) + \int d^3k\, b^{\dagger}(p)b(p) - \int d^3k\, a^{\dagger}(p)a(p). \qquad (85)
\end{aligned}
$$

Clearly B is a baryon number operator and Q is a charge operator. We assign the charges $1, 0, -1$ and 1 to the N, V, θ and $\bar{\theta}$, respectively. The sectors of the ELM are labeled by the eigenvalue (b, q) of the operators (B, Q). According to our formulation the ultraviolet-finite Hamiltonian is obtained by introducing Z-factors, which depend on the UV cutoff Λ and some arbitrary renormalization scale M in such way that effective Hamiltonian does not depend on Λ. The bare Hamiltonian can be rewritten

$$
\begin{aligned}
H &= \int d^3p\, Z_V^2 Z_{M_V} \omega_V(p) V^\dagger(p) V(p) + \int d^3p\, Z_N^2 Z_{M_N} \omega_N(p) N^\dagger(p) N(p) \\
&+ \int d^3k\, Z_\theta^2 Z_{M_\theta} \omega_\theta(k) a^\dagger(k) a(k) + \int d^3k\, Z_{\bar{\theta}}^2 Z_{M_{\bar{\theta}}} \omega_{\bar{\theta}}(k) b^\dagger(k) b(k) \\
&+ \int \frac{\lambda_1 d^3k d^3p}{(2(2\pi)^3 \omega_\theta(k))^{1/2}} Z_{\lambda_1} Z_V Z_N Z_\theta V^\dagger(p) N(p-k) a(k) \\
&+ \int \frac{\lambda_2 d^3k d^3p}{(2(2\pi)^3 \omega_{\bar{\theta}}(k))^{1/2}} Z_{\lambda_2} Z_V Z_N Z_{\bar{\theta}} N^\dagger(p) V(p-k) b(k) \\
&+ \text{h.c.}\,. \qquad (86)
\end{aligned}
$$

We split the original Hamiltonian in the form of Eq. (47);

$$
\begin{aligned}
H_1 &= H(\int_0^\mu), \\
H_2 &= H_0(\int_\mu^\Lambda), \\
V_C &= \int_0^\mu \int_\mu^\Lambda \frac{d^3p' d^3k}{(2(2\pi)^3 \omega_\theta(k))^{1/2}} \lambda_1 N^\dagger(p'-k) V(p') a^\dagger(k) \\
&+ \int_0^\mu \int_\mu^\Lambda \frac{d^3p' d^3k}{(2(2\pi)^3 \omega_{\bar{\theta}}(k))^{1/2}} \lambda_2 V^\dagger(p'-k) N(p') b^\dagger(k), \\
V_A &= V_C^\dagger, \\
V_B &= \int_0^\mu \int_\mu^\Lambda \frac{d^3p d^3k'}{(2(2\pi)^3 \omega_\theta(k'))^{1/2}} \lambda_1 V^\dagger(p) N(p-k') a(k') \\
&+ \int_0^\mu \int_\mu^\Lambda \frac{d^3p d^3k'}{(2(2\pi)^3 \omega_{\bar{\theta}}(k'))^{1/2}} \lambda_2 N^\dagger(p) V(p-k') b(k') \\
&+ \int_\mu^\Lambda \int_\mu^\Lambda \frac{d^3p d^3k}{(2(2\pi)^3 \omega_\theta(k))^{1/2}} \lambda_1 V^\dagger(p) N(p-k) a(k) \\
&+ \int_\mu^\Lambda \int_\mu^\Lambda \frac{d^3p d^3k}{(2(2\pi)^3 \omega_{\bar{\theta}}(k))^{1/2}} \lambda_2 N^\dagger(p) V(p-k) b(k) + \text{h.c.}\,. \qquad (87)
\end{aligned}
$$

Here p' and k' stand for low momenta ($p', k' < \mu$). If the arguments of an operator are all low momenta (p' or k'), this indicates low momentum operators. The arguments in $H(\int_0^\mu)$ and $H_0(\int_\mu^\Lambda)$ means that all the momentum integrations involved in Eq. (82) are running between $0 < p' < \mu$ for the former and $\mu < p < \Lambda$ for the latter, respectively. The configuration space of the high momentum operators are specified by $\{C_I \rightarrow V^{n_1} N^{n_2} a^{n_3} b^{n_4}, C_I^\dagger \rightarrow C_I^\dagger \rightarrow (V^\dagger)^{n_1} (N^\dagger)^{n_2} (a^\dagger)^{n_3} (b^\dagger)^{n_4}\}$ with $n_1 + n_2 + n_3 + n_4 = I$. Aiming at a one-loop expansion the corresponding S and S' operators which preserve the symmetry property Eq. (85), can be chosen as

$$\begin{aligned} S_m &= \int d^3p' d^3k \, S_m^1(p') V^\dagger(p'-k) b^\dagger(k) + \int d^3p' d^3k \, S_m^2(p') N^\dagger(p'-k) a^\dagger(k), \\ S_m^1 &= S_m^N N(p') + S_m^{Vb} V(p'-k') b(k') + S_m^{Va} V(p'+k') a^\dagger(k'), \\ S_m^2 &= S_m^V V(p') + S_m^{Na} N(p'-k') a(k') + S_m^{Nb} N(p'+k') b^\dagger(k'). \end{aligned} \quad (88)$$

We have ignored the $I = 1$ configuration, since there are no tadpole type diagrams. The truncation of S_I in configuration space should be consistent with the loop expansion. Here we confine our attention to the elimination of the high-momentum degrees of freedom up to the first order in coupling constant and second order in μ/Λ. The unknown coefficients in Eq. (88) can be obtained by making use of Eq. (52),

$$\begin{aligned} S_0^V &= \frac{\lambda_1}{(2(2\pi)^3 \omega_\theta(k))^{1/2} (\omega_N(p'-k) + \omega_\theta(k))}, \\ S_0^N &= \frac{\lambda_2}{(2(2\pi)^3 \omega_{\bar\theta}(k))^{1/2} (\omega_V(p'-k) + \omega_{\bar\theta}(k))}, \\ S_0^{Vb} &= S_0^{Va} = 0, \\ S_1^V &= \frac{\lambda_1 \omega_V(p')}{(2(2\pi)^3 \omega_\theta(k))^{1/2} (\omega_N(p'-k) + \omega_\theta(k))^2}, \\ S_1^N &= \frac{\lambda_2 \omega_N(p')}{(2(2\pi)^3 \omega_{\bar\theta}(k))^{1/2} (\omega_V(p'-k) + \omega_{\bar\theta}(k))^2}, \\ S_1^{Va} &= \frac{\lambda_1 \lambda_2}{2(2\pi)^3 (\omega_{\bar\theta}(k) \omega_\theta(k'))^{1/2} (\omega_V(p'-k) + \omega_{\bar\theta}(k))^2}, \\ S_1^{Nb} &= \frac{\lambda_1 \lambda_2}{2(2\pi)^3 (\omega_{\bar\theta}(k') \omega_\theta(k))^{1/2} (\omega_N(p'-k) + \omega_\theta(k))^2}, \\ S_1^{Na} &= \frac{\lambda_1^2}{2(2\pi)^3 (\omega_\theta(k') \omega_\theta(k))^{1/2} (\omega_N(p'-k) + \omega_\theta(k))^2}, \\ S_1^{Vb} &= \frac{\lambda_2^2}{2(2\pi)^3 (\omega_{\bar\theta}(k') \omega_{\bar\theta}(k))^{1/2} (\omega_V(p'-k) + \omega_{\bar\theta}(k))^2}. \end{aligned} \quad (89)$$

It is easy to observe that Eq. (53) will be satisfied if we require $S_m' = S_m^\dagger$, since, up to the first in λ the similarity transformation introduced in Eq. (45) remains unitary. Equally one could use Eq. (54) to obtain S', it is obtained that $S_0' = S_0^\dagger$ and $S_1' = 0$, we will show that the renormalization feature of our model up to this order will remain unchanged, however the effective low-energy Hamiltonian will be different. As was already pointed out, this is because Eq. (54) requires a different truncation scheme. The effective Hamiltonian is now produced by plugging the S and S' defined in Eq. (88) into Eq. (45). With naive power-counting one can identify the potentially divergent terms. At the lower order of expansion, the divergent term is $\langle 0|[V_A, S_0]|0\rangle$, the divergence in this term arises from a double contraction of high-energy fields.

At this step the contributions of the terms $[V_B, S_0(S_0')]$ and $[H_1, S_0(S_0')]$ are zero, after projection on to the high-frequency vacuum. There is one other divergent term, $\langle 0|[V_C, S_0']|0\rangle$, but this is harmless and will be cancelled out by $\langle 0|\big[[H_2, S_0], S_0'\big]|0\rangle$. We thus obtain

$$\begin{aligned} \delta H(\lambda) &= -\frac{\lambda_1}{2(2\pi)^3}\int_\mu^\Lambda \frac{d^3k}{\omega_\theta(k)(\omega_N(p'-k)+\omega_\theta(k))}\Big[\int d^3p' N^\dagger(p')N(p')\Big] \\ &- \frac{\lambda_2}{2(2\pi)^3}\int_\mu^\Lambda \frac{d^3k}{\omega_{\bar\theta}(k)(\omega_V(p'-k)+\omega_{\bar\theta}(k))}\Big[\int d^3p' V^\dagger(p')V(p')\Big]. \end{aligned} \tag{90}$$

¿From this expression one can immediately deduce the renormalization factors Z_{m_V} and Z_{m_N}, we take $\omega_O \simeq |k|$ for $\mu \gg m_O$, therefore

$$\begin{aligned} Z_{m_V} &= 1+\frac{\lambda_1^2}{8\pi^2}(\Lambda-\mu), \\ Z_{m_N} &= 1+\frac{\lambda_2^2}{8\pi^2}(\Lambda-\mu). \end{aligned} \tag{91}$$

There is no mass renormalization for θ and $\bar\theta$ and accordingly there are no vacuum polarization type diagrams. Thus θ and $\bar\theta$ remain unrenormalized, $Z_\theta = Z_{m_\theta} = Z_{\bar\theta} = Z_{m_{\bar\theta}} = 1$. The other contribution of H^{eff} at one-loop which are not zero after projecting on to vacuum come from

$$\delta H(\lambda) = -\langle 0|\big[[H_1, S_1], S_0'\big] + \langle 0|\big[[H_1, S_1], S_1'\big]|0\rangle. \tag{92}$$

The divergent contribution emerges from the first terms, the leading divergence of this expression is logarithmic which means that we can neglect the difference between p and $k-p'$ (for the divergent contribution only). After evaluating a momentum integral we finally get,

$$\begin{aligned} \delta H &= -\frac{\lambda_1^2}{16\pi^2}\ln\left[\frac{\Lambda}{\mu}\right]\int \omega_V(p')V^\dagger(p')V(p') - \frac{\lambda_2^2}{16\pi^2}\ln\left[\frac{\Lambda}{\mu}\right]\int \omega_N(p')N^\dagger(p')N(p') \\ &- \frac{\lambda_1^2+\lambda_2^2}{32\pi^2}\ln\left[\frac{\Lambda}{\mu}\right]\int \frac{\lambda_1}{((2\pi)^3\omega_\theta(k'))}V^\dagger(p')N(p'-k')a(k') \\ &- \frac{\lambda_1^2+\lambda_2^2}{32\pi^2}\ln\left[\frac{\Lambda}{\mu}\right]\int \frac{\lambda_2}{((2\pi)^3\omega_{\bar\theta}(k'))}N^\dagger(p')V(p'-k')b(k'). \end{aligned} \tag{93}$$

¿From this expression we deduce the renormalization factor $Z_{\lambda_1}, Z_{\lambda_2}, Z_V$ and Z_N:

$$Z_V^2 = 1 + \frac{\lambda_1^2}{16\pi^2} \ln \frac{\Lambda}{\mu},$$
$$Z_N^2 = 1 + \frac{\lambda_2^2}{16\pi^2} \ln \frac{\Lambda}{\mu},$$
$$Z_{\lambda_1} = Z_{\lambda_2} = 1 + \frac{\lambda_1^2 + \lambda_2^2}{32\pi^2} \ln \frac{\Lambda}{\mu}. \quad (94)$$

It is obvious from the equations above that one can define renormalized coupling constants in terms of the bare couplings and wave function renormalization

$$\lambda_i = \lambda_i^0 / Z_V Z_N, \qquad i = 1, 2. \quad (95)$$

This definition corresponds for $\lambda_1 = \lambda_2$ with the renormalization introduced to compute the T-matrix for the $N - \theta$ interaction [38, 41]. The one-loop β-function and anomalous dimension γ are

$$\beta_{\lambda_i}(\lambda_1, \lambda_2) = \frac{\partial \lambda_i}{\partial \ln M}|_\Lambda = \frac{\lambda_i}{32\pi^2}(\lambda_1^2 + \lambda_2^2), \qquad i = 1, 2.$$
$$\gamma_V = 1/2 \frac{\partial \ln Z_V}{\partial \ln M}|_\Lambda = -\frac{\lambda_1^2}{32\pi^2},$$
$$\gamma_N = 1/2 \frac{\partial \ln Z_N}{\partial \ln M}|_\Lambda = -\frac{\lambda_2^2}{32\pi^2}. \quad (96)$$

Since the fixed points of the theory are the zero solutions of the β-function, one immediately identifies the trivial solution $\lambda_1 = \lambda_2 = 0$ (we ignore the nonphysical imaginary solution). It is now obvious from Eq. (96) that $\gamma_V = \gamma_N = 0$ only at trivial solutions of the β-functions. This result is in correspondence with property that for real field theories the γ-function is not zero unless at trivial fixed point of the theory [42]. Now to investigate the behaviour of the theory at high momentum, we must compute the momentum-dependent effective coupling constant $\lambda_1(k)$ and $\lambda_2(k)$ by

$$\begin{cases} k\frac{d\lambda_1(k)}{dk} = \beta_{\lambda_1}(\lambda_1(k)\lambda_2(k)), & \lambda_1(k)|_{k=1} = \lambda_1^{ph} \\ k\frac{d\lambda_2(k)}{dk} = \beta_{\lambda_2}(\lambda_1(k), \lambda_2(k)), & \lambda_2(k)|_{k=1} = \lambda_2^{ph} \end{cases}, \quad (97)$$

where λ_1^{ph} and λ_2^{ph} are dimensionless physical renormalized coupling constants defined at the renormalization scale $k = 1$. The coupled equations (97) can be solved by going to polar coordinates $r^2(k) = \lambda_1^2(k) + \lambda_2^2(k)$ and $\theta(k) = \tan^{-1} \frac{\lambda_1(k)}{\lambda_2(k)}$,

$$\lambda_1(k) = \frac{\bar{r}}{\sqrt{1 - (16\pi^2)^{-1}\bar{r}^2 \ln k}} \sin \bar{\theta},$$
$$\lambda_2(k) = \frac{\bar{r}}{\sqrt{1 - (16\pi^2)^{-1}\bar{r}^2 \ln k}} \cos \bar{\theta}, \quad (98)$$

where $\bar{r}$ and $\bar{\theta}$ denote the value at the renormalization scale. The behaviour of the ELM in the deep-Euclidean region is obtained by allowing $k \to \infty$. From Eq. (98) one observes that $\lambda_1(k)$ and $\lambda_2(k)$ in this region are imaginary. This means that the effective Hamiltonian is non-hermitian and the theory generates ghost states when the cut-off is removed. The ghost state appears as a pole in V and N-propagators. Since a theory is said to exhibit asymptotic freedom if (i) $\frac{d\beta}{d\lambda}|_{\lambda(\infty)} < 0$ (ultraviolet stability at the fixed point $\lambda(\infty)$ and (ii) $\lambda(\infty) = \lim_{k\to\infty} \lambda(k) = 0$, Eqs. (98) indicate that the ELM can not exhibit asymptotic freedom at $D = 4$.

8 Conclusion

In this chapter we have reviewed the merits and shortcomings of several approaches for the construction of the effective field theories in the Hamiltonian framework. We have outlined a new strategy to derive effective renormalized operators [9]. The effective low-frequency operator is obtained by the condition that it should exhibit decoupling between the low- and high-frequency degrees of freedom. We have shown that the similarity transformation approach to renormalization can be systematically classified. The non-hermitian formulation gives a very simple description of decoupling, leading to a partial diagonalization of the high-energy part. We showed that non-unitarity representation inherent in our formulation is in favour of economic computation and does not produce any non-hermiticity in the relevant terms. The techniques proposed are known from the coupled cluster many-body theory and invoke neither perturbation nor unitarity transformation. We showed that our formalism can be solved perturbatively. In this way, it was revealed that diagonalization at first order in coupling constant defines a correct low-energy effective Hamiltonian which is valid up to the order λ^3. One can show that the non-hermiticity of the effective Hamiltonian is controllable and might appear in higher order which is beyond our approximation or in irrelevant terms which can be ignored in renormalization group sense.

One should note that Eqs. (48, 50) are not fully consistent with the Hellmann-Feynman theorem [9], although this choice considerably simplifies the diagonalization of the Hamiltonian operator. This potentially leads to a different truncation scheme for the renormalization of other operators. The decoupling requirements in the exact form Eq. (48,50) preserve Poincaré symmetry and the cluster decomposition property regardless of regularization used [9]. Since this is a continuous symmetry, its preservation leads to an infinite set of constraints on the phase space, which has been coded in the decoupling equations. Hence, it is of interest to consider the sensitivity of the Poincaré symmetry with respect to a given truncation scheme in the light-front dynamics.

9 Acknowledgment

One of the authors (AHR) acknowledges support from British Government ORS award and UMIST grant. The work of NRW is supported by the UK engineering and physical sciences research council under grant GR/N15672.

References

[1] K. G. Wilson and J. B. Kogut, *Phys. Rep.* **12C**, 75 (1974); K. G. Wilson, *Rev. Mod. Phys.* **47**, 773 (1975); C. Bagnuls and C. Bervillier, *Phys. Rept.* **348**, 91 (2001).

[2] S. Weinberg, *Phys. Rev.* **166**, 1568 (1968); J. Gasser and H. Leutwyler, *Ann. Phys.* (N.Y.) 158, 142 (1984).

[3] R. J. Perry, A. Harindranath and K. G. Wilson, Phys. Rev. Lett. **65**, 24, 2959 (1990).

[4] R. F. Bishop in: *Microscopic Quantum many body theories and their applications* , edited by J. Navarro and A. Polls. Lecture notes in Physics **510**, 1 (1997), and references therein.

[5] For example: G. Hasberg and H. Kümmel, *Phys. Rev.* **C33**, 1367 (1986); H. G. Kümmel, *Phys. Rev.* **D50**, 6556 (1993).

[6] S. D. Glazek and K. G. Wilson, *Phys. Rev.* **D48**, 5863 (1993); S. D. Glazek and K. G. Wilson, *Phys. Rev.* **D49**, 4218 (1994).

[7] F. Wegner, *Ann. Physik* (Berlin) **3**, 77 (1994).

[8] For example: A. P. Szczepaniak and E. S. Swanson, *Phys. Rev.* **D55**, 1578 (1997); E. L. Gubankova and F. Wegner, *Phys. Rev.* **D58**, 025012 (1998); T. Maslowski and M. Wieckowski, *Phys. Rev.* **D57**, 4976 (1998); T. S. Walhout, *Phys. Rev.* **D59**, 065009 (1999); D. G. Robertson, E. S. Swanson, A. P. Szczepaniak and C. R. Ji, S. R. Cotanch, *Phys. Rev.* **D59**, 074019 (1999); G. Alexanian and E. F. Moreno, *Phys. Lett.* **B450**, 149 (1999); D. Chakrabarti and A. Harindranath, *Phys. Rev.* **D65**, 045001 (2002).

[9] A. H. Rezaeian and N. R. Walet, JHEP **0312**, 040 (2003); *Phys. Lett.* **B570**,129 (2003).

[10] J. S. Arponen, R. F. Bishop and E. Pajanne, *Phys. Rev.* **A36**, 2519 (1987).

[11] J. Arponen, *Phys. Rev.* **A55**, 2686 (1997).

[12] K. Suzuki and S. Y. Lee, *Prog. Theor. Phys.* **64**, 209 (1980).

[13] K. Suzuki and R. Okamoto, *Prog. Theor. Phys.* **75**, 1388 (1986); **76**, 127 (1986); **92**, 1045 (1994).

[14] K. Suzuki, *Prog. Theor. Phys.* **87**, 937 (1992); H. Kümmel, *Phys. Rev.* **C27**, 765 (1983); K. Suzuki, R. Okamoto and H. Kumaga, *Nucl. Phys.* **A580**, 213 (1994) and references therein.

[15] K. Suzuki, *Prog. Theor. Phys.* **68**, 246 (1982); T. T. S. Kuo, P. J. Ellis, J. Hao, Z. Li, K. Suzuki, R. Okamoto and H. Kumagai, *Nucl. Phys.* **A560**, 621 (1993).

[16] K. Suzuki, R. Okamoto, P. J. Ellis, J. Hao, Z. Li, T. T. S. Kuo, *Phys. Lett.* **B308**, 1 (1993).

[17] C. S. Hsue, H. Kümmel and P. Ueberholz, *Phys. Rev.* **D32**, 1435 (1985).

[18] I. Tamm, *J. Phys. USSR* **9**, 499(1945); S. M. Dancoff, *Phys. Rev.* **78**, 382 (1950).

[19] K. G. Wilson, *Phys. Rev.* **140**, B445 (1965); K. G. Wilson, *Phys. Rev.* **D2**, 1438 (1970).

[20] C. Bloch, *Nucl. Phys.* **6**, 329 (1958).

[21] J. P. Vary and A. Harindranath, *In Nuclear and Particle Physics on the light cone*, edited by M. B. Johnson and L. S. Kisslinger (World Scientific, Singapore, 1989), and references therein.

[22] Weinberg, *Phys. Rev.* **150**, 1313 (1966).

[23] for example: R. J. Perry and A. Harindranath, *Phys. Rev.* **D43**, 4051 (1991); K. G. Wilson, T. S. Walhout, A. Harindranath, W. M. Zhang, R. J. Perry and S. D. Glazek, *Phys. Rev.* **D49**, 6720 (1994); M. Brisudova and R. Perry, *Phys. Rev.* **D54**, 1831 (1996).

[24] U. Kaulfuss, *Phys. Rev.* **D32**, 6, 1421 (1985).

[25] R. J. Perry and K. G. Wilson, *Nucl. Phys.* **B403**, 587 (1993); R. Oehme, K. Sibold and W. Zimmermann, *Phys. Lett.* **B147**, 115 (1984).

[26] R. J. Perry, *Phys. Rept.* **348**, 33 (2001).

[27] P. Navratil, H. B. Geyer and T. T. S. Kuo, *Phys. Lett.* **B315**, 1 (1993).

[28] C. Bloch and J. Horowitz, *Nucl. Phys.* **8**, 91 (1958).

[29] H. Feshbach, *Ann. Phys.* (N.Y) **19**, 287 (1962).

[30] P. J. Ellis and E. Osnes, *Rev. Mod. Phys.* **49**, 777 (1977).

[31] K. Suzuki and R. Okamoto, *Prog. Theor. Phys.* **71**, 1221 (1984).

[32] B. Brandow, *Rev. Mod. Phys.* **39**, 771 (1967).

[33] R. F. Bishop, *Theor. Chim. Acta.* **80**, 95 (1991).

[34] for example: R. J. Perry, *Ann. Phys.* (N.Y) **232**, 166 (1994).

[35] M. Gell-Mann, F. E. Low, *Phys. Rev.* **95**, 1300 (1954).

[36] C. Itzykson and J. Zuber, *Quantum Field Theory* (McGraw-Hill, New York, 1980).

[37] T. R. Morris, *Int. J. Mod. Phys.* **A9**, 2411 (1994).

[38] M. T. Vaughn, R. Aaron, R. D. Amado, *Phys. Rev.* **124**, 15, 1258 (1961).

[39] C. M. Bender and C. Nash, *Phys. Rev.* **D10**, 1753 (1974).

[40] J. R. Morris, R. Acharya and B. P. Nigan, *Phys. Rev.* **D21**, 2429 (1980).

[41] M. G. Fuda, *Phys. Rev.* **C26**, 204 (1982).

[42] C. Callan and D. Gross, *Phys. Rev.* **D8**, 4383 (1973).

INDEX

K

L

M

N

O

P

Q

R

S

T

U

V

W